About the Author

Mick was born in Warwickshire into a working-class Catholic family. (Un)educated at a Roman Catholic Secondary Modern whose curriculum centred around football and fighting! Somehow, he managed to escape to train as a teacher working in careers and pastoral education. After fifteen years he moved into ministry becoming a vicar in an ex-mining Urban Priority Area for twenty-four years. Never the traditional style cleric, Mick, together with the people, built up a thriving 'community church'. Moving on from the C of E, he is now a member of the Rugby Meeting of Quakers. Mick is married to Anne with three children and eight grandchildren. *The Vision* is his debut novel.

Mick Vincent.

The Vision

Mick Vincent

The Vision

Olympia Publishers
London

www.olympiapublishers.com
OLYMPIA PAPERBACK EDITION

A CIP catalogue record for this title is
available from the British Library.

ISBN: 978-1-80074-080-8

This is a work of fiction.
Names, characters, places and incidents originate from the writer's imagination. Any resemblance to actual persons, living or dead, is purely coincidental.

First Published in 2021

Olympia Publishers
Tallis House
2 Tallis Street
London
EC4Y 0AB
Printed in Great Britain

Dedication

This book is dedicated to my wife, Anne and to my
mother, Kathleen,
for the wonderful love they have brought to my life.
Thank you.

It is also written in memory of my childhood friend,
Keith Lampard,
who died of Polio, aged five.

Acknowledgements

Thank you…

To my wife, Anne, for her detailed scrutiny and helpful advice on the text. Also, to my daughter, Rachel, daughter-in-law, Emma and friends, Brian and Kathy Atkinson, Jo Miller, Peter Brogan, Robin Muers and Pennie Hartopp, for reading the initial draft and feeding back helpful comments, corrections and criticisms, many of which have been taken onboard!

To Ed Wilson for his article, 'Are you ready to submit?' in the Writers & Artists Yearbook 2020, which was highly entertaining and thought provoking. It extended the re-writing and total reorganisation of this book by at least eight months! Thanks, Ed!

To Peter Brierley and David Walker, for their statistics in Appendix Two, highlighting the continual decline of the Established Church.

To my daughter, Rachel, recalling her archaeological degree at Leicester University and producing the background information on archaeology in the Middle East, used in the character: Penelope.

To friend, Pennie Hartopp, for her inspired and beautiful cover design.

To Nicholas Bradbury for his stimulating account concerning the life of Pierre-Andre Liege in his book,

'Practical Theology and Pierre-Andre Liege' published by Routledge, which I have drawn upon.

To the Abbey Community of Iona for a wonderful Holy Week and Easter of worship (2019) with its profound liturgical words and music, and thereby, inspiring part of this book. A verse of a hymn quoted in the text was from 'Lord of Life and Resurrection' by Pat Bennett.

And finally, a thank you to the author / prophet of a notice I observed hanging inside a declining village Parish Church. The sign, situated by the main exit door, read:

'Will the last person to leave, please switch off ALL the lights'.

Contents

Prologue

His left hand reached out and touched the inside of her right leg. He was amazed at what he was doing, almost as if some mysterious force was acting within him. He could feel her closeness, the subtle scent of perfume, the pure femininity of her body. He was sat at his desk in the study.

She was standing beside him, so near that she felt attached to him, a part of his inner being. Her concentration, that was initially on the papers, was now hard to maintain.

He could feel the softness of her skin as his hand stroked her bare leg. It was the first really hot day of early summer and a light breeze from the garden drifted on the wind, through the open French doors into the room.

She felt his smooth hand as it touched and lightly caressed the inner part of her right thigh. She was wearing a summer dress of floral patterns to reflect the warmth of the day.

He began to move his hand upwards, beginning its journey to a new world. His heartrate increased and he could feel himself becoming flushed. A rising of blood flow to his cheeks.

She noticed her breathing was changing, becoming slightly deeper, expectant and strangely, relaxed. Not feeling threatened but a mixture of warmth, reassurance and love began to glow within her…

Afterwards, they stood as she turned to face him. They

kissed, lovingly, holding each other tightly; never wishing to ever let go of one another. They made a comic picture as they stood together; she with her summer dress partially tucked up around her waist and he, with his white thighs, half-covered by his purple shirt, his trousers around his ankles. There were tears of joy and tears of trepidation flowing down their faces, intermingling with one another.

For the first time in their lives, they both knew a love that before had been outside their experiences in life. A love so deep, profound and pure, that no words could ever speak of it as they melded softly into one another.

But they also began to realise that their explosive time of passionate love was to blow their present worlds apart. The old Vision on the desk would be shattered.

For Elizabeth and Charles, there was now a new beginning.

Part One
Elizabeth
The Family Tree

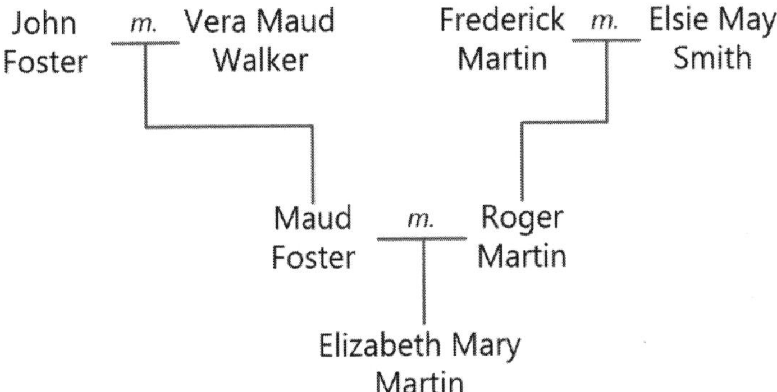

1.1 Pinton-on-Sea

The sky seemed forever grey and the wind lashed the tumultuous seas against the beach defences. In those days, the promenade often saw the waves crashing across the seafront. Pinton-on-Sea during the winter of 1953/54 was grim. Everything was locked up and deserted. A seaside 'ghost' resort town in the depths of February, with the sunny east coast holiday destination now a million miles away. The prevailing wind and rain added to the despondency and despair. There was a constant bleakness bringing a reserved, enclosed existence to the town's residents.

The small seaside town had a two-tone life.

For six months it was alive with a manic bustle of activity, invaded by sunseekers from Easter to the October half-term. They came in their hundreds from the industrial midland and northern towns during the summer work's holiday fortnights. Human forms in all sizes and shapes for their two-week annual break. They were noisy and loud, demanding fun and entertainment, filling the pubs to overflowing for their pints of bitter, mild and stout. Walking the promenade and flocking to the crude humour at the Pier Theatre. They dressed colourfully in bright, summer clothes and were often excessive in their urban language and behaviour. The town bulged and the ice cream vendors and the tacky, summer shops and stallholders grew rich for a short time.

But then, almost as quickly as they arrived, they all departed back to their humdrum factory-life existence for the next fifty weeks. At the end of the holiday season, Pinton-on-Sea changed its colours. The summer shopkeepers put up their heavy shutters and left, the bright reds and blues disappeared, the sun and its rays dimmed. The trees lost their greenness and became bare and stark.

A cruel, hard and heavy winter fell like a grey cloak around the resort and the second Pinton-on-Sea became another reality, bringing an eerie silence in a succession of damp and enclosing sea fogs. An emptiness invaded the town. The townsfolk huddled around their coal fires, through the long, dark nights of winter life.

It was into this darkness that Elizabeth Mary Martin cried out for the first time at 3.50 a.m. on the 15th February 1954. Her mother, Maud, named her Elizabeth after the newly appointed Queen. She was born into the bitterness of a cold, winter night and into the drabness of an off-season seaside resort.

It would, somehow, be a reflection of her early life expressed through her home environment and problematic family.

The birth had been painful, coming a few weeks earlier than expected. There was a sudden breaking of waters and intense pain. Then the birth process followed, with long hours of struggling alone. The stretching of her skin to its limit and beyond. Blood and tears. Maud had screamed out in her pain, with white knuckles clenched. "Never again," Maud vowed, in curses for all in the street to hear. The midwife was overbearing and bullying, the husband absent. Conceived in a functional bed, Elizabeth would always struggle in a vacuum without love.

The night of Elizabeth's conception was an early June summer's day. It was hot and humid, with the evening threatening a thunderstorm. Tempers were short between Maud and her husband, Roger and words were spoken harshly to one another. It was a Saturday, the husband's night and the wife to do her duty. Having spent the evening at the local pub drinking with his mates, Roger entered the marriage bed in a drunken stupor. He rolled over onto his wife, roughly pushing her nightdress up over her face as he thrust into Maud without any foreplay, squeezing her nipples painfully and smacking her bottom harshly. Romance, love or thought for Maud's feelings was not present. There were a number of grunts and thrusts, amidst abusive language ending within a few seconds, with the seed that would initiate Elizabeth's creation, savagely expelled into Maud.

Life began in such a way for Elizabeth.

Maud turned aside from the dead weight upon her with the Saturday night ritual over once again. As her husband snored on in his deep, drink-induced sleep, Maud struggled. The soreness between her legs was an irritation. It was always uncomfortable — the dryness reflected her disgust at the act and the brutal invasion of her. She felt like an object, degraded, used and then cast off.

1.2 Vera and John

Maud was also born in Pinton-on-Sea just after the Great War ended and grew up with her mother, experiencing the hardships of the 1920s and '30s, as high unemployment brought a drop in those who could afford an annual holiday. Then followed the Second World War with the resort completely closing down and sea defences installed on the beaches. Rationing and re-building lives continued the hard times through into the early 1950s. Luxuries were non-existent. It was a tight, restricted and austere world that Maud knew.

Maud's father, John, attended the only primary school in Pinton-on-Sea alongside his wife to be, Vera. It was a harsh regime where beatings of pupils occurred on a regular basis at morning assemblies. The Headmaster ruled with an iron fist and a whippy cane that he carried wherever he went around the school. He appeared to delight in the performance of dragging a pupil onto the stage in the school hall and forcibly caning the boys with six strokes on their bottoms and three strokes on the hands of girls.

John was often pulled out of the assembly of children during the years of his time at Pinton-on-Sea Primary. He hated school and having to sit still and do lessons. He struggled with reading and writing, often having to stay in during playtime to rewrite some illegible script. He loved being outside, playing in the streets or seeking adventures in the nearby countryside. He would often skive off school, rejoicing in the freedom of the open air. However, the next day John would pay for the consequences of his absence, with a savage beating in front of the whole school.

It was in the last year of school that John and Vera noticed each other. Vera was the complete opposite of John. Whilst he was racing around the playground, Vera would stand quietly in the corner, talking to one or two friends. In class she was always studious, constantly trying to do her best. Her neat writing reflected her conscientious approach to life. Vera never appeared on the platform to be caned, only to receive certificates for doing good work in class. It was her shyness and quiet nature that fascinated John and he began walking her home after school each day.

On leaving school, both Vera and John found work with the same employer. Sir Jeremy Eastwood owned the Pinton Manor Estate with over two thousand acres of farmland centred around the fifteenth century Manor House renovated in Georgian times, just one mile outside the seaside resort town. John was taken on to work on the land with its mixed farming of crops and a prized milking herd of Jersey cows. Vera was employed at the House as a maid with general duties including cleaning, making beds and serving at the table. John still lived at his parent's home in Pinton-on-Sea, while Vera had a small attic room in an annex of the main house. Both Vera and John worked six days a week with just Sundays as their day off. However, they were expected on Sundays, to be in attendance at the Estate Church for Morning Prayer, dressed in their Sunday best clothes.

They would look out for each other at the service and try

to be next to one another in the back row. The Squire and his family would always sit in the front pews with other important members of local society, such as the Doctor and nearby village Headmaster, sitting immediately behind. The servants and workers on the estate knew their place which was reflected in the bench seats provided for them at the back of the church, as opposed to the polished pews at the front.

The Vicar, who lived in a large house with his wife, children and servants alongside the fifteenth century church, often preached for thirty minutes during the morning service. He regularly spoke of the godliness of hard work and the need to respect and obey those appointed by God who held positions of authority in society. The Vicar's 'living' was extremely generous and he lived a well-heeled life in the local community. It was the Squire who held the 'living' and who financed the church and its incumbent, hence demanding that the 'Word of God' preached, was loyal to the established way of life.

For John, the long, monotonous service was truly purgatory and only heavenly when it ended. Afterwards, John and Vera would 'walk out' together into the surrounding countryside, sharing a picnic and kisses by one of the many streams running towards the sea. John would enthusiastically recount his life on the farm, whilst Vera would listen quietly to his stories of other workers and their work in the fields. Occasionally, they would walk into Pinton-on-Sea and have Sunday lunch or tea with one or the other set of their parents. Their relationship deepened and when they were both eighteen years of age, they married in the estate church with their parents and employer's permission.

After the wedding, they were allowed a week's holiday to

go on honeymoon to Blackpool before returning to their employment and separate sleeping arrangements. They were very much in love and enjoyed their lovemaking, trying to find precious moments to be with each other. On one occasion, Vera met John late one night, secretly taking him up the servant's stairway to her attic toom, where the excitement of their sexual intercourse was heightened by the danger of being caught.

However, within a few months their life changed dramatically. Vera began receiving the unsolicited attentions of the seventeen-year-old son of the Squire. Time and time again Vera had to defend herself from his inappropriate advances. Amid obscene language he would creep up behind her and either grab her bottom or try to fondle her breasts and push up her skirt to force his hand between her legs. One day, he pinned her to the bed that she was making and proceeded to try to rip off her lower undergarments. Her patience snapped and with a huge surge of anger and strength, Vera turned upon him with a ferocious attack, bloodying his nose as it broke under the frenzied weight of her punch.

Vera immediately went to her attic room and packed her belongings, leaving the House via the servant's door and walked with her heavy suitcase, to her parents' home in Pinton-on-Sea. A few hours later, John joined Vera after being dismissed from his work on the farm. John was angry at the assaults upon his wife and it took all of Vera's quiet reasoning and persuasion to convince him not to go back and 'sort out' the Squire's son. They both soon found alternative work with Vera working in a local bakers and John as an assistant to the town's blacksmith.

After several months of living with Vera's parents, they acquired a small, two bedroomed, terraced house in the town to rent. Both John and Vera were so excited as they could now set up their own home and live together as husband and wife. Their love for each other was so fresh and invigorating that John was full of ideas about the house, while even Vera broke out of her quiet mode to join in with her suggestions.

A month after moving into their new home, war broke out across Europe. John did not volunteer immediately, reassured by propaganda that it would 'all be over by Christmas'. One year later, John was called up and left Vera to 'do his duty'.

He left as a happy-go-lucky, young man in his early twenties but returned three years later as a broken, ill, shadow of his former self. As Lord Grey spoke about the 'lights of Europe going out' at the advent of war, it seemed as if the 'light of life' had been virtually extinguished in John. The youthful, fit man was now unrecognisable, with drooping, hunched shoulders, as he sat each day staring into a vacuum of emptiness, his lungs damaged by poisonous gases.

In his one year on the Western Front, John witnessed such atrocities and distress that his mind was totally smashed apart. Thousands dying to gain fifty yards of mud and potholes. Hundreds of soldiers hanging, trapped upon the barbed wire that was supposed to have been destroyed by guns in the rear. Generals sat twenty miles from the front, issuing suicidal orders, killing thousands of men in an attack, often in one hour of sheer madness. Bodies blown to pieces, filling the gap between the opposing armies with rotting corpses. Within a year, no soldier could even remember why they were at war, minds just filled with endless propaganda about the 'evil Hun'.

On one advance, a shell from his own artillery landed and exploded behind John, throwing him violently through the air. When John came back to consciousness it was dark and he found himself in a shell-hole. Slowly, his senses returned and he felt his own body to ensure he still had all his limbs. Over the months, John had witnessed many of his company lose limbs in agonising pain. It was one of his many nightmares to wake and find a leg or an arm missing from his body.

Then through the darkness, John could see and hear another soldier in the same bomb hole. The soldier began screaming in absolute horrendous pain, lying in a bloody mess with his intestines hanging outside his body.

John relocated his rifle and crawled towards the stricken man. The soldier was near to death and in spasms of agony from the shrapnel wound that had almost cut him in half. Through his screams, he pleaded with John to shoot him, to put him out of his unbearable pain. Moments later, John took his rifle and shot the soldier through the head at point blank range. The soldier's blood splattered all over John's face. It was not a humane decision, but a selfish one taken by John. He did not do it to stop the suffering of the fellow soldier but because he could no longer stand the screaming that tore through him. The shot brought peace for a few seconds, but soon, the man's screams returned and would remain locked in John's mind for eternity.

Morality, ethics, humanity and God were lying crushed in the trenches of this barbaric conflict. John had quickly learnt that to survive meant looking after yourself. Don't make friends as death soon snatched them away. Never be in the first line over the top, always hang back. When in 'no man's land' keep low to the ground and run behind someone else. Locate the shell holes, taking 'time out' in the hope the whistle will sound out a retreat. It had become kill or be killed, friend or foe, a selfish innate desire just to stay alive. He did not want to be a dead hero. Society, order, religion and righteousness was the province of the politicians safely tucked up back home to pontificate about. For John, he had long ago lost his soul. God lay unstirring and buried in the thick slime of the mud, nowhere to be seen in his 'no-man's land'.

Somehow, John managed to crawl back towards his own lines just as clouds of poisonous gas drifted across the battlefield to herald a counterattack. He cut himself to ribbons battling through the barbed wire, eventually falling, half-conscious, into his home trench. He was taken to the field hospital and after his bodily wounds healed, John was transferred back to England to a specialist hospital lung unit to treat his poisoned organs, before he was moved on for a longer spell to a military mental health facility in the Scottish Highlands.

Vera was not allowed to visit John in Scotland so when he finally came home, she could not believe that this man was the same one that she kissed goodbye nearly three years ago. His life force, his vitality, his joy, his freedom of spirit felt as though they had all been extinguished and replaced by a shell of a man, broken in mind and body, often shaking with the terror of his experiences and nightmares.

Vera still loved him, caring for him and his needs but it was hard for her to witness such devastation of a life. There were moments when she wondered if it would have been better if he had been killed in action and like so many other wives, received the news informing her of his death. Surely that would have been an improvement on the living hell he now experienced, where his mind remained sealed in the horrors of barbaric, trench warfare. He was alive and yet, John, her former husband, was gone; dead to her and the world.

In such harrowing and trying times there was only one happy occasion that Vera could recall. One morning she awoke to feel John's hands caressing her back. Since returning, John had not touched Vera in an intimate way. Vera turned to face him and noticed that his eyes were closed, locked away from his present world. She returned his advances and then, pulling her nightdress over her head Vera moved on top of him, placing his erect member inside her, recalling how much John enjoyed this way of lovemaking in the past. Within moments Vera felt a warm surge of his life exploding within her. She looked up and saw John's eyes had opened, tears running down his cheeks. A spark of love, hidden so deeply within his broken humanity had survived the appalling slaughter. Maud was conceived.

The remainder of John's life was a constant struggle through physical and mental illnesses. His decaying lungs led to increasingly long bouts of coughing and retching up of green, slimy deposits. It was almost as if he was trying to rid himself physically of the mud and stench of death he'd witnessed. Vera was most affected by the darkness of his mental life. Everything seemed black and full of despair. His demeanour invaded the home, hanging over them and, like his lungs, John's mind seemed to drown in the unceasing tragedy of his war experiences.

Even Vera's pregnancy and the birth of Maud did not lighten John's life. He showed little interest in his daughter as he failed to be involved in all aspects of life. Sitting in his chair, endlessly looking into the coal fire, watching the flames flicker in shades of yellow, blue and reds. Rarely eating or speaking, John was already in another world, re-living the horrific memories, entrenched in shattered bodies, violence and death. Remembering the moment when he jumped into the enemy trench and in a face-to-face encounter, bayonetted a German soldier who had his hands up in surrender. John's rifle jarring in his hands as the steel struck the man's sternum. Then stabbing him endlessly in a frenzy of fear. The nightmare screams never died.

Vera cared for his physical needs but was totally unable to unlock his closed mind. As the months and years went by, she absorbed his depression and trauma. Already an inward-looking personality, his darkness filled her life. She struggled as a mother to find space from caring for John, to spend the necessary valuable time to build a loving relationship with her new-born child. Often, Maud was left to be cared for by grandparents as mental and physical exhaustion engulfed Vera.

1.3 Maud

Maud's memories of those pre-school days of her life with her parents were minimal. Of her father, her pictures were dim and hazy. Maud remembered him sitting in his chair, hour after hour, day after day, gazing at seemingly nothing in the fireplace. Later in life, she recalled that he rarely spoke and she could never remember being held or cuddled by him. One picture that stayed with Maud was that of her mother, helping her father to go the toilet situated in a shed in the back yard, struggling to hold him upright as she took his weight upon her. Maud's most vivid memory though, was the endless coughing and the green deposits into numerous handkerchiefs which were to be found on every surface around the home.

Of her mother, Maud had more memories of those early years. Good times: visiting the sweet shop in town, of walking along the promenade with the wind and sea spray encouraging then to hurry along, of visiting grandparents and being left with them sometimes for days and weeks. But there were sadder thoughts of a mother too often not being present, seemingly away in darker thoughts and exhausted with coping with a needy husband.

Maud's father died a few weeks before Maud was due to begin school. In the middle of the night, Vera awoke to the most piercing scream she had ever heard. Next to her, John was lying with his eyes wide open and waving his hands out in front of him. He was covered in sweat and the veins on his forehead were highly prominent. His distress was more evident than anything Vera had witnessed before. Calmly, Vera stroked him and reassured him that he was now home and at peace. Eventually, his tense muscles relaxed and he fell asleep. In the morning, Vera felt a coldness close to her. She reached out and touched John, feeling death upon him. Having checked the breath of life was no longer within him, Vera went immediately to Maud's room.

Vera woke Maud and dressed her quickly, escorting her out of their home to Vera's parent's house, saying that she would have to stay for several days. Maud could see that her mother was in a distressed and agitated state but was happy that she would have a few days being spoilt by doting grandparents. A week later, Maud returned home to a half-empty house with no father present. Vera explained that her father had gone to be 'with Jesus in heaven'. Maud was totally bemused and asked whereabouts 'heaven' was and could they go and visit her father. Her mother explained that it was too far away, above the clouds in the sky. Maud was simply confused and bewildered. Jesus had even taken her father's chair as well.

The home now felt strange to Maud. It felt so quiet and yet, her father had spoken so few words. In the following months, her mother seemed to cling to Maud, wanting to be with her all the time. Deprived of the task of caring for her husband, Vera appeared lost and mourning the death of her role in looking after John. There was an emptiness in her life after years of seeing to his every need. Vera wandered around the house, aimlessly searching for something to do, trying to occupy herself with tasks in an attempt to throw off the negative thoughts that she had absorbed from her husband's years at war. The mental anguish exhausted Vera and then was followed by anger, as she began to blame John for the black moods that pervaded her life and home. Getting rid of his chair had not appeared to have lightened the atmosphere.

Maud was also struggling. Trying to cope with beginning school after her fifth birthday and then returning each day to a home with a mother who, at one moment was wanting to spend every minute with her and then the next minute, going off into an angry tirade at the smallest matter. Maud became more and more anxious and uncertain, unable to express her confusion and loss other than through an increase in spiteful behaviour towards other children in the school playground and local town parks.

At school Maud found some relief in lessons and learning. She enjoyed reading and especially then, writing imaginary stories about worlds and places that she learnt of through her love of books. Being a quiet child, Maud melded into the background of the class, often going unnoticed by her teachers. She had one special friend whom Maud played with at breaktimes. Margaret was similar to Maud in nature and they shared happily together in games of tick and skipping in the playground.

When they were eleven years old, Margaret left the school and town of Pinton-on-Sea with her family, to move to an undisclosed address in Birmingham in her parents' desperate search to find work during the hard times of mass unemployment at the beginning of the 1930s. They left secretly, late at night, leaving behind a litany of rent arrears and debts. Maud was bereft. Her only friend had gone completely out of her life so suddenly. There one Friday afternoon, Margaret had disappeared forever by Monday morning. No goodbyes, no sad tears of departure, no future contact. It left Maud empty and lonely, unable to verbalise her feelings of loss to anyone, including her mother.

Maud struggled on alone in the remaining three years at school, relieved that on leaving at the age of fourteen, Woolworths were opening a new store in Pinton-on-Sea and recruiting school-leavers for their brand-new shop. Maud applied and was taken on with several others from her school.

Maud's mother, Vera, was pleased that her daughter could now help with contributing to their living costs. Vera had had to give up her job at the bakers when John returned from the war and had been taking in laundry from the big houses for year after year, in trying to provide for her daughter and herself. It had seemed an endless grind of living just on meagre resources, a constant struggle to survive just above the breadline with no luxuries such as holidays.

For Maud, this subsistence existence was a part of the gloom of her early life. Her mother's marriage devastated by John's war and death, leaving Vera unable to come to terms with her loss. Angry that a war not only ruined soldiers' lives but also spread its evil tentacles deep into family life, bringing emotional instability and turmoil for wives and children in future generations. Later in life, after a second world war, Maud would reflect back to childhood days and remember her mother's vehement anger at politicians talking of the 'glorious sacrifice that our heroes made'. Vera abhorred Remembrance Sunday events and refused to ever attend, speaking of the hypocrisy of such events in glorifying war, when in reality it turned men into taking part in savage and brutal acts of violence. Vera had long ago thrown John's medals into the sea from a nearby cliff.

In Maud's first week of work at Woolworths, the small group of new shop assistants were shown around the store and given a series of talks about how the shop operated, its ethos and history. They were informed that a certain Frank William Woolworth had opened the first store in 1879 in New York State, in the United States of America. It was known as the 'five cent' shop as all its products sold for five cents or less. It was a hugely popular marketing tactic and stores spread rapidly across America in the following years. In 1909, the expansion reached England when the first store opened in Liverpool. The five-cent concept changed to the 'sixpence' shop. The new store in Pinton-on-Sea that Maud worked at was its three hundred and thirty-fifth shop in the United Kingdom, demonstrating its popularity with ordinary working people who flocked to F.W. Woolworths, consuming its cheaper products.

Maud soon settled into the routine of her working life. Each day standing behind the counter, serving her customers on a one-to-one basis. As the years went by, the monotony of home and work became one of a lonely routine, even more so after the death of her mother when Maud was twenty-five years old. A brisk nine minute walk each morning to work and a slow, tired, twelve minutes to walk back home. In between, eight hours of routine labour with one hour for lunch and two fifteen minutes tea breaks. 8.30 a.m. to 6 p.m., five days a week, with a sixth, half-day off on Thursday afternoons. It went endlessly on, year after year.

The plainness of Pinton-on-Sea in the off-season matched Maud's life. Into her thirties and still single, no-one was ever seriously romantically interested in her. There were only distant second cousins and cool neighbours. No deep friendships. Set in her ways, already worn down by life's spartan routine, she was beginning to feel old at thirty-three with no prospects of marriage on the horizon.

1.4 Roger

Elizabeth's father, Roger, was a travelling salesman visiting towns such as Pinton-on-Sea to sell toys for a national firm based in London. He stayed in cheap guest houses, living on his wits, a good talker. He was a flashy, outward-going man, who was a loud and seemingly, self-assured, confident person. Busy, on the move all the time with no roots, no lasting relationships.

Roger was originally from the 'big smoke', a son of family traders at local markets in Cheapside, London. His father, Fred was a bully, an aggressive and dominant husband and parent. His word was law in the home and Roger learnt quickly that to avoid a good strapping from his father's belt, it was advisable not to speak unless spoken to. Roger was a quick learner and fast on his toes, as home-life taught him when to duck and weave from the heavy clubbing of his father's hand around his head.

His mother, Elsie, was the total opposite of her husband. She was quiet, withdrawn and reserved, speaking little. In Roger's eyes she appeared as a shadowy figure in the background, suffering constant verbal and physical assaults from her domineering partner. His mother often displayed bruises and Roger occasionally heard loud slapping and whimpering from his parent's bedroom after his father returned home, the worse for wear, after a late night at the pub.

With all the constant restrictions within the home enforced by a tyrannical father, Roger expressed all his pent-up energy in the outside world at school and play with friends. As a child, he bubbled with enthusiasm and life, using his innate intelligence to invent numerous schemes to raise monies for sweets and 'fags'. With little love at home from either father or mother, Roger learnt quickly to be independent, looking after himself, to be 'number one' before anyone else. As he grew into adolescence, his personality reflected his narrow view that the world was about what he wanted and needed.

He began helping on his parent's stall from a young age and then after leaving school, he was selling full-time on the family vegetable pitch. Calling out, chatting up the lady customers, attracting the punters, competing for their attention and then spending time with them, joking to get their future custom, ensuring they would return time and again for the laughter and fun. But then, moving on quickly after the sale and eyeballing the next possible client. His conversation flowed, with his confidence exuding a quick, smart wit, reeling in the next catch.

The war years were when Roger came into his own. Now in his early twenties, he had already built a reputation for 'wheeling and dealing', buying goods at a cheap price and selling on for profit, all unknown to his father and family. He called it his 'evening' job after a hard, long day on the market stall. Having rented a 'lock-up' under the arches of the local railway line, Roger stored and sold a variety of dubious products. His gift of the gab served him well and he gained a 'go-to' name tag, as someone you could approach for a cheap bargain.

With war looming in 1939, Roger was thinking ahead. No

way was he going to be gun-fodder for generals and so planned accordingly to avoid military service. Roger had witnessed so many first world war-damaged veterans on the streets with missing limbs, sat on pavements begging for money for basic food or to drown their horrific memories in alcohol. He started wearing glasses and telling everyone about his poor eyesight. Secondly, he began delivering free vegetables that were left over at the end of the day from the stall to a local doctor, who had been appointed to the Army Recruitment Board in early 1940. When his call-up papers arrived in the summer of that year, Roger failed his medical on extremely poor vision, telling everyone that he could not 'hit a barn door at ten yards!'.

As the war progressed so did Roger's business. His parent's vegetable stall became increasingly denuded of produce and Roger spent more daytime hours, flourishing in dealing in the 'black market'. With the bombing came plentiful opportunities to acquire tradable goods. Roger could often be found in the early hours of the morning helping at bomb sites. Supposedly clearing rubble, Roger was also helping himself to anything that he could conceal and trade.

The risks of being in the path of falling bombs was considerable but Roger thought solely about the possible profits to be made. By 1942, he had moved out of his parent's home and acquired his own rented, terraced house. In the following year, his life changed for the better. The Americans arrived in town with their love of the English and, more importantly for Roger, with lots of money in their pockets. Gone was the need to scour bombed buildings and endanger his life. Cigarettes and nylons became his stock trade supplied by a long list of American 'buddies' he cultivated, through his salesman's easy flowing conversation.

Business boomed for Roger with the nylons trade bringing him into contact with many middle-class young women. The war had broken down many social and sexual barriers, encouraging young people to live for the moment; uncertain that there was to be any future. Some stayed overnight at his home, paying with favours for the nylons, while others wished to enjoy a one-off sexual relationship with an 'east-end' lad from a different culture than their own. One of his well-heeled ladies referred to him as a 'bit of rough on the side' from her officer husband, who was serving abroad in the Armed Forces. On one occasion, he paid dearly for his philandering with a blooded nose and severe headache, when the husband of one of the women he bedded was a professional boxer prior to the war. His profits from his tax-avoiding enterprises were soon wasted away on loose living and his love of drinking.

A year or so after the war ended, Roger's freelance trading ceased. He was on his way home one night from the local pub when, taking his usual short-cut down a dark alleyway, two menacing figures emerged from the shadows. One was the talker, the other the enforcer. The shorter man spoke menacingly saying that his boss, 'Charlie', was upset at Roger for interfering in their business interests and suggested that Roger take a long holiday. This was just a warning, the rotund speaker concluded.

Roger nodded and went to move away, not seeing the fist of the much larger man until it crashed into his chin. Roger fell and knew nothing of the following 'kicking' that broke his arm, three ribs and caused intense bruising and swelling to his 'privates'. When he regained consciousness half an hour later, Roger staggered home, shakenly packed a case and after visiting the hospital, caught a train to Brighton, booking into a cheap guest house. Roger knew all about Charlie's gang's violent reputation and the way others who had crossed Charlie, found themselves in a brick-weighted sack at the bottom of the Thames.

A month later when Roger returned to the East End, he went back to his father's vegetable stall, keeping an eye open for any trouble, watching his back and especially avoiding dark alleyways. The area was now under 'Charlie's' gang's total control with protection rackets, prostitution and illegal trading all sewn up. It was a tough area and Roger decided to 'keep his head down' and wait for other opportunities to arise.

That opportunity, when it arrived, shocked Roger's family when he told them of his new job with Whites. He had got fed up with the long hours on the market, the cold winter days outside. He was young, in his early thirties with the world before him. It was time to move on into a bigger, more exciting life. Post-war, early 1950s and new horizons could be just around the corner away from his now restricted home patch.

He had applied, and in his interview, impressed the recruiting panel of Whites Toy Company with his confidence and passion for selling. He was offered the job of Eastern Region Toy Salesman for Whites. The possibility of a car was promised, sometime in the future and a salary based largely on his success as to how much he sold. Selling in a suit, he now had a respectable job. There would be no more street markets with noise, banter and coarse comments. No more danger from rival gangs, just a golden future with huge commissions begging to be achieved. For Roger, he felt the future was bright with the possibility of rising through an old established firm. Laid out before him was the opportunity to be the best company salesman and the chance of moving onwards and upwards.

1.5 Maud and Roger

Maybe it was the opposites that brought Maud and Roger together. The worldly, outward-looking, confident man, in contrast to the contained, quiet, reserved, small-town woman. Roger first saw Maud one lunchtime, sitting alone on a bench on the front at Pinton-on-Sea, eating her pack of home-made sandwiches. She was sat watching the waves breaking upon the cold, wind-swept sand. Maud was enclosed in her full, long coat, scarf, hat and gloves, protected against the winds of life, enwrapped in her solitary world. He sat beside her and easily drifted into conversation. Her quietness allowed him the stage, her timidity encouraging him on.

Later, at six o'clock, Roger was there to meet her at the staff door as she finished work. He walked her home through the rain and so began Elizabeth's parent's courtship. They met mainly at weekends — Roger travelling away through the week with his work. He was still trying to sell Whites' selection of toys in the eastern regional town shops. Then, he would return to Pinton-on-Sea on Friday evenings, to woo his new-found love. He had found weekend lodgings in the town to pursue his goal.

Maud was confused by the salesman's attentions. In her youth, young men had not given her a second look. She excused her lack of boyfriends on the need to look after her widowed mother, whose spirit was broken and whose mind began to wander in her grief and confusion. Maud felt she had had no time for herself but now, with Mother dead and Maud in her thirties, time was moving past her.

She had no experience of courtship to draw upon. There was no close family or friend to turn to for advice and no one to offer her a listening ear. Her only knowledge was half-truths and whispers about men. Maud recalled her mother's warnings about an undefined evil. It was something that 'nice' people do not speak about, something hidden away, something unpleasant and something dirty.

Maud looked into the full-length mirror in her bedroom. She did indeed look so ordinary, unskilled in making herself attractive and feminine. But she did have attributes as she slowly undid her blouse and slipped off her undergarments.

Her breasts were full and firm with erect, brownish nipples. They were rounded and desirable. A slight tremor ran through her. Then, a hot flush followed, as she quickly covered herself up. Her shame was reflected in a burning face but also in a coldness shuddering through her body.

Their courtship stumbled on, with Roger leading the way while Maud struggled with mixed emotions. It was after two months that they first kissed; an embarrassing coming together. He was too passionate, pushing, thrusting into her mouth with his tongue, while she was untutored, feeling awkward. Their teeth clashed and grated together.

A month later, during a kiss goodnight, Roger placed his left hand on her right breast. Maud immediately stiffened, became tense, unsure, ashamed and later, in the darkness of her bed, she burst into tears, confused at her mixed feelings of pleasure and disgust as she recalled that moment of touching.

Roger reflected that life was improving and his courting

of Maud was progressing, as he made his way home through the poorly lit, terraced streets. The rain had stopped. His overtures were slowly moving towards his goal. Although she had taken his hand away from her breast, it was after a few moments. He had felt her nipple through her clothing. It had become erect, responding. Roger whistled as he walked on, remembering previous women he had known. Those brief relationships which never lasted more than a few weeks or months, always moving on, wanting more and different new conquests. Life was good.

But then, another reality intervened.

He reached into his coat pocket for a cigarette. It was his last one and he realised that he had no money to buy any more until the next payday. Maybe life was not quite so good. Sales were down again and his commission would be lower this month as a result. Money in the towns was scarce for everyone and used only on basics. He journeyed from town to town, visiting store after store. No sales or only small orders of the more popular lines.

His life was an endless series of squalid lodgings with few comforts. Often, only a bare room with a basic sink and cold water to wash in. Third rate food was all he could afford on his basic income. The glamour of the travelling salesman was becoming lost in the monotony and routine of the job. There was the difficulty of getting to see managers at stores and their demeaning of him as a travelling salesman. The suitcase was a lonely companion.

It was time to change, to settle down and to find a base with home comforts. Slippers by the fire, dinner cooked and on the table each day, a warm full bed. He needed a home, a woman, a centre for his life. The woman, Maud, well she would provide for some of his basic needs. An ample body with full breasts, but she was a bit ordinary looking. Love? He wasn't much of a romantic and all that 'sloppy, feeling' courting. The rain started again, this time falling heavily, dripping off his hat. He stopped whistling, hurrying on into the night, hoping for a new day.

Through her tears Maud saw her suitor as a way out from the dreariness and routine of her life in Pinton-on-Sea. Maybe it was the opportunity for a more colourful, exciting life in the future. Possibly, it could offer a new world ahead, full of change and variety. Maud hoped Roger would signify a new beginning, a chance to move out of her set, enclosed world. A Sales Executive for a national firm with real prospects to move into management. Roger said how highly he was regarded by Head Office. He said that they described him, 'as one of their top salesmen in the country' with 'a dynamic personality'. And his stories of all the wonderful places he had visited and all the experiences he had encountered sounded a world away from Maud's mundane daily life.

Maud had only one hesitation.

It was when he touched her. She inwardly shrank and retreated into herself, something closing down and a barrier came up. Maud's mother's words echoed through her. This was wrong, something 'good girls' do not do. The touching, the wandering hands, the tongue intruding, was leaving her with feelings of shame and disgrace. Maud felt herself shrinking into herself, questioning her heightened arousal and guiltily remembering the Vicar's message from the pulpit about sins of the body. His thunderous word, shouted out about the evils of lust and fornication and the importance of keeping oneself clean and pure. Her only knowledge of her sexuality was how one should suppress one's emotions, subdue bad thoughts and hold everything within, tightly. Maud drew the blankets up securely around her neck and her insular world.

It was a beautiful late summer's day when Roger proposed to Maud. They had taken a picnic basket into the countryside, away from the sea and the crowds. Sitting hand in hand on the bus ride through the country lanes, was followed by a walk across the fields and through a wood to arrive at a quiet, idyllic spot on the banks of a small stream.

Away from the real world and alone together they shared their packed lunch of egg sandwiches, pork pie and cake, with a bottled beer for Roger. Maud was happy and the sun shone brightly on her summer frock leaving her feeling warm and content.

After their picnic, they lay upon the grassy bank as she listened to his endless stories of his travels and the towns he visited. Maud liked being with someone and not alone and it was good having Roger pay attention to her. Another person just being there. Slowly, with the afternoon sun at its height, Maud drifted into a light sleep feeling secure in his arms.

Half asleep, half awake, Maud felt his hand upon her leg. Instantly, she became tense. A tightness enwrapped and gripped her. But, patiently and tenderly, Roger continued to stroke her leg through her dress and the tension passed for Maud.

She began to relax again and with a mixture of drowsiness and warm sun, Maud felt more reassured by his caressing. Roger recognised the change in Maud's body and took this to be a sign to proceed further, a mistaken indicator of encouragement and agreement.

He moved his hand up inside her dress, across her nylons

to the bare skin of her thighs. Maud froze, unable to respond in any way. She was incapable of moving and was struck dumb in terror. All emotions held in abeyance, the body tightly clamped down, her breathing stopped. Maud, in her inexperience of life, was powerless to react in any way. He pulled aside her knickers, lost now in his own personal lust, totally unaware of her needs or feelings. Roger was rushing to gorge himself in his carnal desires, not understanding her body, just seeking his own gratification and pleasure.

As his fingers forced their way into her, Maud fainted.

It was afterwards, as Maud recovered, that Roger proposed to her on that riverbank. Guiltily, he suggested that maybe it might be a good idea if they got married, the right thing to do. Still in a daze, mixed-up in her emotions, Maud nodded her consent. The afternoon had worn on and the sun was going down behind the dark woods. The warmth of their day had ended and the threat of a storm was in the air.

Two months later they were married. It was a sparse affair with only twenty guests invited. None of Roger's family attended as he had not bothered to keep in contact.

Moving on for Roger, also involved not looking back, his working pattern merging with all aspects of his life. Maud got hold of a second-hand wedding dress that just about fitted and Roger wore his best suit that he kept for visits to Head Office. There was to be no honeymoon. That would come later, explained Roger, when the sales picked up and the car, he kept telling Maud he would soon have, could transport them to Scotland or Wales for two romantic weeks together.

The marriage service took place at St. Mary the Virgin Church, a huge, barn-sized, Victorian, red brick building with numerous statues of Our Lady prominent. The vicar introduced himself as Father Harold, a high churchman. He had met them a week before in a gloomy side-room of the church and told them about the 'sanctity' of a life-long marriage. He had talked non-stop for half an hour, never once seeking their thoughts or feelings. Telling Roger of his duty to provide and Maud of her duties in the home. Instructing them of the need to only have sexual intercourse for the raising of a family.

A routine talk that he had given for the past thirty years in exactly the same way. His obscure language, spoken in a strange, churchy voice, continued into the service using words beyond their understanding such as 'sacraments' and 'procreation'. The liturgy centred around old-fashioned words such as 'thee' and 'thou': phrases that were not used in everyday language by Maud. She was bewildered and confused by the meaningless service.

The priest even got her middle name wrong but she felt too much in awe of his power and position to correct him. He raced through the service and they were out in twenty minutes, bumping into the next couple waiting their turn in the queue.

Maud left the church with a feeling of merely being a part of one of those new production lines found in the big factories, merely a number, uncared for, an entry in the church register, another fee collected. Roger left the church pleased it was so quick and looking forward to the first of many pints. As they walked away from the church, a sea mist rolled into the town, covering it with a blanket of grey and blotting out the low autumn sun.

They had hired the back room at The Bosun's Inn for the reception. Roger, being a regular visitor to the pub, had done a deal with the landlord. Sandwiches, sausage rolls and pork pies were the mainstay of the food provided, with a small wedding cake made by one of Maud's cousins. Roger drank too much and Maud sat waiting. Eventually, the party broke up and they made their way to Maud's home for their first night spent together.

The memories of that first night would shape the marriage that they shared together. Roger, fuelled with beer, was eager and lustful. He had decided not to touch Maud again after the riverbank incident and to wait for this night. For him, the waiting was now over and he was desperate to claim his rights.

Maud was anxious, uncertain and not really knowing what was to come. No one had ever explained to her what this night fully involved. She only knew of something about duty. On hearing that she was soon to marry, one of the older women at work said she just had 'to grin and bear it' on her wedding night. The rest in the store's canteen all laughed and cheered, assuring her that the men soon got fed up with it. All of which just added to her apprehension.

It was all over in a few moments. She had changed into her best nightdress in the spare bedroom while he had got into bed. The moment she joined him in bed he climbed on top of her. Maud was amazed at the hardness of his member and the pain she experienced as he entered her. There were no words of endearment, no soft whispering in her ear, no thought as to her feelings. He grunted and pushed deeper into Maud with her legs flapping inelegantly in the air. Within seconds he came and she could feel a surge of wetness within her.

He rolled off, lighting a cigarette before falling asleep.

Maud lay there in shock and dismay.

1.6 Elizabeth's childhood

Elizabeth's memories of her father were few. She remembered his hat, how he wore it half-cocked on his head. She could still recall sitting upon his shoulders as they walked down the town's promenade on a warm, summers day and stopping for an ice cream cornet. Her father argued with the ice cream man about his prices being far too high. Elizabeth recalled laughing as she noticed the fast-melting ice cream dripping onto his ever-present hat. Another memory was playing ball with him in their small backyard. Her father trying to teach Elizabeth how to kick the ball, but she insisted on always picking the ball up, determined to play ball the way she wanted.

But there were other darker memories too.

There was the shouting and the loud banging of doors being slammed in the house.

Of the raised voices in arguments that seemed endless to her. Waking one night and sitting on the stairs, listening to her parents argue and that sound that she would never forget. The sound of a hand viciously slapping a face; hard skin upon soft, accompanied with her mother's screams and tears. Of rushing back to bed and hiding away, shaking uncontrollably under the blankets.

And only one other memory remained of her father and that was his many visits to her bedroom on his return from the pub. He would stagger into her room, often waking her as he bumped into and fell over her toy box. Elizabeth remembered him always so close to her face, with his beer-laden breath, followed by his endless talking to her about his work. On and on he would speak about how good he was at his job, 'the best salesman in the world' he would claim. Story after story, spoken through his stale breathe as Elizabeth tried to snuggle lower into her bed. With no one else to listen to him in the house, it was to Elizabeth that he turned for reassurance.

One Monday morning, he had left with his case to visit shops in towns along the coast, never to return. Out of the door and out of their lives. The following week when he had not returned, Maud rang Whites Toy Company's Head Office, to be told he had been dismissed for missing his sales targets for the last six months. Gone out into another world, gone without a word.

Elizabeth was just three and a half years old when her father left. She was unable to put her feelings of loss into words, unable to articulate her emotions. Here one day, he was gone forever the next. Elizabeth returned to wetting the bed, to regular tantrums, to being disobedient and awkward. Subconsciously blaming her mother for her loss but also, deep within her, guiltily relieved there was no more shouting and screaming, no more of his interrupting her sleep with his constant talking about himself.

Later, looking back in life, Elizabeth came to understand that at this time in her early life she appeared to lose the closeness and love of both parents in that one moment of time. Her father had walked away from a sour and acrimonious marriage; gone apparently, with the barmaid from the Bosun's Inn, to manage a pub in the Midlands. Elizabeth was left alone, bereft, feeling unwanted and unloved. Her mother turned inward into herself. She was angry at the abusive relationship with her husband, being deserted, unable to express her feelings to anyone. But she still saw him every day in Elizabeth's eyes and in other aspects of her daughter's personality.

After a while, Elizabeth's life settled again and the bedwetting became less regular and her tantrums were fewer. Her mother had lost her job at Woolworths when she became pregnant with Elizabeth, as was the company's policy in those days. To make ends meet with only Roger's meagre wage, she had returned to work after Elizabeth was six months old and weaned from the breast. Maud was now employed at the local grocers' shop around the corner from their home.

Elizabeth was left for a shilling a week, with a childless lady down the street for the five weekdays that Maud worked. Ethel was a kindly lady in her late forties who had been married for over twenty-five years. She brought a balance into Elizabeth's life with her care and interest. Ethel had a collection of toys accumulated from local rummage sales which Elizabeth spent the morning alone playing with. Ethel always seemed to find a new toy each week to add to the toy box. Then, after Ethel had done her housework in the morning, they would have a sandwich and drink of milk for lunch. But it was the afternoons that Elizabeth loved most when Ethel played games with her and taught her nursery rhymes to sing.

Her mother was always too tired when she came home from work to play with her.

By the time a meal was prepared it was bedtime for Elizabeth. Her mother was too exhausted trying to cope on her own, to bother with reading Elizabeth a good-night story. Only at weekends did they spend time together. Going to the local park and playing on the swings and the roundabouts. Walks along the front, dodging the waves on windy days, as the sea hurtled its spray-like way across the promenade. On some Saturdays when Maud had to work overtime, Elizabeth would go with her mother to the grocers and enjoy helping in the shop. Saturdays always ended with the evening visit to buy their fish and chip supper wrapped in newspaper. To sit and eat, looking out to sea watching the endless waves rolling in. Elizabeth often wondered where the waves kept coming from, they seemed inexhaustible, on and on, never stopping.

There were some good moments but Elizabeth also remembered the deep sadness that surrounded her mother. The stigma Maud felt from gossiping neighbours of being left for another woman and now alone. The times when she seemed apart and distant, enclosed in another far-away world. Pre-occupied with inner thoughts and stunted by bad experiences. Swamped by a heaviness, a darkness, something she seemingly could not shrug off.

At the age of five, Elizabeth started school and entered a different environment. She still continued to be looked after by Ethel who took and collected Elizabeth to and from school each day as well as caring for her during school holidays. Elizabeth's mother, Maud, became even more distant, not on hand to share Elizabeth's school experiences.

It was Ethel who asked her what she did each day at school. Ethel who helped Elizabeth with her first day tears, cuddled and reassured her when she was upset. Ethel who listened to her early efforts at reading and counted along with her. Together, Elizabeth and Ethel would listen to Children's Hour on the Home Service with a drink and biscuit in the late afternoon. Only at the weekends did Maud show any interest in her daughter's school life, occasionally helping her with homework that Elizabeth had to have ready for Monday morning.

Elizabeth's school was in dark, Victorian-built buildings. It was divided into two halves with boys in one section and girls in another. In the playground wall that divided the schools, there were holes where you could look through and see the boys playing football. The classrooms were large with high ceilings and each had a stove which burnt coal and gave out heat but only to those who sat nearby. In the centre of the school was a large hall with the classrooms attached all around. Her first teacher was a Miss Taylor, an elderly spinster, who always had her slivery hair in a bun at the back of her head. She was very experienced with young children, being kind and gentle, like a grandmother to the children.

For Elizabeth, this was the first time she had been with other children. Initially she was frightened and withdrawn. The noise and the frenetic rushing around in the playground found Elizabeth standing alone in a corner. As others began to make friends in her class, Elizabeth was left behind, not knowing how to play with other children. As birthday party invites circulated, Elizabeth always found herself left out.

She rarely spoke in class, only occasionally putting her hand up to answer a question. One day she wet herself rather than bring attention to her desperate need, so it was left to a girl sitting nearby who shouted out, "Elizabeth has wet herself," bringing upon Elizabeth utter shame and humiliation — one of those dark moments that remained locked into her memory through the whole of her life.

Gradually, over time, Elizabeth got used to the routine of school life. She loved story time towards the end of each school afternoon and was often transported to wonderful places in her imagination, to fairy kingdoms and glamorous palaces with charming and handsome Princes. The stories took Elizabeth to a much happier place than her own. Elizabeth was quick to learn how to read and was aided by Ethel who now acquired old children's books from a second-hand stall on the market, instead of the toys of Elizabeth's early days.

After Children's Hour finished on the wireless, they would sit together on the settee, taking turns reading from the old books Ethel brought home. It carried Elizabeth to places such as tropical islands searching for treasure with the characters becoming vivid within her. The parrot attached to Long John Silver's shoulder, his crutch tapping out on the road, his scarred face with an eye patch and long hair under that funny-shaped hat. His frightening messages with 'back spots' held Elizabeth in awe, half-way between wonder and being scared out of her wits.

But these imaginary worlds contrasted deeply with her life experiences in Pinton-on-Sea. At home, her mother seemed to be sliding further away from her. Often Elizabeth would find her sat in an unlit room staring, seemingly, into the darkness. Her mother would go for hours without speaking, apparently wrapped up in her own private thoughts. Eating little and uninterested in her food, often forgetting to cook dinner and sending Elizabeth out to get some fish and chips. Sometimes disappearing for hours on end, returning without explanation, looking lost and in a daze, unaware where she had been.

At school, Elizabeth progressed steadily making one or two friends but no deep relationships. Occasionally she was invited to other children's homes for tea but never returning the invitation for the other child to come to her house. Apart from her reading and writing, Elizabeth struggled at other schoolwork, particularly with sums and number work where she was in the remedial group.

At the age of eleven, the school decided that Elizabeth was not clever enough to be entered for the Eleven Plus examination and so the following September, she moved to the new concrete-built secondary modern school on the outskirts of Pinton-on-Sea, as opposed to the ancient grammar school in the nearby wealthy market town of Tuxbury.

On the first day at her new school the Headmistress, Miss Crosby, addressed the new entrants from high on a stage in the assembly hall informing them of the rules and aims of Pinton High School for Girls. The rules were exhaustive and enforced by staff keeping to the letter of the headmistress's law. The aims, Miss Crosby explained, included preparing 'her' girls to take on their future role of serving society in offices and shops and particularly, in learning the skills necessary for being good housewives later in life.

Elizabeth found everything about life at the secondary school very regimented and structured. Walking along corridors on the left side, no running within the buildings, referring to all staff as 'Miss', regardless as to whether they were married or not, no speaking in class unless replying to the teacher, chairs placed on desks in a particular way at the conclusion of the final lesson of the day. As well as staff enforcing Miss Crosby's endless rules and regulations, twenty of the senior pupils were dragooned into a regiment of 'prefects', who lined the main corridors to ensure that no-one spoke to and from morning assembly.

School uniform was rigidly adhered to with no variations whatsoever allowed. Woe betide any girl who arrived at school in any footwear other than the prescribed, out-of-date, formal, laced-up, black shoes. With the explosion of 1960s fashions in society and the freedom to wear outrageous clothes, school uniform was one of Miss Crosby's main battlegrounds to maintain 'decent' standards.

These were just some rules from hundreds of rules and regulations that she would remember and which remained within Elizabeth for years to come. Failure to follow these strict rules resulted in punishments: beginning with lines writing out one hundred times, 'I must not…' followed by the crime committed. The ultimate sanction for consistent infringement of Miss Crosby's ordered regime was six strikes with the ruler across the hand, administered privately in the headmistress's study. For a more serious offence, the punishment was in full public view during assembly before the final hymn was sung.

Elizabeth concurred with the endless rules of the school wishing to keep a low profile. Within her though, was a growing yearning to be able to express herself, to be away from the petty restrictions imposed upon her, released from the smallness of her hometown. Elizabeth listened to her mother's account of her grandfather's tragic life, of a young man who loved the open-air freedom of the countryside life until maimed and restricted by war. On another occasion, whilst lying awake one night, Elizabeth pondered that maybe it was her father's job as a travelling salesman, always moving on, restless, that was a part of her increasing need to break free.

The lessons at Pinton High reflected Miss Crosby's aim to produce homemakers or girls to work in respectable jobs, such as office work, with a curriculum of Cookery, Needlework, Typing and Shorthand, alongside a little Biological Science,

Mathematics, English, History, Geography and Physical Education. Elizabeth coped with most subjects but particularly disliked the Games lessons, standing in the freezing cold, winds blowing in off the sea, as she waited forlornly for someone to throw the netball to her. If the weather was too wet, the girls would be herded into the assembly hall and taught dancing where Elizabeth always ended up as the man taking the lead, which she loathed.

Elizabeth found some solace in the English lessons and her love of reading was encouraged by her teacher, Miss Hughes. The reading of novels was guided by her teacher and she read works by Dickens, the Bronte sisters and her favourite author, George Eliot. Elizabeth would spend hours alone in her room devouring the three books she borrowed each week from the Town Library. As well as her English lessons, Elizabeth also enjoyed Typing and Shorthand classes with her love of words, obtained from her extensive reading, helping her come top of her class in this subject.

Elizabeth continued avoiding any deep friendships with other children at her secondary school fearing that they might want to come to her home and with that, experience her mother's dark moods. As a loner, with few friends, she was occasionally a target for hurtful comments by other children. They taunted her about her absent father and her strange mother, leaving her in floods of tears.

In her third year at the school, this baiting reached a new level. Teachers at the High School did not look forward to lessons with third year classes. This, they believed, was the most difficult and unpleasant year group of girls to teach. Years one and two still displayed interest and enthusiasm for the new school and its different approach compared to their primary schools. Then, in year four, pupils were focussed more upon achieving some success in external examinations. But year threes' attitudes and behaviour seemed to reflect the girls' changing bodies and movement from children towards adulthood. Physical changes in menstruation, pubic hair and emerging breasts combined with emotional turbulence as image and adolescence took hold, in an era where little or no social or sexual education was available, either in school or at home from parents.

With Elizabeth at this time, the pressure upon her increased as other girls saw an easy opportunity to ridicule someone with no friends to defend her. A lone target who lacked confidence to stand up for herself. On one occasion after school, two girls followed Elizabeth home, knocking on her door, which was opened by her mother and thereby they gained entrance to the house. The next day, their distorted and exaggerated account of Elizabeth's mother and her home was all over the school. Everywhere Elizabeth went around the school, there were small groups of girls laughing at her or making snide and hurtful comments. The two girls were revelling in the limelight of their capers and their profiles were heightened for a short time at Elizabeth's expense. The following couple of days, Elizabeth feigned headaches and sickness, avoiding school until the following week.

Outside of school, life was changing rapidly.

The austere, hardship days of the war and the rationing of the early fifties were giving way to a new era. The 1960s saw new freedoms with pop groups bringing youthful rebellion to the fore through their loud and popular music. The town was invaded on Bank Holidays by the new youth cultures of Mods and Rockers. Their scooters and motorbikes tearing through the seaside town, with pitched battles taking place between the groups hurtling along the front and the beach, scattering the sunbathers and overturning the ice cream stalls. Groups of youths, with transistor radios, menacingly gathering on street corners, blasting out the music of The Beatles, the Rolling Stones, Manfred Mann, The Hollies and others, to the annoyance of older residents. Clothes fashion was revolutionised with more colourful and outrageous outfits sold in trendy new shops opening on the High Street. New words arrived in the country's dictionary with concepts such as 'hippies', 'flower power' and 'free love'.

But for Elizabeth, all this appeared to pass her by. She took little interest in the 'pop' scene and she dressed modestly. It was almost as if she was unable to break free from the enclosed life that she had led throughout her childhood; unable to throw off the shackles and restrictions life had dealt her.

Her home remained the same. It was still enveloped in the darkness of her mother's grey moods with little colour, even the heavy wood panelling adding to the gloomy atmosphere. Stained cupboards and wardrobes, together with poor lighting, increasing the mood of bleakness that prevailed.

As Elizabeth entered her adolescent years, her relationship with her mother became more estranged. Few words were spoken between them and they did fewer things together, even the Saturday night fish and chips had disappeared off their menu.

One day in the spring of 1966, Elizabeth discovered some tablets belonging to her mother that were half-hidden in the kitchen cupboard. When Elizabeth asked about the tablets in a rare conversation with her mother, Maud explained that she had been to the doctor because she had felt a bit 'down'. The doctor had told her 'to pull her socks up' and 'to give thanks that she had so much in life' and wrote her out a prescription for the tablets. Her mother said she had taken one or two but they did not make any difference, so she had given up on them.

Elizabeth now walked to and from school on her own every day and on return after school, let herself into the house. She occasionally visited Ethel down the road but as the years went by, they drifted apart, especially when Ethel began looking after another little child.

It was Miss Hughes who became the closest adult to Elizabeth and it was to her English teacher that she turned to for help on the school day, when she discovered blood in her underwear in June 1967. Her teacher took her aside and explained that this happened to all girls and was a part of growing up. Miss Hughes asked as to whether her mother had told her anything about this and then went on to explain more about sanitary towels and how babies are created. Elizabeth listened intently, amazed at the words she heard. Her own knowledge was limited to overhearing some of the girls whispering about boys' 'parts' and one of the girls who had seen her brothers, describing it, amidst the girls' giggles. From that conversation with Miss Hughes, Elizabeth used her pocket money to buy her sanitary towels, never saying anything to her mother. Her mother never enquired.

At the age of fifteen in 1969, Elizabeth left the High School and applied to the local Technical College in the principal town of the county, to take a Typing and Shorthand course. She had only taken two CSE examinations in English and Cookery and a City & Guilds exam in Typing and Shorthand, but the 'Tech' was hugely impressed by her wide range of vocabulary and the expertise of her typing and so offered her a place. It meant an hour-long bus journey each day and a ten-minute walk from the bus station to the college. Then there was a repeat journey back after a long day's study.

This was a defining moment in Elizabeth's life. She loved the study and the atmosphere of the college with its more relaxed regime. There was extra freedom with quiet study periods where you looked after yourself with a more adult and casual relationship with her tutors. As well as typing and shorthand lectures, there were also tutorials about the structures of offices and people's responsibilities within workplaces, about deportment and dress codes. It was a two-year course and Elizabeth blossomed. She loved the whole ethos of the college and showed that determination of character that had been hidden so deep in her persona. Each month, she would be at the top of her class in the assessments that they undertook and at the end of the first year, was awarded the Year One prize for the Best Student; a certificate and presentation evening she did not bother telling her mother about.

Elizabeth felt like a different person. It was as if she had escaped the blanket of despair that cloaked her home and the town of Pinton-on-Sea. She walked through the lighter, pleasant county town of Tuxbury from bus station to the college with a confidence and freer spirit. She began noticing the green, well laid out parks and the wonderful trees, whilst feeling a huge sense of release, of bonds becoming unshackled.

But at the end of each day came the return journey. To go back to a cold home, with a mother who had ceased working and become increasingly a hermit-like figure locked within her walls, unable to share Elizabeth's joy of having found a new life. The small, dingy house, with its unpleasant smells and depressing decor, contrasted with the openness and light of the college and the county town. The restricted home lifestyle reminded Elizabeth of the lack of real love in her early life.

Elizabeth had also changed physically and was now a young lady. With the college course and talks on deportment and dress codes in the office, she looked more to her appearance. Elizabeth started to value herself and began confidently buying clothes that made her look more mature and grown up. She also learnt about make-up and its appropriate use in the office setting and used her part-time weekend work wages from selling rock and sweets on a sea-front stall, to finance her new look. She knew she was not glamorous but she had beautiful, wide, dark brown eyes and a lovely, full smile, inherited from her father.

Young men began noticing Elizabeth and one day, on the bus journey back home, a fellow traveller and student sat next to her on the crowded bus and began 'chatting her up'. Bill was on the motor mechanics day release course attending college every Wednesday. Just before Elizabeth got off the bus, Bill asked Elizabeth if she would like to go to the pictures with him on Friday night. This was the first time any young man had ever spoken to her in such a way. Elizabeth had attended an all-girls school and now a secretarial course for young ladies only, so there had been no intimate contact with the opposite sex before this bus journey. Elizabeth was totally flustered and at a loss as to how to respond. She blushed deeply, stammering some made-up excuse saying that she was busy this Friday and rushed to get off the bus. The following Wednesday, Elizabeth caught the later bus back home.

1.7 Maud

It was after that first night with Roger that she had realised her mistake. Then, it gradually dawned upon Maud in the following weeks and months, that he had no real love for her. He was too interested in his needs, too centred upon what he wanted. Maud felt trapped into a marriage that had nothing for her. She hoped that becoming pregnant would help and a child would bring them together but it was not to be. Roger remained steadfast in his selfish ways demanding sex and a wife to serve him home comforts. Maud heard the rumours of him with the barmaid at the Bosun's Inn, but he denied everything, saying it was just small-town gossip. They argued increasingly and on one occasion, he hit her.

Initially, Maud was glad when he left, never to return and she threw his remaining clothes into the dustbin. But as the months went by, Maud became more and more troubled. Being called names by neighbours, the snide comments made behind her back, the knowing looks some people gave her and the disgrace of apparently being judged as not having been a good enough wife, piled up for her.

She tried to provide for her daughter, Elizabeth but those big, brown eyes haunted her, reminding her daily of Elizabeth's father. Maud made an effort, especially at weekends, taking Elizabeth to the park, on walks and treating her to fish and chips on Saturday nights. But she couldn't get over the memories left by Roger, of the abuse, the hurtful sex, the drunken nights, the shouting and swearing at her, the absence of any tender love. Maud tried to shut it out of her life but unintentionally she shut out Elizabeth, as she transferred her hurt onto her daughter.

As the years went by, she locked all of this within her and as she did so, life became even more desolate for her. There was no-one to turn to, no close friend, no loving relative. Alone, Maud struggled on, turning more and more inward.

On one occasion, she went to the doctors but her GP was of the old school, prescribing tablets almost before she had sat down. He then talked about getting on with life and putting one's back into it and similar unhelpful phrases. Eventually, Maud found it harder and harder to get out of bed in the morning. There was no energy, no interest, no life and it felt like she was walking through a thickness, a fog, that slowed her down.

She lost her job at the grocers and became more and more a recluse, sitting for hours in the dark rooms of the house, walking aimlessly around the town during sleepless nights, dozing through to the afternoon and not bothering to eat; neglecting herself and her daughter.

Maud rarely spoke to Elizabeth when they met in the home. Elizabeth was away at college all day and at weekends and holidays worked on a stall on the sea front. She barely registered that her daughter was growing up, wearing new clothes and using make-up. All of this passed over her in the haze and dark world in which she had regressed into.

Maud decided that she could no longer continue in this living hell. She stepped out of her house into the cloudy night, her empty tablet pot left on the sideboard. It was late February and the cold, east wind, blew a light drizzle through the air. She walked down to the sea front, onto the sands and kept on walking. The water was freezing cold but she seemed not to notice as she became enclosed in her watery grave. She had walked out in the early hours of the morning into the darkest and coldest of all nights.

Her body was recovered the following day, half a mile down the coast on a deserted beach.

1.8 Elizabeth

Elizabeth got out of bed on that cold February morning, washed quickly, put on her make-up, dressed and went downstairs to have some breakfast before leaving to go to college. Her mother was not around but that was not unusual as she often slept all morning since retiring from work. On this Thursday, she had an extra class in the evening and did not return home until late. The house was in total darkness and Elizabeth went straight to bed, presuming her mother was already asleep.

During the late afternoon lecture the following day, a message came requesting that Elizabeth go immediately to the Principal's office. As she entered, Elizabeth noticed that the Vice-Principal, Mrs Lomas, was also present with Mr Taylor, the Principal. A police officer, who was sitting on the far side of the room, stood and came towards Elizabeth. Her mind was in a whirl and the words he spoke made no sense to her. "I have some bad news for you, I'm afraid," he said. She was encouraged to sit down next to Mrs Lomas on a leather settee before the officer continued to inform Elizabeth that her mother had been found dead.

Elizabeth just sat, totally stunned, in a dream-like state, not knowing how to respond. Speechless and unable to put any coherent questions together; shocked into silence. The officer continued to say that her mother's body had been found at the deserted Chatsburn Beach at lunchtime yesterday, by two cliff path walkers.

All that went through Elizabeth's thoughts were the words, 'Why?', 'How?'.

Elizabeth began to shake, trembling uncontrollably. She looked down at her hands wondering why they were moving without her permission. Elizabeth felt that she was sweating but inside she was icy cold. No tears emerged from her eyes in those surreal moments, just the belief that this was not really happening, that she was somehow in the midst of a bad dream. This scene Elizabeth was witnessing was 'make believe'; it was not real. In a moment, the police officer would disappear into nothing and she would wake up, sat at her typewriter surrounded by fellow students in class. Normality would be returned.

Mrs Lomas gently placed an arm around Elizabeth's shoulders and gave her a comforting hug. Quietly, she explained that she would take Elizabeth to her locker to collect her coat and bag and that she would then drive Elizabeth home and ensure someone could be called to be with her. Had she any close relatives or friends that Mrs Lomas could contact? Elizabeth tried to comprehend the question, to process it through her scrambled brain, to think of an answer. To make some sense of the last few minutes.

Eventually Elizabeth replied, "No," she uttered, "there is no one, no one at all."

The car journey home passed in a blur. All Elizabeth could remember was Mrs Lomas trying to be kind, reassuring her that the college would give every possible support to ensure that Elizabeth would be able to complete her course. Mrs Lomas tried to be positive and was confident that Elizabeth had the character to cope with this tragedy using a popular catchphrase that 'time heals'. These words Elizabeth would hear on several occasions over the following days and weeks but Elizabeth did not find that this was so.

Later, as she sat at home, questions started pouring into her mind. How did this happen? What was her mother doing there? Was there an accident? Did she fall? Did someone kill her? The police officer had just stated that further investigations into the cause of her death were proceeding. Elizabeth felt divorced from reality, somewhere alone. The world was continuing outside and around her but she felt no part of it. She was lost in a separate life, apart from any previous human experience she had ever known. Elizabeth could not cry. No tears flowed, not until many years later. It was Ethel, who having lost her husband twelve months before, came to her and helped Elizabeth with the arrangements that had to be made.

The following day the local newspaper had the headline, 'Local woman found drowned: suicide suspected'. It stated that the police believed there was no foul play involved but after the Coroner's deliberations, an Inquest would take place. Elizabeth was aghast and devastated, unable to comprehend what could have driven her mother to take her own life.

Meanwhile, Ethel took Elizabeth to register the death and to visit the only Funeral Directors in town. The Registrar, in a bare, functional office, was efficient in her role but showed little sympathy for Elizabeth's situation. Asking Elizabeth questions concerning details and dates about her mother's life, which in her shocked state Elizabeth found difficult to answer. The Registrar became impatient, pointing out that the interview was for only half an hour and that other people were waiting to be seen.

The Funeral Directors premises were a sombre facility, with dark furnishings and minimal light as if the building was a half-way storage place between the light of life and the darkness of death. The gentleman who dealt with them was dressed in a black, formal suit, very solemn and slow in his mannerisms and movement and in the way he spoke. Mr Gardiner, of Gardiner & Sons Funeral Parlour explained to Elizabeth that as a result of the manner of her mother's death, the local vicar would not allow Maud to be buried in the churchyard, as the ground had been blessed and was holy. Therefore, it was inappropriate for someone who had possibly taken their own life to be interred in sacred ground, as committing suicide was considered a grievous, mortal sin in the eyes of the established church.

Instead, Mr Gardiner respectfully suggested, especially as funds were sparse, that Elizabeth's mother be buried in the paupers area of the Municipal Cemetery behind the Gas Works and that a Free Church minister be asked to say a few prayers at the graveside. A date, two weeks later, was provisionally booked dependent upon the Coroner's enquiries.

A week before the proposed date of the funeral, Mr Gardiner informed Elizabeth that her mother's body had been released by the Coroner and a Death Certificate issued, thereby allowing the arranged funeral to take place the following week. He further inquired as to whether Elizabeth might wish to view her mother in the Chapel of Rest. Elizabeth replied that she needed time to think and would let Mr Gardiner know if she decided to do so.

Later, Elizabeth spoke to Ethel and asked her opinion as to what the correct procedure was in whether to visit a deceased relative. Ethel advised against doing so due to her mother's body having been in the sea for so many hours. Elizabeth was relieved by Ethel's words that she did not have to see her mother, in what could be such a distressing state.

In the morning post on the day of the funeral, Elizabeth received a letter from the Town Hall stating that as she was not yet an adult, she would not be allowed to remain in the council house and should therefore make other arrangements for her future accommodation. They informed her that she had thirty days from receipt of the letter in which to vacate the premises and return all keys to the housing department at the council offices in town. The letter also reminded Elizabeth that she was liable for the rent due in the coming month. There was no mention of offering condolences.

Ethel came to Elizabeth's house and together they walked across town to the Municipal Cemetery. Only three others were present: a neighbour, Mrs Adams who, in earlier days, had worked with Maud at Woolworths, Mr Crawford, the owner of the grocery shop where Maud had worked for many years and the Minister from the local Congregational Church, a Mr Griffiths. The funeral directors came and deposited the cheap, unnamed coffin in the grave, gave Mr Griffiths a small, brown envelope and then drove off. The minister recited several formal prayers then he too, walked away without any words of sympathy to Elizabeth. Maud's life of fifty-one years was all over in less than five minutes. Rejected by 'decent' society and the institutional church, she was entombed in a deep hole, on a cold blustery March day, behind two massive Gas Towers throwing out their waste products into the grey sky above.

Elizabeth and Ethel walked back home in silence.

Ethel offered the spare room in her home to Elizabeth, who gladly accepted and moved in the following week. There was little of Maud's belongings to sort out and Elizabeth packed her mother's meagre belongings, giving her clothes to the Salvation Army. It was strange going through her mother's clothes and possessions, seeing the smallness of her life in the few things she owned. Elizabeth kept just one brooch that Maud often wore in earlier, happier days as a memory of her mother.

Elizabeth offered to pay some rent from her part-time job but Ethel would not hear of it. Three weeks after her mother's death, Elizabeth returned to her course at the college but found it difficult to concentrate on her studies and was often aware that she was struggling to take in the information imparted to her in the lectures.

Her emotions were all over the place. Coming through the early stage of grief and shock, Elizabeth's feelings began to turn to anger. How could her mother do such a thing to her? Why did her mother not talk to her? How could she just leave her in such a state? Had her mother thought as to how her action would impact on Elizabeth's life? Where did she think Elizabeth would live in the future? Did she not love her?

'How could she…?' the words echoed unceasingly through Elizabeth's mind. The anger, the hurt, began to bury itself into her very soul. She could not rid herself of these feelings and her unexpressed angst moved to a hatred of her mother, questioning whether she, Elizabeth, had ever been loved or cared for by either of her parents. There was no one to share these feelings with, no one to hold her hand and listen. Ethel was kind and caring but not the sort of person to understand such mixed-up emotions and Elizabeth could not express to her verbally such deep, dark thoughts.

The suppressed anger came out in different ways. At the college, she found herself verbally hitting out at fellow students. Any little incident would provoke her into an angry tirade and as a result, most students avoided her and she became even more isolated. Her teachers noticed the anger, finding her less cooperative and moody, rarely joining in class discussions, seemingly in a private, enclosed turbulent world of her own. The staff on Elizabeth's course had a partial understanding of the feelings that they imagined Elizabeth was going through and kindly took this into consideration in their dealings with her.

One member of staff, Mrs Andrews, Elizabeth's shorthand tutor, had lost her husband from cancer the previous year and was therefore more empathetic to Elizabeth's emotions. One lunchtime, they sat together and Mrs Andrews shared the death and bereavement of her husband with Elizabeth. She particularly related to Mrs Andrews feeling angry that her husband had died at such a young age leaving her a widow at only forty-five years of age. Elizabeth warmed to her tutor and shared some of the anger she felt at her mother's death but she was still too raw in grief to go on and say what the reasons were for her distress. It still hurt too much and was concealed deep within her. They arranged to meet again but Elizabeth found an excuse not to attend.

Elizabeth also took her unresolved anger out on Bill. They had met again on the Wednesday night bus home and Bill asked Elizabeth if she would like to go for a drive in his Morris Minor Shooting Brake, that he had recently acquired from the scrap heap; renovating it in his spare time outside of his motor mechanics course.

This time she agreed and the following evening they drove out of town into the countryside. They stopped in a farm gate entrance in an isolated country lane and within moments of kissing, Elizabeth encouraged Bill into the back seat of the car where they proceeded to take off their clothes. Elizabeth indulged her pent-up feelings of anger in heated and prolonged sex with a surprised and delighted Bill. She never felt any pain in losing her virginity and took no precautions such was the state of her confused and turbulent emotions.

After an hour of frenzied sexual activity, Elizabeth put on her clothing and left an exhausted and shocked Bill, walking alone through the dark night of her thoughts; not truly understanding what had driven her to such actions. Shame and guilt at her behaviour flooded through her as she stumbled along the road to Ethel's home.

After a bath to try to wash away the previous hour of sex, Elizabeth wrapped herself deep into her bed and wept bitterly under the bed covers. Never again, she resolved, would she do such a thing. She never saw Bill again.

Later, Elizabeth found that as the anger became less intense, it was now replaced by feelings of guilt. Should she have done more to help her mother? Was she solely focussed on herself and her secretarial course to the exclusion of her mother? Why had she not made the effort to talk more to her mother and taken time to listen? Surely, she was aware that her mother's dark moods were a sign of depression and mental illness that required medical help? How had they become so estranged? Was it her fault that her mother had killed herself? Her selfishness? Elizabeth's lack of care for the person who had given her life?

These thoughts were not helped by people's reactions to her. Elizabeth noticed that as she walked along the local streets, neighbours coming towards her crossed over to the other side to avoid talking to her. They even made exaggerated detours to view shop windows on the opposite side of the road, in their overacted desire to ensure they did not have to speak to Elizabeth.

In the local shops, people who would normally have acknowledged her with a greeting, now avoided any eye contact, suddenly becoming intensely focussed upon the magazine that before they were lightly browsing. The shop assistants would speak to her but not look at Elizabeth, seemingly blanking her out. Did they all believe that it was her fault that her mother had taken her own life? An uncaring, self-centred daughter who had driven her mother to such a desperate act?

And then, even later, there came a growing realisation that her childhood had been a damaged one. A father, who had left, deserting her and never bothering to ever make contact again. No Christmas or birthday presents from him, not even a card on her birthday from the moment he walked away through the front door with no kiss goodbye. A mother who rarely cuddled or held her tight, not kissing her goodnight or tucking her up into a warm bed. A parent figure who was often so distant and in a seemingly different world from Elizabeth. Unable to share her thoughts and feelings, locked away in her own dark times, incapable of reaching out to Elizabeth and loving her. Constantly reprimanding Elizabeth that her large, brown eyes were just like her 'rotten' father's, leaving Elizabeth with the negative feeling that she too, like her father, was not loved by her mother.

But despite all these worrying thoughts there was, within Elizabeth, a real determination to put all these things behind her and to live her life. That strong aspect of character now began to surface and with it, the realisation that she had to get away from the past and create her own future. To break away from the small, inward-looking town of Pinton-on-Sea and her family's fractured history in that place to a new, lighter beginning in a fresh setting.

The college helped Elizabeth find employment as a Trainee Secretary at a local Solicitor's firm in the county town of Tuxbury, beginning in September. During the summer, she found a bedsit just down the road from the solicitors and moved in on the 1st September 1971 to begin her new life, even though she realised that hidden, deeply within her, were issues from the past that would trouble her for years to come.

It was a sad farewell to Ethel who had supported Elizabeth as best she could but apart from one or two neighbours, there was no-one else to say goodbye to. Elizabeth packed her two suitcases and caught the bus on which she had often travelled to her Secretarial studies. Despite the last troubled months of her course, Elizabeth had passed all her exams getting distinctions in typing and shorthand.

It was a bus journey that Elizabeth spent in deep thought. The route began at the town's coach station situated near the centre of Pinton-on-Sea where many of the summer visitors alighted for their annual holiday. The bus then wound its way through the town, picking up at various stops including along the promenade. It was the last week of the summer school holidays and the town was at bursting point with parents desperately trying to find something to occupy the children on a grey, dull and windy day with showery light rain coming in off the sea.

Elizabeth noticed the rock and sweet stall that she had worked at during her holiday breaks from her further education course. Colin, the owner, was wrapped in his raincoat as the wind and rain blew the stall's tarpaulin in crazy patterns. The fish and chip shop where they had bought their Saturday night meal flashed by, packed with punters getting their lunch and trying to avoid the inclement weather. Both places brought back memories, some happy but others, reminders of a childhood that was lacking something crucial. Suddenly, her father's hat came to mind with her ice cream cornet dripping onto it as he carried her along the promenade on his shoulders. She shuddered and closed her eyes until they had left the sea front.

The bus was soon full of holidaymakers seeking refuge from the wet coastal town and heading inland to visit the historic town of Tuxbury. Elizabeth looked out of the window as the bus travelled through the outer edge of the town, taking in her ugly, concrete, secondary school which darkened her mood with its memories of a restrictive and repressive atmosphere.

The grey, dismal day of departure spoke volumes to Elizabeth as she reflected upon her stunted and depleted early life. So, little of the bright colours of the summer's seaside resort but sadly dominated by the more desolate character of the off-season tone of life in Pinton-on-Sea.

Elizabeth intended never to return to Pinton-on-Sea. That life was gone forever and she wanted to bury it, to blank it out completely. Elizabeth's only way of coping with her past was to try and concentrate on a future. Her childhood life was too difficult to come to terms with. It was beyond her ability to cope with its sadness and hurt.

Generations of her family had struggled in Pinton-on-Sea, trying to break free from the claustrophobic circumstances that life had brought to them. War, suffering, despair, depression and suicide were all wishing to be left behind by Elizabeth. To be buried in the past.

She looked out of the window as the town disappeared from view and was no more. It was replaced by the beautiful countryside. The endless, green fields interspersed with the gradual rolling hills and valleys containing a wonderful selection of native trees and hedges. It spoke to Elizabeth of a possible new time heralding a break from the past. The animals of rural life, the cows, sheep and horses grazing in the pastures appeared at peace and content with their environment, unhurried and happy with their situation in its idyllic setting.

The journey felt to Elizabeth that maybe she was now beginning to move towards discarding the past shackles of life and breaking free into a brighter and lighter period of her life.

'Then, reality intervened into Elizabeth's mind, as a picture of her mother emerged, walking down the beach towards the sea in the darkness of that final night-time of life, clouding Elizabeth's thoughts for her future.'

1.9 Hampson and Elliot

Hampson & Elliot were a long-established legal firm in Tuxbury with offices in a Georgian, terrace house near the town centre. A gold plate on the pillar by the front door announced the three present partners' names: J.B. Small, S.N. Harthrop & C.G. Onsell, the two original partners long since deceased.

It was a very formal office setting with a reception and waiting area on the ground floor containing a stairway leading upstairs to four offices on the first floor, one for each of the partners and one shared by secretaries and administrative staff. The next floor was where all the client's files were stored together with other office equipment and supplies. The fourth floor was a flat, which at the time Elizabeth started work in 1971, was occupied by an elderly spinster.

The three partners in the solicitor's' firm were very different characters. John Small was officially recognised as the Senior Partner, this being based upon the length of time he had served in the partnership. In all respects, the three solicitors worked in an equal partnership. This ethos was established from the original partners, Malcolm Hampson and Michael Elliot, who were members of the same meeting house of The Religious Society of Friends. As Quakers, they believed in equality of partnership, people working together in harmony and respect for one another. They insisted that future partners also subscribed to this manner of working. This exhibited itself at the regular Monday morning meetings where, after discussion, decisions were made on consensus with each partner having to nod any proposal through in unanimous agreement. Where there was disagreement, the matter would be deferred for further thought and later consideration.

John Small was to become the solicitor that Elizabeth was to work most closely with. He was a very precise and a well-organised person who took seriously his 'senior' role in maintaining the traditions of the legal practice as set out by its founders. He was a family man who loved his wife and children whose photographs he proudly displayed upon his very large desk. Always correct in his dealings with staff and clients, keeping to the formality and old-fashioned principles of the legal profession, Mr Small dealt with all land and property affairs. He was a quiet, unassuming man who brought a sense of decorum and solidity to the office. His only exception to his ordered working routine was an occasional afternoon off to play his beloved golf at the local Tuxbury Golf Club, where he was proudly Club Captain on two separate occasions.

In complete contrast to Mr Small, the second most senior member of the firm in the number of years served, was Stuart Harthrop. He was a 'larger than life' type character. Well-built at over six foot and fifteen stone, one always knew when he was around the building with his raucous laughter and loud voice. He had the gift of being able to talk to all sorts of people, at ease speaking to everyone he met.

Compared to Mr Small's impeccable appearance in sober, meticulous grey suits, Mr Harthrop was often seen in a sports jacket and flannels with his tie inevitably askew. Maybe his demeanour and appearance reflected the clientele that he had to deal with in the criminal fraternity. He was often out of the office attending local Magistrates and Crown Courts or called out in the middle of the night to represent clients being held in the police cells.

The junior of the three partners was Colin Onsell, who specialised in divorce proceedings and the drawing up of wills. He was in his early thirties, married, a small man with a big ego. Mr Onsell dressed impeccably in modern suits and was very aware of changes in fashion. He rarely spoke politely to junior staff, the only exception being if they were young, pretty and female. His divorce work often brought him into contact with vulnerable, female clients who occasionally he would meet outside of office hours. He always wore a hat which, when entering his personal office, he threw at the hat stand in attempts to get it to land on one of the protruding hooks. This attempt to imitate the 'James Bond' character trying to impress Miss Moneypenny resulted in very limited success. Mr Onsell was the only member of staff that Elizabeth did not warm to but it was years later before she eventually associated his hat with her father's.

Elizabeth was obviously nervous and unsure of herself in those first few weeks. Her immediate superior was a Miss Grayson, the Senior Secretary, who instructed Elizabeth in her duties. Elizabeth began with general office tasks: learning routines that were followed, understanding and then doing filing on the third floor and keeping in touch with her shorthand and typing skills. Occasionally, Miss Grayson would allow her to be present with her when one of the partners wished to dictate a letter, getting Elizabeth to take the shorthand and then to type up the letter under her supervision.

Initially, Elizabeth was in fear and awe of Miss Grayson. In her early fifties, Miss Grayson had worked for Hampson & Elliot for over thirty years before Elizabeth arrived. She ruled the office with a firm but fair hand, ensuring that all administrative staff were disciplined in performing their working tasks to a high standard. She was totally aware of all that was going on and ensured that the very highest levels were achieved and maintained by the secretarial staff. Miss Grayson kept strictly to an ethos of what she considered to be appropriate for the legal profession. She never spoke of her personal life and it was not until Elizabeth visited Miss Grayson when she was ill in hospital many years later, that Elizabeth discovered her first name.

Gradually, Elizabeth's confidence grew and she began to be trusted with more responsibility. After only six months, her excellent progress had been recognised by both Miss Grayson and the partners, so much so that she became Mr Small's link secretary, attending to his requests for files, doing follow-up work on client's cases and the taking and typing of letters relevant to Mr Small's work. At the end of her first year, the firm were so pleased with Elizabeth that she received a modest increase in her wages.

There was little jollity at Hampson & Elliot. It had a respectable air which reflected the majority of clients who called to discuss serious matters in land deals, divorce arrangements, the buying and selling of houses and the writing and reading of wills. Consequently, the office ethos and individual members of staff, had to be reserved and show respect and decorum in their contact with the public.

Occasionally, there was a little light relief in the secretaries office with the tradition of birthdays being celebrated with cakes bought from the local baker's shop. At morning coffee break, the secretaries would gather and share the cakes bought by whosever birthday it was. It brought a lighter atmosphere with the moment and there were smiles and occasional laughter. Generally, though, Miss Grayson kept a tight ship insisting on everyone concentrating on the seriousness of their allotted work.

This atmosphere suited Elizabeth as there was little time for small talk and only very rarely would anyone enquire about her personal life or family. This was to be Elizabeth's life and home for the next fifteen years. The elderly lady occupying the upstairs flat died suddenly from a heart attack in early 1973 and Elizabeth asked if she could take on the tenancy. The partners were delighted to have someone whom they could trust and agreed. Elizabeth gave a months' notice on her bedsit and moved into her new, spacious, furnished flat.

In those early years of working, Elizabeth coped by putting everything into her career. She did not want time to think and to remember, so in the first eighteen months Elizabeth would always happily volunteer to work late if required. Increasingly, Elizabeth would be the last to leave the office, sometimes at eight o'clock or even later, totally absorbed in her job. The partners saw the benefit of someone whom they viewed as eager and enthusiastic and also competent in her work, off-loading some of their routine tasks on to Elizabeth.

Mr Small, as the solicitor in the firm who specialised in the house market, encouraged Elizabeth to follow a Legal Executive course at Night School to further develop her career and to allow, though not mentioned by Mr Small, more time for him on the golf course. Hampson & Elliot paid her fees and expenses for the course and Elizabeth spent one evening a week during term time for three years, eventually qualifying as a Legal Executive, again achieving a distinction in her final examinations.

Moving into the flat at the top floor meant Elizabeth had keys to the office and took on the responsibility of opening and closing the premises each weekday. It also meant that Elizabeth could do some work at the weekends as well, using up some of the time she found hard to fill; time when those difficult thoughts and memories came tumbling back.

Elizabeth noticed that she slept well during the weekdays with a regime of working up to twelve hours a day, followed by the cooking of a meal, concluding with watching some television, before going to bed. But at weekends it was different. She slept fitfully, waking several times and often finding hours when sleep would not return. It was in those long and lonely nights that Elizabeth struggled with her demons. Her anger and her guilt, buried deep within her during the busy week, emerging out of the darkness to envelop her. It always surprised her with its continual and endless intensity.

She was struggling with her dreams which were becoming increasingly more vivid and including horrific nightmares. The most common one which constantly recurred time and time again, was located in the sea close to the pier back in her home seaside town. In this nightmare, Elizabeth dreamt that she was floundering, trying to keep her head above the choppy waves, as she desperately reached out a hand to save her mother beside her. Try as hard as she could, Elizabeth could never quite manage to grasp hold of her mother's fingers. Her mother's hand was always so cold, so distant, that she slipped away from Elizabeth's desperate reach. Constantly,

Elizabeth's head would disappear below the waves and then re-emerge with gasps of water and spluttering breath, as she watched her mother slowly moving away into the deep, swirling grey water. Elizabeth felt that she was drowning next to her mother, failing to help as the waves of death overwhelmed them both.

Right from the early days at the firm, Elizbeth had taken her hour's lunch break away from the office. In the first few months, she had wandered around the historic county town, walking beside the River Tux that wound its sleepy way through the meadows that were a feature of the lower town. In this beautiful setting, the tower of the cathedral rose majestically into the blue sky, surrounded by green lawns and ancient buildings used as Diocesan offices, the Bishop's Palace, a private school and individual homes for the wealthy and well-to-do in society. A past Prime Minister lived here in the Cathedral Close alongside the rich some of which, commuted weekly to the City of London financial markets.

Elizabeth spent all of that first autumn, winter and spring exploring her new hometown, stopping to visit historic buildings and looking in interesting shops that were so different from the gaudy shops of Pinton-on-Sea. For Elizabeth, Tuxbury was a breath of fresh air, light and interesting, contrasting with her childhood memories of the dullness of her hometown.

In the early summer, Elizabeth noticed an ancient stone-built church tucked away down a side-street near the original town centre. Inside, it was cool from the summer heat and she sat to eat her packed lunch in the quietness of the building.

Due to its out of the way location no one else was there; Elizabeth was alone. She could never really explain, even years later, what happened that day but a deep peace invaded her as she sat quietly. It was almost as if time stopped and some wonderful feeling of love and peace was descending upon her. Elizabeth felt a warmth flowing through her, a feeling outside of previous experiences. Elizabeth returned each week to the church and enjoyed the peace and tranquillity it provided but never again did she experience the same feelings as that first time.

Her nightmares and dark times lessened and she learnt to manage her life but Elizabeth was even more aware that within her, all was not well. She had outward control but an inner part of her lay unfulfilled and darkened by the unresolved past.

This was especially so when it came to relationships with the opposite sex. After that first experience with Bill, Elizabeth retreated into her shell. Her work environment only consisted of three men, all of whom were married with children, although Mr Onsell had on one occasion, brushed past making unnecessary contact with her. Her demeanour in response made it quite clear to Mr Onsell that she did not approve of this slight contact or conduct. Mr Onsell did not repeat his attempts at touching Elizabeth but turned to another secretary, where he appeared to have more success. Many clients that Elizabeth dealt with were male but she kept them all at a professional arm's-length, maintaining the appropriate behaviour and standards of a legal office. Elizabeth did not seem to outwardly notice the lonely world in which she existed.

One weekend, Elizabeth met Edward in a coffee bar in town and after chatting, they went to his flat to listen to records. They sat together on the sofa talking about the music and general superficial daily matters. Elizabeth enjoyed the male company and the togetherness of their conversation, it being a new experience for her as she rarely spoke to anyone during Saturday and Sundays. Elizabeth ascertained that Edward was a Trainee Quantity Surveyor with a local firm in Tuxbury but returned to his parents' family home who lived up north, most weekends.

The afternoon moved on and Edward leaned forward and kissed Elizabeth. She responded and they moved across to his single bed where they began having sex together in this cramped space. This time, Elizabeth was totally passive, frightened of her only previous sexual moments with Bill and therefore, treading an opposite path. Edward was inexperienced and the initial advances were a collection of fumbles and apologies. Any momentum was also interrupted by Edward struggling with the contraceptive he used and its off-putting odours. Non-involved, it was all over in a few minutes for Elizabeth in the functional movements of two bodies. Desperate to control her emotions, she felt nothing and did nothing. It seemed as if, even in the close proximity of two people making love, Elizabeth was isolated and alone.

As Edward lapsed into a doze, Elizabeth got up, dressed and left, quietly closing the door behind her.

Elizabeth returned to her flat and bathed, wondering why this supposed act of 'making love' had been so mechanical and lacking in feeling. The inner awareness of how love had been absent in her earlier life, leaving Elizabeth unable to love at a deeper level in her adult life, was buried far within her and as yet, unconnected. Elizabeth never returned to the coffee bar and had no other sexual encounters for years to come.

One lunchtime, as she sat eating her lunch in the quietness of her newly discovered, out of the way church, the vicar arrived seemingly in a bit of distress. He did not notice Elizabeth sat at the back of the church and went to his seat at the front. In a loud voice Elizabeth heard the vicar shout out, "Why God, why did you allow this to happen?" He then broke into huge sobs as he sat crouched over in his stall.

Elizabeth moved to go out to respect his privacy but as she did so, dropped the lid of her lunchbox. Alerted that someone else was present, the vicar came to Elizabeth and apologised for disturbing her peace. He was a youngish man in his late thirties, softly spoken with a caring, warm personality expressed through his eyes. He introduced himself as Richard and explained that he was the local Hospital Chaplain and had been with a mother at the bedside of her dying three-year old daughter who had cancer — hence his outburst of pent-up grief and frustration.

In the following months, they met occasionally at the church and eventually Richard invited Elizabeth to come along on a Sunday to the morning service. He explained he was only part-time priest at the church as it had a small congregation being so close to the cathedral. Richard spent most of his working week in the local hospital where he worked alongside chaplains from other Christian churches.

Elizabeth was apprehensive about making such a commitment. She lived in her own self-contained world; in control. This would be a step outside of her isolated and lonely lifestyle into a new experience of being in a community of people. Her only knowledge of church was over a short period of time when she was sent to Sunday School as a child. She remembered the frightening, booming voice of the vicar as she sat rigid in the uncomfortable pews of the cold and austere building. Elizabeth recalled how he always wore dark clothes, enfolding himself in a long, black cloak, which swirled around him as he walked through the churchyard; of being scared by his appearance and manner.

However, Richard was different. He dressed in lighter coloured clothes, always wearing a grey, clerical shirt often accompanied by a selection of sloppy, bright jumpers that appeared to be several sizes too large for his slim build. The serious, powerful and foreboding image that Elizabeth had previously of clergy was totally dissipated by Richard's appearance and character.

Richard was so kind and considerate, listening quietly and attentively without interrupting or being domineering. Elizabeth shared with him a little of her life but was careful not to go into too many details, avoiding the hard issues of those early days. It was still too difficult to go there. Richard always responded in a positive way, never judging or criticising, just encouraging and building up her confidence and trust. Eventually after several months, Elizabeth, now in her early twenties, began her association with church life.

On that first Sunday, Elizabeth was amazed how few people were present and how old they all seemed. They sat in the top part of the church with overhead electric heaters glowing, in an attempt to fend off the coldness of the building. An elderly lady sitting next to Elizabeth helped her follow the service by showing her the pages to turn to and the hymns to sing from another book. When it came to the moment people went forward to receive Holy Communion, which Elizabeth knew as the bread and wine, Richard announced that if you were not confirmed you were welcome to come forward to receive a blessing. Elizabeth was unsure what 'confirmed' and 'blessing' meant but encouraged by the elderly lady, went forward and Richard placed his hand on her shoulder and said a prayer.

Afterwards, they all had coffee together and the elderly lady with one or two others chatted to her about where she lived and what work she did. Elizabeth was pleased that she had coped and had had the courage to attend. She returned each week and began enjoying the attention of the other attenders who were delighted a young person had joined them. Elizabeth liked the feeling of being 'mothered' by the older members of the congregation. It reminded Elizabeth of Ethel from her childhood days; her own mother did not enter these positive thoughts.

Over the next few years, she learnt a great deal about the Christian faith. Elizabeth discovered the deeper meaning of the seasons of the church year, the festivals celebrated, the liturgy of the services, the ornaments of the church and their relevance. Most important for Elizabeth were the explanations of Jesus' words and actions Richard gave during his sermons, especially how it should and could relate to our present-day way of living our lives. Of course, she had known an outline of Christian beliefs through religious education lessons at school but this was different, as Richard helped her explore a whole new dimension of her hidden spiritual life.

There was one particular sermon from Richard that inspired Elizabeth and moved her along her spiritual journey. Richard spoke of the commandment 'love thy neighbour' and the importance of not just thinking of yourself but of also, helping others less fortunate across the world. He referred to Jesus who always reached out to the poor, the hungry and the sick. Elizabeth already gave a weekly amount to help the work of St. Cuthbert's but, as she was leaving the church at the end of the service, she passed by the noticeboard near to the main door. Her attention was caught by a Christian Aid poster depicting a starving, black African child, with swollen head and exposed ribs, lying listlessly in her grief-stricken mother's arms. Elizabeth turned back, sought out Richard and volunteered to take part in the house-to-house collection in the forthcoming Christian Aid Week in May. The following year, Elizabeth was the organiser for her church and on the town's Christian Aid Committee.

As her involvement with the church deepened, Elizabeth was confirmed, joined the Parochial Church Council and represented the parish on various committees including deanery and diocesan synods. She began to apply that same determination and energy to her life at St. Cuthbert's Church, that had helped Elizabeth to cope with her working life at the solicitors.

Richard organised a parish weekend retreat one summer and Elizabeth went along, not really understanding what was involved. It was at a retreat centre in the countryside and accommodation and food was provided for them. On the Saturday morning, Richard gave a talk to the group of twelve about God's healing love through the life and actions of Jesus. He then asked them to go away and spend the next few hours in silence, thinking upon this theme. They could go for walks, sit in their rooms, use the chapel or common rooms but to think how God's love and healing could help them in their lives.

Elizabeth wandered out into the grounds of the retreat house in the hazy sunshine and found a wooden bench, in the beautiful rose garden, to sit on. As she made herself comfortable, her first thought was of her mother and Elizabeth burst into floods of tears. As her mother's image passed through her mind, memories engulfed Elizabeth as she recalled the sadness of her mother's life, the long years of loneliness and despair, the inability to give love to Elizabeth. She tried to imagine that final night of her mother's life, the struggle and the courage it must have taken for her mother to walk that journey to the sea. The difficulty it must take to drown, to stay under the waves, to fill one's lungs with water.

Elizabeth returned to her room and slept from emotional exhaustion. When she awoke in the late afternoon, her first thought was that maybe her mother was now healed. The hope that her mother's troubled spirit was now transformed through the loving arms of a God, held in goodness and light to be made whole again. And that belief from her new-found faith brought some comfort to Elizabeth.

After eight years at Hampson & Elliot, Elizabeth's line manager, Miss Grayson, became ill and had a prolonged time off work. The partners asked Elizabeth to take on her role on a temporary basis. This meant effectively that Elizabeth, at the age of twenty-five years, was running the administration of an important and historic solicitor's office.

She now had to attend the partner's weekly meeting on Monday mornings and to generally ensure that all was working smoothly across the firm. Her salary increased to reflect the extra responsibilities. The partners were so impressed by Elizabeth's zeal and enthusiasm that, when, six months later, Miss Grayson was diagnosed with breast cancer and decided to retire, they offered Elizabeth the permanent position.

In the next few years, Elizabeth was fully occupied with her managerial role at work and her life around the church. She learnt new skills attending courses in management and dealt with staff training and supervision. Under Elizabeth's guidance, the firm expanded and a fourth partner was engaged and extra secretarial staff employed to cope with the increased work generated. The other half of Elizabeth's life also grew, with Richard asking her to be a churchwarden and through this, getting involved with the institutional structures of the Anglican Church, meeting Rural Deans, Archdeacons and Bishops. She encountered a whole new world and vocabulary in words like 'faculties', 'mission audits', 'terriers' and such like.

There was little spare time to think beyond her immediate world of work and church. No real time to ponder those early years. But occasionally, something brought it to the fore again. There was the death of a colleague's mother in a road crash when the grief and tears of a sudden tragic bereavement reawakened memories for Elizabeth of her own time, trying to come to terms with her mother's suicide.

There was also the break-up of a marriage, leaving another colleague with a young child three years old, while the father walked away, reminding Elizabeth of her own single parent childhood. It was Elizabeth, as the Office Manager, who had not only to deal with the practical arrangements such as staff cover but who also had to be there for her junior colleagues: to listen, to hold their hands and to share in their grief and sadness.

On each of these occasions, two years apart, it brought back for Elizabeth the sleepless nights with the aimless wandering around the flat and even when sleep came, the return of those bad dreams. The questions returned as vivid as ever, the doubts entering into her well-structured life and bringing the painful reminder, that much within Elizabeth had not yet been resolved. At work, she still maintained her high standards but at these times, there was an edge to her, with instructions a little more curtly given, her manner slightly more aloof and distant.

It was the second of these occasions that distressed Elizabeth most and she found it increasingly difficult to hold the public, 'I'm in control' image, whilst within her all was turmoil. Elizabeth seemed to absorb the member of staff's distress and found herself in touch with emotions she believed she had buried long ago. Once the member of staff had returned to work, Elizabeth requested annual leave for a holiday that was long overdue and she found a cottage to rent in mid-Wales for a week. There, in the beauty of the country during walks and time alone, she managed to find some peace and calmness again, practising her new-found skills of meditation, which brought some relief. During a quiet time towards the end of the week's holiday, Elizabeth came to a decision.

On return to Tuxbury, Elizabeth contacted Richard and arranged to call one evening at his vicarage situated near to St. Cuthbert's. After welcoming Elizabeth with a cup of coffee and enquiring about her week's break, Richard, sensing that something was amiss, asked if he could be of help. Elizabeth recounted the situation at work concerning the junior colleague whose husband had left the marriage leaving the secretary with a young child. As she did so, Elizabeth became increasingly distressed and had to stop speaking on several occasions before recovering to recount the whole story. Elizabeth was surprised to feel a tear run down her cheek, as in the past she had always avoided expressing emotions in the company of others.

Richard had sat perfectly still, concentrating intently on Elizabeth's words and feelings. He had got to know Elizabeth well over the last few years and was aware how reserved she always was with regard to her emotions, holding back in a disciplined, controlled way. Through the professional counselling courses that he had attended to assist him in his work as a listener in the hospital chaplaincy, Richard recognised that Elizabeth's colleague's difficulties had awakened some pain and hurt in Elizabeth's own early life.

After a time of silence, Richard asked, "Is your father still alive, Elizabeth?"

Richard had remembered during those intense listening moments that in a previous conversation with Elizabeth, she had spoken about her mother dying when she was quite young but recalled, as he listened to her story about the junior colleague, that Elizabeth had never mentioned her own father.

Elizabeth sat, stunned by the question, her mouth half-open in amazement. It was one of the many questions she had asked herself in that final quiet, yet troubled meditation in her holiday cottage in central Wales. Usually when Elizabeth recalled her childhood, it was always her mother who was the focus of her anger. This time it had felt very different and it was her father's image that was before her. Thoughts had tumbled one after another through her mind, searching for answers. 'Where were you for nearly all my life?' 'Why did you not care about me?' 'How could you just walk away and leave me?' 'Where are you now?' 'Have you got other children? 'Do I have brothers and sisters?' 'Have I a family and am I not really all alone in this world?'.

The intensity of that meditation whilst on holiday persuaded Elizabeth of the need to speak to someone, whom she could rely upon to listen and be helpful. Someone who would value her; an understanding, considerate person who could be relied upon to keep confidences. Elizabeth had known Richard for almost ten years and gradually over those times, their relationship had become the closest to a friendship that Elizabeth had ever experienced. Richard had spoken to her recently that he was looking for a full-time Hospital Chaplaincy and after several applications, now had an interview at a London hospital. Soon Elizabeth would be alone again.

Eventually, after a long pause, Elizabeth replied, "I have no idea, my father left before my fourth birthday. I have not seen or heard from him since." The words were finally spoken. Some of the hidden hurt and pain that Elizabeth had carried alone for nearly thirty years was shared.

Over the next few days, Elizabeth reflected upon the conversation with Richard. After she had replied to Richard's question, they had talked further about her father and those memories she still retained. Elizabeth began to realise that her anger towards her father had been buried deeply within her and superseded by the negative feelings she held towards her mother.

Initially, Elizabeth had felt a warm glow within her that after so many years of holding these feelings within herself, she had found the courage to trust in another individual and speak of some of her past loveless experiences as a child. It was not long however, before the negative thoughts reappeared and the questioning of herself as a loving person dominated her mind. Did her father leave and her mother reject her because Elizabeth was so unlovable; a child resulting from a union where no love existed? Why had she not made friends, not been approached romantically by men, not able to share herself with others? She plunged once again into the depths of despair, trying to seal herself away from thinking about the pain of the past, locking herself in a pretend reality that all was well.

Difficulty in getting to sleep was added to by strange dreams occurring when finally, insomnia was overcome. In one such dream, Elizabeth found herself walking along a street with everyone around her frantically searching for their husbands, fathers and brothers. No one could find any males: they had all disappeared into nowhere. Hundreds upon hundreds of women running aimlessly, all shouting out the names of their loved ones. Calling out into a vacuum, helplessly. The hundreds turned into thousands, then into millions, the panic and the noise of the desperate women; frightening and deafening.

The morning after that nightmare, Elizabeth sat quietly in her flat before work in her daily few minutes of meditation. She recalled her dream of the previous night and pondered upon what meaning it had, if any, for her. It was very similar in its vividness and intensity to the nightmare of the drowning in the sea next to her mother. The word 'searching' came into her mind at the same moment as the alarm on her clock rang out to signal the conclusion of her quiet time.

Throughout the day, in between meetings with solicitors and clients, Elizabeth's mind returned to why the nightmare focussed upon everyone frantically searching for men. At the end of the working day, as Elizabeth climbed the stairs to her flat, her father's name, Roger, came into her thoughts. She had been with a client that day, Mr Roger Whitmarsh, advising him in her role as Legal Executive about a possible house purchase. 'Roger,' 'father,' 'searching'; the connection was made for Elizabeth. The revelation frightened Elizabeth and she felt an overwhelming surge of that panic the women in her dream had experienced.

Elizabeth spent the next few days reviewing the discovery that had come about from her time with Richard, the nightmare and the connection she had made concerning her father. Words had not fully healed; maybe action might help.

Mr Onsell, through his divorce work and Mr Harthrop, with his criminal brief, made regular use of a Private Detective, a Mr Tom Pearson. Elizabeth had met Tom on a variety of occasions concerning various cases that he had helped with and knew him to be a professional man whose confidentiality could be relied upon. Mr Pearson had served for thirty years in the Police Force before retiring and setting up his own investigative business. Tom not only specialised in gathering information for use in divorce cases, tracking those committing adultery but also investigated missing persons, mainly in the pursual of the recovery of debts.

Elizabeth rang Tom the next day and made an appointment to meet with him at his office in Tuxbury, reassuring him that this matter had nothing to do with the solicitors' work and was a personal issue that she wished to resolve. Elizabeth explained that she would like Tom to trace her father, whom she had not seen for the past thirty years. Tom accepted the case and after ascertaining more details from Elizabeth, he informed her that he would send a written report of his findings within the month.

Two weeks later. a handwritten letter arrived in Elizabeth's post box.

Dear Elizabeth,

With regard to the search for your father, Mr Roger Martin, I wish to inform you of two matters. Firstly, that locating his whereabouts was a lot easier due to his very colourful life, hence quicker than I expected. Secondly and most importantly, I'm afraid I am also the bearer of sad news and realise the information enclosed may be a great shock to you.

It appears that your father's venture into the managing of public houses after leaving Pinton-on-Sea was rather short lived. After a year, he was dismissed by the brewery, Ansells, for mismanagement of the accounts. From Birmingham, he moved back to London where he became involved in the growing and evolving drugs trade during the 1960s. He was convicted at Southwark Crown Court on two occasions for supplying dangerous drugs and duly served prison sentences of three and five years respectively.

On release from Durham Prison after his second sentence he returned to London. By this time, he was addicted to heroin and within six months of release from prison he was sadly found dead in an alleyway from an overdose of the heroin drug. A friend of mine in the Metropolitan Police at that time informed me that there was some concern relating to his death and a suspicion that the overdose was administered by others. At that time, there was violence between rival gangs trying to establish territories and it was believed that your father may have been a victim of the resulting gang war. No conclusive evidence could be established so the death was recorded by the coroner as an 'open' verdict.

The date of his death was the 5th January 1973. Your father's funeral service was handled by the local council at

Chapelfields Crematorium on the 14th March 1973 at 9 a.m., with only the council representative present. His age in the crematorium records was recorded as fifty-four years. As no-one claimed his remains, the ashes were later scattered in the grounds of the said crematorium.

With regard to your request to discover whether your father had other children, I found no evidence in Public Records to indicate that he had any further children. However, in today's freer society my research in this area may not be conclusive.

I am sorry that I cannot bring you better news but please accept my condolences and my thoughts are with you at this time of grief.

I do not include an account for my fees. I think the news I have sent to you is enough for you to cope with and therefore waive any payment.

Best wishes,

Tom Pearson.

Elizabeth read the letter three times before its contents began to sink in. She just did not know how to react. This account of her father's life was a story of a stranger, someone whom Elizabeth could not identify with. Violence, drugs and prison was a world outside of her experience. A foreign environment that her father appeared to live in. The memory of her sat upon his shoulders walking along the promenade at Pinton-on-Sea seemed a different life, alien to the picture that the letter painted of his later existence.

Over the next few weeks, life for Elizabeth became a challenge in searching for her own identity. Mr Harthrop had on various occasions in the past, talked about some of the criminals he encountered through his work and the desolate lives that many of them led. Elizabeth had listened but in a detached sort of way. These were people outside of her personal experience, merely names, cases, files, paperwork. She had never personalised these people, never sat thinking about their everyday lives. Now her father had been one of them. Elizabeth was the daughter of a criminal, a prisoner, a gang member. She was no longer just a respectable Senior Secretary in a county town firm of solicitors.

After the initial shock, Elizabeth began to feel a profound sadness. It seemed to gather slowly, deepening day after day, as if she was continually being immersed and saturated in a flood of tears of sorrow. Drowning in grief. Now a father was there alongside her mother in those waves of death. Before the letter, Elizabeth did not know if he was dead or alive. Before, she could hold onto the thought that he might one day return and say 'sorry'. Before, she was not totally alone. Now she was a real, proper, full-time orphan, confirmed as being totally without any family.

Elizabeth met with Richard and handed him the letter from Tom Pearson. He asked Elizabeth how she felt although he could sense her distress. She replied that after the shock of the news of her father's life and death, sadness now appeared to be enveloping her. It had become like a cloak, cutting her off from reality. She still functioned at work but found lengthy concentration difficult and decisions increasingly impossible to make.

Richard spoke about the process of bereavement and how it takes time and support to eventually work through the confusing emotions. Elizabeth felt Richard was a little distracted, his mind at times, elsewhere. He had had his interview for the Hospital Chaplain's vacancy and been offered the job and would be leaving Tuxbury in a months' time. Richard was spending a lot of time staying with friends in London searching for a small flat to rent near to the hospital and meeting other staff in the chaplaincy team. Time was short and he was in a rush to move on.

The month soon passed and after a 'goodbye' party in the parish, Richard left with a promise to Elizabeth he would keep in touch and if she was ever in London, to give him a ring so that they could meet up. Later, after clearing up the remains of the party, Elizabeth walked home alone realising that she did not know Richard's new address or phone number. A father gone, now a friend. Loneliness was present in every fibre of her being, in every step Elizabeth seem to tread in life.

Over the next few months, Elizabeth returned to her old way of coping. She clothed herself totally in being busy, working regular twelve-hour days and overtime at weekends. Alongside this, Elizabeth, as churchwarden of St. Cuthberts, was in charge of the parish during the interregnum, busy with arranging for other clergy to cover services and with meetings to consider a new appointment to the church. Elizabeth buried her feelings, hoping the sadness would disappear, unable to deal with its intensity. Elizabeth gritted her teeth and called upon that determination that had seen her survive before.

About four months after he had left, Richard wrote to Elizabeth. He apologised that he had forgotten to leave his address and phone number in all the flurry and confusion of moving on. He hoped that Elizabeth was well and that she was coping with her grief, together with the added burden of the extra parish duties. Richard explained a little of his new job and how excited he was in leading a team of four chaplains in this large hospital. However, the main point of the letter was to draw her attention to an advertisement in the Church Times where her newly enthroned Bishop of Tuxbury was wishing to appoint a new Personal Assistant. In the very large envelope with the letter, was a job description of the vacancy which Richard felt would suit Elizabeth's skills. He encouraged her to apply and begin a new and challenging time in her life.

Elizabeth's spirits lifted immediately and that evening she sat and wrote back to Richard, thanking him for his letter and of thinking of her concerning the Bishop's Personal Assistant role. Elizabeth had read through the details of the job and was interested by its description but doubted whether she would be confident or competent enough to take on such a high-level role in the diocese. She had briefly met the bishop once at his welcoming service and reception and felt that he appeared to be a kind and warm person.

It was now nearly fifteen years that Elizabeth had worked at Hampson & Elliot and on receipt of Richard's letter Elizabeth wondered, for the first time, as to whether she should move on. As she pondered about the Personal Assistant vacancy, Elizabeth decided to ring Richard for more details as to why he thought she might be appropriate for this appointment. Within her, there was also the need to hear Richard's voice and confirm that she did still have a friend. Someone to talk to.

They spoke for over an hour, covering much more than just the job with the bishop. Richard spoke about his new role, his incredible small bedsit accommodation and his new nurse girlfriend he had started dating. Elizabeth explained how busy she had become since receiving news of her father's death, realising she was shielding herself from the hurt. She also gave an update on how the Church of St. Cuthberts was progressing and the hope a new incumbent would soon be appointed. It was at this point that Richard enthusiastically encouraged Elizabeth to apply for the Personal Assistant job with the Bishop. He felt that she would bring a freshness and vitality to the role, helping to awaken a sleepy, established institution and bring to it new insights as she had done at St. Cuthberts.

His last words to Elizabeth on that first phone call were, "Go for it." Elizabeth applied and to her surprise, was called for interview.

The interview took place at the Bishop's House in a large room with a panel of three people sat behind a desk with a chair set out in front of them. The bishop was present, flanked on either side by the Archdeacon and the lay chair of the Diocesan Synod. Elizabeth was invited by the bishop to give a resume of her career so far and then was asked questions by all three. On reflection, Elizabeth noticed two things.

Firstly, her eye contact with the bishop left her with questions, something seemed to stir within her, something, she could not logically explain.

Secondly, she noticed an edge to the Archdeacon Colin's questions. Did she feel a slightly aggressive, unfriendly note in his voice or was it her being too sensitive?

A week later, Elizabeth received a letter offering her the appointment of becoming the Bishop's Personal Assistant. She wrote back to accept and two months later, having worked her notice, she sadly left the solicitors and moved on to a new beginning with excitement, and also much trepidation.

Elizabeth was thirty-two. It was 1986.

Part Two
Charles
The Family Tree

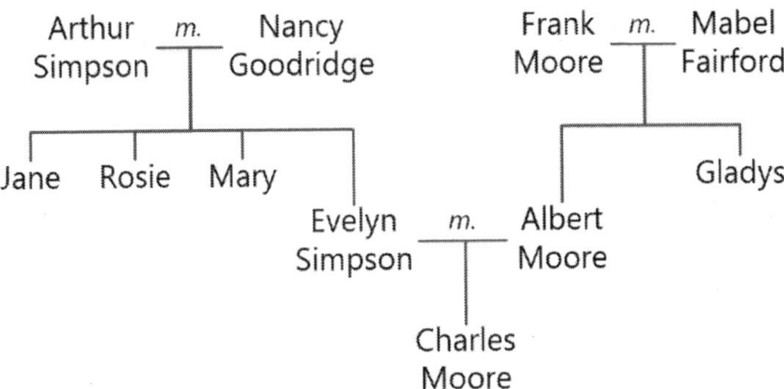

2.1 Gattingford

Gattingford in the late 1940s was a tough, North Midlands mining town with row upon row of identical coal-pit, terraced houses. They were all two up, two down with an outside loo in the back yard, sharing a jitty running along the back of the terraces. Built in the early twentieth century and rented out by the coal mine owner to house his employees, they were, by 1948 blackened by the smoke of the town's factories and coal fires of the homes. The bleakness of the town was particularly noticeable on cold, wet days, especially when the late afternoon 'pea-soup' fog was made even more dense by the industrial waste pumped into the air that hung over the town.

The black stuff was in the very blood of the people of Gattingford. Coal mining was the main employment in the town and the four pits surrounding the town employed thousands of men and women, directly and indirectly. It was the living dark artery that drove the lives of the residents. By 1948, the town had seen three generations of miners increasing the town's population to over forty thousand people.

It was as if the darkness and the hardness of life in the underground pits reflected itself onto the surface existence of the people of Gattingford. In the winter months, miners would see only darkness for five days out of seven. Walking to work, down the pit and then returning home, there was no daylight for them until Saturday afternoons and Sundays dawned. They were on ten-hour shifts of physical graft at the coal face, armed with pickaxes hacking away at the solid coal wall, often in small, cramped and dangerous conditions. It was a hard, gruelling existence for fifty to sixty hours a week and it was no surprise that the men brought that hardness back to the surface through the way they lived their daily lives.

The original owner of the pits was a Mr Alfred Chambers, who in earlier times, had been a landowner on the outskirts of the once-village of Gattingford. When coal was discovered in the Victorian era, it was his enterprise in buying up more land that saw the beginnings of mining in the area. His eldest son took over the running of the mines in 1910 and was ruthless in his exploitation of land and men to make profit.

Mr Joseph Chambers considered a miner simply to be a cog of his production wheel. The miner's labour was cheaply bought and used. If they could not work through long-term sickness, they lost their job which usually resulted in the miner's family losing their home as well. Safety and the welfare of his miners were foreign words to Mr Joseph Chambers. He was a determined, self-centred man driven by the sole desire to maintain his wealth and position in society. Sentiment was not in his vocabulary and he knew there was always someone else desperate for a job, if a miner did not pull his weight. His philosophy was simple; these miners were hard men and if he treated them softly, they would cause him grief.

As the mines expanded, so did the town. Gattingford was on the Great Western Railway north-south main line and with the advent of coal, new branch lines were built to connect the mines with the main line. This led to sidings and sheds for the storing of railway stock and the growth of the junction into a major railway hub employing hundreds from the town.

Alongside this, there was the growth of factories associated with the mining industry, with engineering firms and steel production. Separately, but adding further to the desolate and bleak industrial scenery, was the development of several quarries and a couple of coal-fired brickworks.

Gattingford was not a pretty town in 1948. It was a working town fuelled by industrial needs that determined its landscape. It had been battered by years of mining and factories and latterly, also by the effects of war as shown through the missing homes in the midst of the terraces and the bomb holes that had become wasteland and children's play areas. The town centre with its Co-op and smaller shops was dominated by an Edwardian, brick-built Town Hall erected by Joseph Chambers in memory of his father, Mr Alfred Chambers. It was a town that you hurried through, with little of interest to visit and nothing picturesque to hold one's attention. A grimy landscape of mines, factories, quarries and worker's terraced homes.

A working-class labour force dominated the make-up of the populace, with a few white-collar workers and managers alongside who lived in the new suburbs in their three-bedroom, semi-detached houses. The labourers were a people who worked hard and long for small reward to try to provide for their families. They were a community who were rough and ready, quick to turn to fists to settle arguments and yet, there to support one another when in need. They were a people who had experienced severe hardships through the General Strike of 1926, the economic collapses of the 1930s followed by the effects and shortages of the Second World War. A community bombed out of homes and factories without the support received by other more important and publicised towns and cities.

It was into this community and town that Charles Albert Moore was born to his parents, Albert and Evelyn Moore, on the 30th of November 1948 in an upstairs room of his grandparents' end-terraced house. Evelyn named him after the recently born first son of Princess Elizabeth, with his middle name that of his father.

2.2 Evelyn

Evelyn Moore, Charles' mother, was a foreigner to Gattingford. Originally named Evelyn Annie Simpson, she came from a nearby mining town of Sheddingworth. It was smaller than Gattingford but also centred its life around the one coal pit that gave work and homes to its residents. Being just three miles away from Gattingford, there was a keen rivalry between the two communities and especially between the young men, after the consuming of a bevvy-full of beer on Saturday nights. At closing time at the Dance Halls and Working Men's Clubs, the fighting would erupt out onto the streets as the young bucks from each town fought to impress the girls with their strength and manhood.

She was the eldest of four girls in her family. Her father was a miner and constantly expressed his frustration and anger in not having a boy to continue the family line, to follow him into the pit and Working Men's Clubs. He was a man's man and found life difficult surrounded by five women, taking refuge in the Miner's Welfare Club most evenings and weekends. The leather football he bought before Evelyn was born, ready to teach his son basic football skills, still lay, flat and gathering dust under the sideboard.

Evelyn was born in 1928 in Sheddingworth, a huge disappointment to her father, who had been bragging to all who would listen about the forthcoming birth of his son and heir.

Instead of celebrating Evelyn's birth, he spent the night drowning his sorrows at his local drinking club, much to the amusement and jibes of his work mates. This same routine was repeated over the next two daughters that arrived into the world, so when Evelyn's mother was pregnant for the fourth time, her father kept quiet, not telling anyone of the imminent birth. However, it soon became common knowledge that Evelyn's father now had four daughters and the ribbing of him was even more intense, much to his anger. This led to his blooding the nose of one young baiter who came too close, suggesting that he now had four weddings to pay for.

Evelyn's early life was dominated by the prevailing culture of an inward-looking, male-centred ethos of a small mining town. The home was all about her father's needs: his food was required to be on the table when he arrived back from a shift, his slippers needed to be warming by the fire and the girls always had to be quiet and still whilst he listened to the radio. If any of these traditions were not in place, together with numerous other petty rules, he would fly off into a rage, taking his belt and strapping the girls' legs. Evelyn, being the eldest, was often the focus of his rage and his belting — his frustration an outward expression of that first huge disappointment. The anger and violence overhung the children's home life, creating a permanent state of fear and anxiety. For Evelyn's mother, the beatings often came at the end of another drunken Saturday night binge when he staggered home, demanding food from an empty pantry and violent, sexual gratification.

For Evelyn's family, the struggles of the depression of the 1930s or the rationing of the 1940s made little difference as there was never any money and what little there was available, was mostly drunk away. Evelyn's father worked hard through his days in the pit but also drank hard, giving only a portion of his weekly wage packet to his wife. To make ends meet, Evelyn's mother took in extra laundry from the big houses of the local headmaster and doctors.

Evelyn can remember many days of her childhood when the only food on the table was 'bread and dripping'. Meat was a luxury, only appearing on the table if Evelyn's father had successfully poached a pheasant or a rabbit from under the gamekeeper's nose on the local Chambers' estate. There were no annual summer holidays to the seaside and the only memory Evelyn had of going anywhere, was a free day-trip with the local Miners Welfare Club to Pinton-on-Sea. Evelyn was so excited, loving the beach, making sandcastles and jumping the waves, watching the donkeys and visiting the noisy, colourful arcades. It was one of the few childhood memories which she treasured.

As the eldest child, Evelyn was given responsibilities around the house by her beleaguered mother. Every Saturday morning it was Evelyn's job to clean the brasses. In her early childhood this took several hours but as her drunken father kept selling the brasses to pay for his drinking, the task became less onerous. After school ended in the afternoon, Evelyn was often given the 'tic-book' to go to the local corner shop to get one or two items. On several occasions the shopkeeper, Mr Collins, shouted, "No more tic until yer mother's pays summat off," refusing to give her the bread or milk she had come for until the bills were paid. Evelyn remembered and hated this public humiliation in front of gossiping neighbours.

It was in such a setting that Charles' mother grew up. The threat and reality of domestic violence, the endless cycle of poverty and the taken-for-granted role of women as being subservient to men's needs, were to her simply life as she knew it. Evelyn knew no other way.

As she grew, her character reflected her life's experiences. Evelyn became quiet and withdrawn, often avoiding eye contact with anyone. She had learnt through the violent reactions of her father to avoid catching his eye because one could never know how he would react. Sometimes it would be a smack around her ear with his hardened hand, other times with a strapping from his belt, and occasionally, if lucky, she would be totally ignored.

Evelyn rarely spoke for being afraid of drawing her father's anger and made efforts to keep out of his way, hiding away in the girls' bedroom, reading her books. She made few friends, for she was frightened to bring them home in terror of her father's violent and unpredictable moods.

Her school was one of the few safe refuges for Evelyn away from the home and knowing that her father would never enter its walls. Sheddingworth School was run by the local Church of England Education Board and was the only school in the small town. Evelyn began school when she was five and remained there until leaving, aged fourteen.

Regular visitors to the school to take scripture lessons and to lead prayers at assemblies, were the local vicar, Reverend Jennings and his curate, Reverend Jones. Evelyn found the vicar a rather serious and dull person but she loved the young curate who always seemed so happy and willing to talk to the children. Reverend Jones opened up for Evelyn, a whole new world with his stories that were so full of kindness and good deeds. She loved the stories about how Jesus helped people by making them better and how he fed so many people who were hungry from so few fishes and bread rolls.

It all seemed a world so far away from Evelyn's experiences of life. She began Sunday School soon after beginning day school, wearing her best and only frock, as she skipped happily away from her home on Sunday mornings to discover another place of safety. Evelyn had a very caring, elderly lady, a Mrs Walker, as her Sunday School teacher who soon recognised the sadness within Evelyn and the hardships and bruises that she was enduring in her childhood. Mrs Walker often chose Evelyn to read or to share with the class the picture she had crayoned or the little prayer she had written. These small acts of kindness would be treasured by Evelyn, in comparison to the harshness of her home life.

As a part of the Sunday School, the Church of St. Andrew, during the 1930s economic recession, recognised that many of the children were often malnourished and in need of sustenance, so a breakfast was provided by the Mothers' Union members as a part of the morning's activities. After hymns and Bible stories, there was a break for food and drinks, followed by activities and then finishing with prayers. Evelyn loved these Sunday mornings away from her home and father. She always walked back very slowly, taking a longer route home, hoping that he had already gone out for his Sunday lunchtime drinking session. She knew the afternoon would follow with the waiting and the dreading of his return.

At school, Evelyn struggled with her studies. She had never been encouraged to learn at home anything other than domestic tasks. Her personality was to keep her head down and stay out of the limelight, living quietly in her own little world. Never putting herself forward, always wary and afraid the teacher may be angry with her and call her out in front of the class to give her the cane, ruler or strap.

Eventually, Evelyn learnt to read and write and enjoyed going to the Town Library to sit and read story books in the warmth and safety away from the threats and abuse of her father. The library was another sanctuary that Evelyn discovered in her search for a normal life. The books took her away to other happier worlds with bold knights rescuing maids in distress; bringing that love into her world that she had so rarely experienced in her home life.

Evelyn also enjoyed the practical lessons at school. She learnt how to sew and knit and the basics of cooking. But best of all, Evelyn loved sport, where she excelled at running, representing the school in cross country races. Here, Evelyn felt a deep sense of freedom, running across fields and through the open countryside with the wind blowing through her hair and the light rain refreshing her, as she ran away from the hardness and fear that was in her life.

As Evelyn came into her teenage years, she began to blossom into early womanhood. She was a pretty, young lady with jet black hair and a lovely smile, unfortunately so often hidden in the sadness of her life. She began to attract the attention of some of the older boys from the adjacent boys' school, who would ask to walk her home. At the same time, Evelyn's mother spoke to her about the 'facts of life', about boys and how babies are created and the 'women's curse' of coping with periods. Evelyn was so used to her own company and self-contained, that she was not interested in 'courting' and avoided boys as much as possible.

Her father also noticed Evelyn's body changing into that of a young lady and often 'bumped' into her or 'accidently' touched her budding breasts or her bottom. He also changed from shouting and hitting out at her, to trying to get her on his side in any family arguments.

One evening when Evelyn was fourteen years of age, she was at home alone, while her mother and the younger girls were out visiting an aunt. Her father arrived home worse for wear after another drinking session at the Miners' Welfare Club. He burst into Evelyn's bedroom where she was lying on her bed reading a book and started to talk about her growing breasts. He became excited and despite Evelyn asking him to leave as she was reading, he fell onto her bed and pinned her down. He pulled aside her blouse, ripping savagely, causing buttons to fly off. He pushed up her bra and started touching her breasts. Evelyn was exposed to him with her tender, small, white breasts before his lustful eyes. He then put his hand up her skirt and tried, unsuccessfully, to tear her knickers off.

Evelyn struggled and squirmed underneath her father and when he started to thrust off his braces and lower his trousers, Evelyn managed to get an arm free and in desperation, reached out to her bedside table, picking up an iron pot that she kept her pencils in. As her father lurched forward again, Evelyn smashed the pot down forcefully upon his head, scattering the pencils over the room.

Her father fell off the bed with his head pouring with blood from a three-inch gash. As he staggered to the door, he tripped over the trousers that had dropped around his ankles, to fall again and collide with the door frame, banging the other side of his head, causing a lump to appear almost immediately. He went downstairs to the kitchen sink and Evelyn jumped off the bed and jammed a chair against the bedroom door so he could not return.

Later, Evelyn heard him explaining to her mother that he had fallen and cracked his head on a wall. Even later, he visited the doctor and had to pay for six stitches in his head wound. Her father never attempted to touch Evelyn and she made sure that she was never alone in the house with him again.

In that same year, Evelyn left school and began work at the Co-op shop in Gattingford. She was one of five trainee school leavers that the Co-op took on every year, recruited from the local schools. The five girls were allocated to different departments within the store but came together one day a week for collective training. The other four girls came from Gattingford and were not aware of Evelyn's home circumstances in Sheddingworth, so Evelyn felt more relaxed and confident in their company and for the first time in her life, began to make friends.

In particular, Evelyn got on really well with Gladys, a tall, blond headed girl with twinkling, blue eyes. Gladys was full of fun and always up to mischief, playing practical jokes on the other trainees. Maybe what brought them together in friendship was Gladys' free, loving character, which Evelyn longed to be as well. They worked in adjoining departments on the first floor and tried to ensure they had the same tea and lunch breaks so they could spend time together. Alongside this new friendship, Evelyn was also liked by the managers and supervisors as she always volunteered to do any overtime that was required, sometimes spending weekends stocktaking. For Evelyn, it was another retreat away in a safe place from her unloving home environment.

Evelyn would travel by bus the three miles to work in Gattingford, arriving at the town's bus station where Gladys would be waiting so they could walk together past the Town Hall to the Co-Op store in the centre of the town, arriving at 8.30 a.m. Occasionally on their five-minute walk, they would witness the damage from the previous night's German Air Force raid. Although most of the bombing was concentrated on the factories and mines, there were also stray bombs that brought devastation to the town centre and to surrounding housing estates. One night a hardware store, just two buildings away from the Co-Op, was reduced to a pile of rubble.

As their friendship grew, they discovered they shared the same birth date and when they both reached sixteen years of age, Gladys invited Evelyn to share their birthday celebrations together at her home and then stay overnight. Evelyn's family had made no plans to celebrate her birthday.

After work the following Saturday, Evelyn walked with Gladys to her home in Gattingford instead of catching the bus back to Sheddingworth. Evelyn carried a small, overnight bag containing her nightclothes, washbag and a change of clothes for the evening's party. Although Evelyn gave her mother most of her wages to help with the housekeeping, she also had some money left to spend on herself. Together with the store staff discounts, Evelyn was able, with Gladys' advice, to buy clothes that suited her growing good looks.

Gladys' family home was an end-terraced house, larger than Evelyn's claustrophobic home. It had a greater depth to the building at the back allowing the family to have three rooms downstairs and three bedrooms upstairs. As they walked, Gladys explained that her older brother, Albert, would not be there as he was now in the Army doing basic training. Her parents would be there and that other relatives and friends would be dropping in throughout the evening. Evelyn had not mentioned the party to her parents, simply telling them that she was spending the night at Gladys' home. As they neared Gladys' home, Evelyn could feel herself getting nervous and anxious, not knowing what to expect; wondering if Gladys' father was like her own.

Evelyn need not have worried. The moment Gladys opened the front door both her Mum and Dad came rushing to the door, singing Happy Birthday to Gladys and greeting Evelyn. They were so happy and joyful, warmly welcoming Evelyn to their home, both of them giving Evelyn a hug and a kiss on the cheek, saying that they heard such nice things about her. Within minutes, they had taken her coat and bag and sat her down in the front room with a cup of tea and a piece of fruit cake. In the corner of the front room, there were several of Gladys' opened birthday presents from her family.

Evelyn thought back to earlier that morning when her father had left the house without even acknowledging her birthday and her mother just gave her a card and a small brooch as her only present. Evelyn was stunned by the warmth of Gladys' parents and their love and concern for her. Maybe, thought Evelyn, they recognised the deep sadness in Evelyn's eyes concerning her own home-life or more probably, Gladys had mentioned one or two of the stories Evelyn had shared with her about her drunken father and the fear that she felt within her own home.

The evening was something that Evelyn had never experienced in the whole of her life. So many people visiting the home, such laughter and fun and so much food laid out in the back room for all to share. Gladys' parents were Chapel people, attending the local Methodist Church and so there was no alcoholic drink, only pop or tea. All the family, neighbours and friends who visited had all been asked to bring two small presents, one for Gladys and one for Evelyn. She was amazed that the family had been so thoughtful and kind, so much so, that she was lost for words as to how to express her feelings. She was just overwhelmed by such love and generosity.

But there was one moment during the evening that Evelyn would never forget.

At about 9 p.m., as Evelyn stood talking to Gladys in the hallway, the front door burst open and a young man in army uniform rushed into the house, singing Happy Birthday at the top of his voice. Gladys ran to him and jumped into his arms, shrieking with laughter. The young man was Albert Moore, Gladys' big brother, who had managed at the last minute, to get a weekend leave pass from his initial training camp. His unexpected arrival brought the family together in a joyful scrum of hugs and back-slapping.

As Albert extracted himself from the hugs and greetings, he turned and saw Evelyn. His mop of brown hair shook as he moved and his twinkling eyes, a family trait, together with a gorgeous smile, had Evelyn's heart beating rapidly and knees knocking, as she blushed at his attentions. Evelyn had never seen such a handsome, happy, young man. He marched towards her with some intent but before he got to Evelyn, Gladys arrived between them and halted his advance and introduced Evelyn to Albert. Shaking hands, Evelyn noticed she was trembling and felt her face red and hot. Much later in their courtship, Albert told Evelyn that on that first meeting his intent, as he walked towards her in the hallway, was to pick her up and twirl her round and tell her that she was the most beautiful woman he had ever seen.

Later in the evening, there was much laughter in the family as Gladys and her parents realised that with the unexpected arrival of Albert, there would have to be a changing of sleeping arrangements. Evelyn was to have had

Albert's room and bed and Gladys laughingly teased Evelyn about sharing the bed with Albert and his snoring. Evelyn blushed deeply, especially when Albert came and gave her a kiss on the cheek, and called her, 'the Mrs'!

And so, it was that on her sixteenth birthday Evelyn met Albert.

2.3 Albert

Albert Edward Moore was born in 1926 in the upstairs, front bedroom of the family end-of-terrace house in the mining town of Gattingford. Albert's mother had worked in the textile industry making stockings until she became pregnant, while Albert's father was a foreman carpenter at the local pits. Albert's parents had been married for four years before Albert was conceived. They had begun to worry as to whether they would ever have children.

They were very much in love with one another and when Albert's mother realised that she was pregnant, they shed tears of happiness together. As the months of the pregnancy advanced, they happily planned for their child's arrival. Happiness and joy seem to fill their home during these months of waiting, despite the hard times of the General Strike.

Due to Albert's father's job and its position of responsibility in overseeing a team of carpenters across the four pits, he was allocated an end-of-terrace house by the mine owner's agent. Downstairs was a front parlour and a dining/sitting room with a scullery further down the extended depth of the house. Upstairs, there were three bedrooms with a small washroom, later to have a bath added. Albert's father and mother slept in the front bedroom and they prepared the nearest bedroom to them ready for the forthcoming child.

Albert's father and mother had known each other through

childhood with both of their families attending the same chapel in Gattingford. In those early days of the twentieth century, it was a very strict code of behaviour that the chapel imposed upon its members. The evil of alcohol was constantly preached from the pulpit by the minister, drawing upon examples of violence and damage to family life that drink could bring. Its use was banned in all aspects of the chapel's spiritual and social life with members encouraged to lead sober lives. The Holy Communion 'wine' used in the chapel, was therefore a non-alcoholic, cordial drink.

Victorian values of sexuality still formed an important part of the way chapel members were expected to conduct their relationships, in keeping strictly within the boundaries of married life and the respecting of the holiness of each other's bodies. Hard work and civil duties were encouraged, with loyalty towards family and nation, embodied in the chapel's teaching.

One of Albert's earliest memories was being held in his mother's arms in the chapel and listening to his mother's whole-hearted singing of the hymns. In those early years of his life, going to chapel three times each Sunday was a natural part of his upbringing. The morning service was attended by all members of the chapel and was a mixture of Bible readings, hymns, prayers and a sermon, often with a visiting preacher leading. In the afternoon, Albert would go to junior chapel where there would be Bible stories and activities. This was Albert's favourite time at chapel and he always ran down the hill to try to get there first ahead of his smaller sister, Gladys. The evening service was dreary and Albert would often fall asleep in his mother's arms.

In Albert's family home, Sunday was a special day. He

always wore his best clothes and was not allowed out to play in the street. His parents explained that this was the Lord's Day and the time was to be spent at chapel or at home with family.

The day also included the best meal of the week with a special cooked Sunday lunch and after junior chapel in the afternoon, there were family games together.

Albert's favourite game was playing 'hide the thimble' which involved searching through the house, with his sister in tow, to try and find the small object with their parents shouting that they were getting 'colder or freezing' until eventually, the growing excitement mounted as they were 'getting hotter' as they homed in on the thimble.

When Aunts and Uncles occasionally visited for Sunday tea, the evening service at Chapel would be missed and Albert loved to play a family game called 'stations' which involved racing around the front room, competing with one another to grab the one empty chair. Albert always chose Wolverhampton as his named station as he and his father, supported the Wolves football team. Albert loved the game especially when, whoever was in the middle without a seat, shouted 'General Post' and everyone had to rush and change seats, creating absolute chaos and fun.

One particular Sunday evening game of stations ended, with one of Albert's more portly aunts getting stuck in one of the narrower seats, much to the endless laughter of all present. This family event was even mentioned at this aunt's funeral many years later! The final act of a full Sunday was the weekly bath in the tin tub in the kitchen and the change to fresh new pyjamas and underclothes. Each Sunday ended with a goodnight story from his Enid Blyton books, followed by prayers and a goodnight kiss from both his mother and father.

A deep, warm and contented sleep ensued.

As Albert got a little older, his father allowed him to enter the shed that was in their back garden. It was a special place, usually 'out-of-bounds', where Albert's father kept his precious woodworking tools. Albert's dad taught him how to use the various pieces of equipment, showing Albert how to plane, to saw and how to use a chisel. Albert loved these times, usually on a Saturday when his father was not on a shift at the pit and with parental help, Albert made little wooden toys to play with. His father also used his carpentry skills to bring a little extra into the household budget by making bookcases or small tables for neighbours. Albert loved the smell and the feel of working with wood and spent many happy hours alongside his father in their workshop.

Occasionally, as Albert was learning these new skills with the carpentry tools, there would be an accident when the chisel would slip and his finger would be cut. His mother would be called to bind up the wound and would chide her husband for allowing Albert to do such dangerous work. Albert's father would stand quietly by, accepting his telling off but from behind his wife's back, he would wink at Albert and they would smile together, in a father and son bond, quickly changing to a 'straight face' as his wife turned her attention towards him to reinforce her scolding.

Albert attended the local school where he excelled at practical subjects and sport. He achieved a creditable level of reading and writing but his main love was outside of the formal classroom setting. In his later years at school, while the girls did cookery, Albert perfected carpentry skills, learnt initially from his father, to become top of his woodworking class.

Albert also loved his football and played for his school

team where he was the centre forward. One of his best Christmas presents was the gold and black football shirt that his mother made for him when he was eleven. Occasionally, Albert's father would take him to see the nearby Wolves team play where he was able to watch his heroes: Bry Jones, Stan Cullis and Billy Hartill perform their wizardry. Returning home after the match, he would play football with his friends in the local streets and park where he would imagine scoring the winning goal in the Cup Final to the cheers of thousands of supporters.

From his secure and happy family home, Albert would spend many hours out playing in the streets and roaming across the nearby countryside with other boys of his age. They would meet up after breakfast and play football in the road until the local police constable, a PC Harry Hughes, came pedalling along on his bicycle causing all to scatter into the side-alleys to hide. On other occasions, there would be games of 'cowboys and Indians', which would be all-day games of sieges and ambushes, especially around some half-built houses on the new building sites on the edge of town.

As his sister, Gladys, grew up she would accompany Albert on trips out into the surrounding countryside. Often, they would take a picnic with them and explore the local woods nearby, spending time making dens amidst the undergrowth. Some of the old quarry workings provided them with huge reservoirs of water in which to bathe and swim. The summer holidays provided an adventure every day in the sun-drenched weeks of their childhood. Albert loved looking after his little sister and they grew up sharing one another's lives and dreams, in the loving environment in which they were both nurtured by their parents.

The highlight of the summer was the family's two-week holiday to stay with an aunt and uncle in Bristol. They would catch a coach from the town's bus station, changing at Cheltenham onto a black and white company bus for the final part of the trip. Albert's uncle worked on the Great Western Railway and always took Albert and Gladys to the railway sheds and allowed them to climb up onto the footplates of some of the huge steam engines. Every other day, there was a railway trip on one of the smaller steam trains to the seaside resorts at Weston-Super-Mare, Portishead or Clevedon. Days would be spent on the beach building sandcastles and dams, climbing rocks or swimming in the sea. Albert's mother would always produce a mid-day picnic with jam sandwiches to eat whilst on the beach.

At the age of thirteen, Albert sat with his family and listened on the radio to Mr Chamberlain, the Prime Minister, sadly declare that their country was now at war with Germany. Initially, nothing seemed to change and it was not until the middle of the following year that the town's first air raid took place. In the meantime, Albert had helped his father build a shelter at the bottom of the garden.

Albert's father had earlier left his employment with the coal mine and had set up his own carpentry business, after securing permission to continue renting their house. When Albert left school in July 1940, he joined with his father as an apprentice. Together, they established a good reputation for quality work at a fair price and were able to scrape through the difficult war years.

Just before his eighteenth birthday in 1944, Albert received his papers calling him to enlist for service in the army. On the day of his departure, armed with his travel warrant, there were heart-rending and emotional scenes on the platform of the local train station with his mother and sister in tears. His dad shook his hand strongly, telling him to take care and look after himself. Albert's mother clung to him for a long time, reminding him to behave and to be good; her first-born child. They waved their son away to an unknown future.

Albert's training was at a camp near the South Coast. He joined with a group of other new entrants all about his age. Their life together was a communal one, with thirty recruits living in barracks. There was the sharing of the hard, exhausting times of marching and drill, combined with the fun times as a company of young men about to enlist on an adventure together. There was a much-hated Sergeant-Major figure who seemed to take great pleasure in inflicting pain on the Parade Ground with endless hours of drill and daily inspection of their kit. The three months training brought the company together in the support of one another, producing a concern and comradeship to the group which would see benefits in time of action.

Albert became great friends with a Cockney lad from the big city. They seemed to click from the first week of training, helping each other across the assault course to make sure both covered the distance in the set time. For Albert, the whole experience was extraordinary, so different to anything he had ever known before. To meet so many varied characters and outlooks upon life, as against the narrower perspective of working-class people from a traditional mining town that had been his childhood. To listen and talk with young men about their childhood and beliefs was enlightening and enriching to Albert. He blossomed in this company of others and his confidence grew as he coped with whatever was put before him in training.

After three months, the new recruits were considered ready to move across the Channel to form a back-up company behind the main advance through France and Belgium. Before embarking, the company were all given a weekend leave to visit family back at home. It was his sister's sixteenth birthday and it would change Albert's life forever.

The following day after Gladys' and Evelyn's sixteenth birthday party, the two of them walked with Albert to the railway station, where he would catch his train to return to his unit and then on to the unknown challenges of war. At the station, Gladys disappeared to find the toilet and Albert took this prearranged opportunity to take hold of Evelyn's hand, saying how much he liked her and could he write to her as a boyfriend. Evelyn again coloured but nodded, saying that she would like that and that she would in return write to him. Albert lent forward and kissed her lightly on the lips just as Gladys reappeared cheering, happy that her and Albert's plan had worked so successfully.

It would be eighteen months before Albert met Evelyn again. In the meantime, they wrote each week to one another. Through their letters they shared so much of their thoughts and feelings for one another, telling each other of their hopes for the future. In one of her first letters, Evelyn sent a picture of herself which Albert placed in his army uniform pocket next to his heart.

In Albert's absence, Evelyn spent more and more time with Gladys and her family in Gattingford. Most weekends Evelyn would stay overnight, sleeping and dreaming in Albert's room and bed. That small kiss on the station platform was her first and treasured by Evelyn. She lay in his bed, wondering what it would be like lying in his arms, being stroked tenderly and lovingly by him, imagining Albert making love to her. She wrote in her letter to him the next day about her feelings and he responded by sharing his dream of wanting to lie beside her and make love together with her.

Fortunately, Albert's unit was not on the front line. Their task was to follow behind the advance, mopping up any remaining isolated resistance from the German Army. The reality was that the majority of the time was spent marshalling surrendering German infantry, who had had enough of the war and wished simply to find safety and survive. Most of the soldiers they escorted to holding camps were subdued but also often friendly, occasionally some spoke English and shared with Albert details about their families back in Germany, showing them to be ordinary family men and dissipating the propaganda that Albert had been told about the evil Hun.

However, there were moments when Albert came across the brutal reality of war. On one occasion, he was involved in an operation to oust a German sniper from a farmhouse. They succeeded in flushing out the soldier only to discover he had brutally killed the farmer, his wife and three small children. Albert was in the detail to bury the family, carrying the cold, stiff bodies of the children to the newly dug graves. He would never forget the injuries that had been inflicted upon those innocent children, their open eyes of terror. Although he wrote a little to Evelyn about his army life, he did not mention this incident to her until months after his return to Gattingford.

As Albert's company followed the advance into Germany, he was to witness the destruction that war brought through the blanket bombing of German towns. He was aghast as they entered a German city, which was virtually obliterated by incendiary bombs, which together with high winds, had caused a firestorm, trapping thousands of civilians in an inferno of death. One elderly man who had survived the fire was in tears, asking Albert through his broken English, why had such a beautiful city consisting of just old men, women and children, with no military targets, been destroyed? Albert was lost for words to explain such horror and just held the old man, as he sobbed tears for his wife of sixty years who had been killed in the slaughter. These events deeply affected Albert, with his chapel background of the stories about Jesus' love for all.

Meanwhile back at home, Evelyn's family life continued as before with her father drinking even more, to the extent that he began missing days at work. Evelyn loved the weekends when she escaped to be with Gladys and her parents. They welcomed her into their home and treated her like a daughter. They were aware that their son, Albert, was writing to Evelyn as her letters from him came to their home and outnumbered by four to one the letters he wrote to his parents; a matter which they playfully teased Evelyn about. Sometimes, Evelyn would read parts of Albert's letter to Gladys and her parents, sharing his news with them. Other parts of the letters she kept strictly to herself, although occasionally she did share some of the more romantic parts with her ever-closer friend Gladys. Although Evelyn worried for Albert's safety, she seemed to have a belief within her that he would return and that all would be well.

2.4 Evelyn and Albert

In October 1945, Albert was demobbed and returned home, arriving one wet Saturday evening. As he came through the door, this time it was Evelyn who rushed into the hallway and jumped into his arms to be swung round and kissed by Albert. Gladys and her parents stood back and waited, recognising that their son had a new love to acknowledge before turning to greet them.

Albert and Evelyn were inseparable over the next few months, spending as much time as they could together. In quiet moments they both found it hard to keep their hands off one another, with their loving kisses leading to such a passionate desire to explore each other's bodies. However, Albert was determined to wait until their marriage night before realising the bliss of being able to make love to each other as husband and wife.

On Christmas Eve of that year Albert officially proposed, getting down on one knee in front of Evelyn and the family at a Pre-Christmas supper. This time there was no blushing from Evelyn, just an overwhelming joy and radiance as she uttered one word, 'yes'. They became engaged and began planning their wedding in the following spring at the chapel that Albert's family had attended for many years.

One cold winter's Saturday night in January 1946, Evelyn's father was making his drunken way home from another heavy drinking session at the local Miner's Welfare Club in Sheddingworth. He stopped to buy fish and chips and ate them hurriedly to ensure he would not have to share them with his family. On entering his home, he ignored his wife and made his way upstairs to bed where he slumped into a deep sleep, still dressed in his day clothes.

Evelyn's mother decided not to risk waking her drink—sated husband and possibly experience his physical violence or sexual aggression but stayed downstairs and slept on the settee. The following morning, she entered the marital bedroom and touched him to wake him up. He was cold, deadly cold, with a deposit of vomit and blood around his mouth. Evelyn's mother raced downstairs and across the street to the neighbour in the road who always came to lay out the dead. A brief inspection by the neighbour confirmed death and the doctor was called.

The funeral took place two weeks later in the Victorian-built Parish Church followed by burial in the churchyard in a single grave. It was a cold, overcast day and as the cortege arrived at the church gates it began to spit with rain. Few people attended the service, with only a handful of neighbours and close family present. The curate, draped in a black cloak, was delegated to take the proceedings and routinely followed the text from the Book of Common Prayer. Evelyn's father's name was mentioned only twice: once at the beginning of the service and secondly, at the graveside. Nothing was said about his life. No tears were shed by Evelyn, her mother or any of the family. Afterwards, they gathered at the family home for tea and sandwiches where few words were spoken. No gravestone was ever erected.

Later that day, Evelyn was alone with Albert and

desperately wanted him to hold her close, touch her and make love to her. Somewhere, within her, Evelyn was in contact with the terrible lack of love she had experienced from her father throughout her early life. She wanted, nay, desperately needed, the reassurance that a man could share true love with her. Albert held her tightly but at some level within him, he realised that this was not about their togetherness but about Evelyn's childhood absence of fatherly care. He resisted the temptation to make love to her, instead holding her in his arms stroking her and reassuring Evelyn that he loved her deeply and that all would be well. Evelyn, finally relaxing in his comforting arms and feeling his deep love for her, cried copious tears for her loveless childhood days.

Albert and Evelyn married on a beautiful, sunny day in early May. The chapel was packed, not only with family from both sides but also with worshippers from the chapel. Having spent so much weekend time with Gladys' family in Gattingford over the past two years, Evelyn had become a regular and loved member of the congregation. With Albert's agreement, Evelyn had asked Albert's father if he would give her away and walk her up the aisle. With tears in his eyes, Albert's father had replied that it would be a wonderful privilege and an honour to do so. Gladys was to be chief bridesmaid and Evelyn's three sisters to be the other bridesmaids. Albert's war-time friend from his unit in the army came up from London to be his best man. Evelyn's mother was present and for the first time in many years, Evelyn noticed that she was smiling happily.

After the service, there was a reception in the hall attached to the chapel where an evening meal was provided by the Ladies Guild. After speeches and the cutting of the cake, a local Methodist band provided music for the evening of dancing. The evening ended at 10 p.m. and Albert and Evelyn were waved off from the hall to spend their first night together. Initially, their home was to be with Albert's parents until they could get their own house. On the wedding night, Albert's parents and sister, Gladys, had made arrangements to stay with other relatives so that Albert and Evelyn could spend their first night together alone. As a wedding gift, Albert's father had made a double bed for them and his mother had prepared new sheets and blankets for their marital bed.

On reaching home, they went straight to their room and began undressing one another. Evelyn was so happy; it had been a perfect day and likewise, Albert was overjoyed and so proud of his new wife. He could not stop calling her, 'Mrs Moore'. They climbed into bed and kissed and held each other. For both of them it was a joyful night of discovery. For Albert, it was to be about finding areas of Evelyn's body that responded to his touch and how he loved the small moans she uttered as they made love. For Evelyn, it was an experience of joy and wonder, both before and after making love, of being loved by someone so much, so deeply.

The following day, the family returned and there was lots of teasing with Evelyn blushing when Gladys asked, with tongue in cheek, if everything went well! All the family could see the happiness and contentment in Albert and Evelyn's eyes for one another, to know that their lovemaking had been fulfilling. After a few days honeymoon at the small seaside resort of Pinton-on-Sea on the east coast, Albert and Evelyn returned to their family, home and work in Gattingford.

Life was beginning to change around them. The year previous, a new Labour government had been elected with a reforming socialist mandate. In June 1946, coal mines were nationalised and the National Coal Board was set up by the Atlee Government. The private coal mine owners were compensated and replaced and Gattingford saw a new era of mine management with an increase in trade unions. Many of the miner's homes were taken over by the Town Council and Albert's parents now had to pay their weekly rent at the Town Hall.

For Albert and Evelyn, it would be some time before acquiring their own home as the effect of war bombing had decreased the housing stock. There were the beginnings of new building but there were still many shortages, including materials for the house-building trades. However, they were both extremely happy in their home with a loving family around them. Most nights they would come together in their double bed and quietly make love, becoming increasingly aware of the parts of the bed where the springs were noisy. They loved evenings when the other members of the family were out and they were alone and could be as loud and as free in their lovemaking as they wished. It was during one of these evenings that Evelyn experienced her first orgasm and was so amazed by the feelings that flooded through her. The sense of release and fulfilment was overwhelming. The reassurance of being loved touched the very depths of her soul.

The following year, Albert's father had a heart attack and decided to retire and leave his carpentry business to Albert. The parents decided to get away from the polluted air of Gattingford and move to a mobile home on the coast near Pinton-on-Sea. They arranged with the local council that Albert and Evelyn could take on the tenancy of the house. Gladys also moved away, after gaining promotion and a position in management with the Co-operative Society in the nearby city. Albert and Evelyn now had their own home and space for one another.

It was a year later that Evelyn gave birth, in their double bed, to Charles. It was November 1948, sixteen days after the birth of Princess Elizabeth's son. Charles was to be their first and only child.

2.5 Albert, Evelyn and Charles

Charles' birth had been a difficult one. Evelyn had been in labour for over twenty hours and was beginning to weaken. To assist the delivery, she was cut to make room for Charles' head to emerge. Afterwards, the midwife counselled that they should wait some time before thinking of any other children. After the pain, came the ecstatic joy of holding the child created through the great love they shared together. Evelyn was just amazed at the bundle placed in her arms, holding Charles' small fingers and feeling his pure, soft skin.

Albert had been excluded from the birth, being told by the midwife that it was no place for a man. He had waited downstairs, nervously and patiently, feeling powerless to help his wife through the shouts of pain uttered by Evelyn throughout the long labour. Eventually, after everything was cleaned up, Albert was allowed in for a few minutes to see wife and son. He, likewise, was in awe of such an incredible gift of creation. Tears came to his eyes as he held this precious parcel of love.

Both Albert and Evelyn doted upon their first-born son and watched with joy and delight, his rapid growth and development. The first smile, chuckle, roll onto his side, beginning to crawl, were all recorded in his immaculately kept baby book. Gladys and Albert's parents were regular weekend visitors to the family home to experience the wonder of having a grandchild and to share in his parent's happiness of Charles' first year of life.

Evelyn's mother was also thrilled with her first grandchild. She caught the bus from Sheddingworth twice a week to come and help out, proudly pushing the pram around the streets to give Evelyn a much-needed break and some quiet time for herself. Evelyn was pleased to see that her mother was beginning to find a new life, free from the tyranny of her past over-bearing, demanding, selfish and brutal late husband. Evelyn began to discover her mother's love for her, hidden for so long in the terrifying marital relationship that she had experienced for so many years.

Once Evelyn had recovered from her difficult childbirth experience, Charles was christened during the Sunday morning service at the chapel and a shared lunch was provided for family and friends in the chapel hall. Charles was a happy baby who slept through each night from six weeks of age. At his christening he was on top form, with everyone commenting upon his beautiful, broad smile which captivated all. His big, twinkling, happy eyes seemed to speak of his contented nature and the love that surrounded him.

Just a week before his first birthday, Charles took his first step, walking out into the world. Albert and Evelyn knew he was close to walking as he had begun pulling himself up on the furniture and standing. They were both at home playing with him when he took the initial two steps from one to the other of his parents.

Soon nothing could stop him as he became more mobile, getting into more and more mischief as he discovered and explored everything around him. On his first birthday, Albert gave Charles a wooden train set which he had made in his workshop, working late into the nights to complete. He had painted the engine in the bright colours of red and blue. It was to be Charles' favourite toy for many years; indeed, it was to become a life-long possession.

Charles' early childhood continued serenely. He loved the daily pattern of his family life. He played with his toys in the morning while his mother busied with her housework. Then, in the afternoon came a trip out to the shops or to visit family or friends. His favourite afternoon trips were to the park that had been recently built from a bombsite, by the town council. He loved soaring into the sky, pushed on the swings by his mother or on the see-saw going up, then down with a bump that made him chuckle. Most of all, Charles loved the evenings when his Dad returned from work and after tea, together all three played games before bed-time, followed by the reading of a goodnight story.

Then, when Charles was nearly four and a half years old, his whole world fell apart.

Charles' father, Albert, had continued in his father's business of carpentry and had recently begun to work with a big housebuilder, providing the construction of roofs on a new, large estate on the fringes of Gattingford. The early 1950s saw a surge in house building to construct new housing to replace the war-damaged stock, as well as to provide homes for an increasingly large workforce in the rapidly expanding industrial growth in the town. The builder was under pressure to build quickly and cheaply. Contractors such as Albert were harried and rushed to provide finished houses, with a blind-eye turned towards any safety precautions that would prevent the builder from completing on time and thereby reduce the builder's profit. Delays incurred financial punishments for the builder, so speed was the main priority.

One blustery Tuesday in late April 1953, Albert fell to his death. He had delayed beginning work because of the wind but the site foreman insisted that the job had to be done quickly and there could be no delay. If Albert did not go up, he would be released and another contractor employed in his place. Half an hour later, Albert was dead. A fierce gust of wind caught him off balance and he fell from the roof level onto the concrete base of the house, fracturing his skull. An ambulance was called but Albert was certified dead, on arrival at the hospital.

Evelyn was washing up the breakfast dishes when the knock at the door came. Charles was playing with his red and blue train, pushing the engine round and around the wooden track.

The policeman was brief and formal, giving only the barest details of Albert's accident. As the door closed behind him, Evelyn retreated into the darkness of death. She was stunned into a shocked silence, unable to think. Release came eventually through huge sobs that racked her body. Unable to control the tears that poured out of her, she almost stopped breathing, so profound were the wrenching shudders of her grief-stricken body.

Charles watched his mother, confused. Despite his young years, he never would forget those minutes that would scar his inner life for years to come. Such profound shock, sadness and pain would not be released by Charles until a lot later in his life. The utter devastation of his much-loved mummy was too much for Charles to face. Too hurtful to recall, something he could only cope with by locking it away, hidden far within him.

There was a knock at the door and a moment later, Evelyn's mother appeared in the room. She rushed to her sobbing daughter and held Evelyn in her arms as they sat together on the settee. Charles jumped up to give his Nan a hug, desperately needing comfort too in the face of his mother's tears. Looking into his Nan's eyes, there too, were tears pouring down her face. Charles felt anxious and was becoming frightened and worried. In a fraction of time, the happiness of his loving home was shattered — broken, like the faces before him. Everything felt wrong, outside of his normal, happy life. His mummy was still not capable of words, the huge shaking of her body in grief was scaring him. He began to tremble and cry.

At that moment, his Aunt Gladys arrived and seeing that Evelyn was being comforted, turned her attention to Charles. She picked up Charles to carry him into the backroom away from the crying and distress, removing him from the intense scenes of grief. As they left the room, Evelyn called out Charles' name — it was to be the last word she spoke.

In the other downstairs room, Gladys sat and held Charles tightly, whispering softly in his ear, telling him that everything would be all right, trying her best to reassure him. Charles stopped crying and his shaking lessened as he allowed the love and comfort of his Aunty to calm him. In those moments and through that cuddle, a life-long bond was formed and Gladys was to become a second mother to him.

The long day unfolded as more and more friends and relatives arrived, adding to the mayhem of the front room. Care and love were expressed to a dumb-struck Evelyn, who remained transfixed in a separate world on the settee. There were also the platitudes of those who struggled for meaningful words to speak. Phrases were trotted out: 'he's in a better place now' and 'at least it was quick, there was no suffering'.

In the evening, Albert's parents arrived from their home near Pinton-on-Sea. Again, another time of family tears as everyone held each other, trying to find words to express their tremendous grief and shock. Albert's mum, dad and Gladys were making efforts to hold their intense pain within, recognising Evelyn's brokenness and despair. The family resorted to small talk, with Evelyn's mother and mother-in-law busying themselves with providing food and cups of tea, while Charles' Grandad and Gladys played toys and read books with Charles in the back room.

Evelyn remained fastened to the settee; the shock so severe that all communication had closed down, unable to hear, or to comprehend the words of condolence spoken to her. Evelyn was not responding and incapable of speaking or expressing any emotion other than those initial tears and sobs. The small morsel of food eaten was tasteless and bland and the tea only sipped occasionally. She simply sat and stared into the abyss. The family became more and more worried as the day went on and they tried to get her to talk but with no response. Evelyn had already gone into another world.

Within Evelyn's emptiness, a memory was stirring. A dim and yet, at the same time, vivid recollection of their last evening together. Of Albert arriving home, with Charles rushing down the hallway as he always did, to jump into his dad's arms for a cuddle. Of Albert's greeting kiss to her which lingered long on her lips, containing a message that he was eager for her. The recollection of a laughter-filled game of hide-and-seek where Albert hid in the airing cupboard, lost to them for minutes, until Charles spied his dad's foot waving to them from the partially-open door. The reading of a goodnight story to Charles and a last kiss for his son. Then together, Albert and Evelyn quietly stealing downstairs to the settee and making love, tenderly and beautifully, locked together in their ecstasy.

As the day wore on, the family conferred. Evelyn remained unreachable and out of contact with any reality, rooted in a silent world of bewilderment on her settee of love. Her total distress was expressed through her wild, almost manic looks. It was decided that to protect Charles from such overwhelming distress, Evelyn's mother should take Charles back to her house in Sheddingworth for a few days, away from the painful sight of his mother's suffering. Aunty Gladys explained to Charles that he was to go on an adventure with his Nan and have a 'three-night sleep-over' at his Nan's house. Charles helped his Aunt pack his bag with his favourite teddy, his train set and his goodnight book. With a confused and worried look back towards the front room, Charles together with his Nan, quietly slipped out of the back door to catch the bus and travel the three miles to his Nan's home.

Charles would never return to his childhood home until many years later.

As night came to the devastated household, sleeping arrangements were planned. Evelyn remained affixed to the settee, refusing through gestures to leave her cocoon of love. Blankets were brought and a bed created for her on the settee.

Evelyn lay down, staring into the blankness of death; unable to comprehend what had happened. With sleep elusive, at around 3 a.m., she rose from the settee and left the house.

The wind was still raging and the rain poured down. Without a coat, Evelyn was soon drenched and battered by the inclement weather. Somehow, in her wanderings, Evelyn made her way to the building site where Albert had been working. The house where the accident occurred was still roped off, but Evelyn climbed the ladders to stand at the exact place where Albert had fallen from. The wind and rain swept around her as she reached out to Albert to hold onto him and prevent him from being blown away. Reality had left her long ago.

Evelyn landed on the same hard concrete where Albert had lain not eighteen hours before.

She was discovered when the first worker came on site four hours later. An ambulance was called and Evelyn was taken to hospital. She was still alive but had severe head injuries and was in need of surgery. The family were alerted to Evelyn's disappearance by her father-in-law coming down at 8 o'clock to make a cup of tea. With her nowhere to be seen, he shouted up the stairs but at the same moment, there was a harsh knock on the front door. The same local policeman who called yesterday, stood, his face set and grim as the bearer of bad news once again.

He was invited in and sat on Evelyn's settee. Gladys and her mother arrived as the policeman explained that Evelyn had had an accident at the building site and was seriously ill in hospital. Again, he gave the barest of details, refusing to give speculative answers to their numerous questions, leaving the family to wander in their imaginations, trying to fill in the missing hours.

As the police officer left, the family quickly washed and dressed and raced to the local hospital. At the hospital reception, they were directed to an accident unit where a waiting room was provided. A doctor would be with them as soon as possible. They sat for over an hour, waiting and wondering. Questions poured through their minds as to how the accident evolved, followed by their own doubts and guilt. Should someone have stayed with Evelyn through the night? Should they have called out a doctor? Did they do enough to move her out of her shock? Questions tumbled out as they thought back over the past twenty-four hours.

The doctor finally arrived. Evelyn was still alive but only just. She was being prepared for surgery to treat the head injuries she had suffered. It would be touch and go as to whether she would survive and then, her future was unsure as it depended upon the severity of her injuries. It was to be the longest day of their lives; waiting for news.

Sitting, helpless and unoccupied with nerves stretched to the limit, time ticked slowly by. Eventually, late in the evening, the doctor returned to explain that Evelyn had survived but unfortunately, the brain damage was considerable and a normal future life highly unlikely. More would be known in the coming days and weeks. They were allowed to see her for a few minutes before going home.

Back at Albert and Evelyn's home they sat, dazed at the events of the past two days. The death of a son and brother, the brain-damaged daughter-in-law and the consequences now for a grandson bereft of parents. It was Gladys who recognised the need to lead and to bring some order and structure to what needed to be done. At the centre of her thoughts was Charles and his future life. There were hours of discussion over the next couple of days and eventually it was decided that Charles should stay with his Nan at Sheddingworth and at weekends and holidays with his other grandparents near Pinton-on-Sea. Gladys would take him to her parents each weekend and be with him to give support. This decision was confirmed after conversations with Charles' Nan and the news from the hospital that Evelyn's condition was worse than first thought. Her remaining life would require twenty-four-hour care in a home. The doctor referred to her condition as a 'vegetative-state'.

It was Gladys who travelled to Sheddingworth to speak to Charles. Time and time again she went over in her mind how she should put into words the disaster that had happened to Charles' parents. How do you tell a four-year-old that his life has been turned upside-down in twenty-four-hours? How will he react? How do you explain death to an infant? Gladys prayed on that bus journey as she had never prayed before. She had to be the strong one. She had to place her grief on hold. She had to be there for Charles. She had to have enough strength for them both. On that journey, Gladys decided that she would tell the truth to Charles; to be honest. Not to tell Charles that Daddy and Mummy had just 'gone away' to try and protect him but instead, to try and explain in simple language about the accidents. To reassure and comfort — but to be straight as well.

That following hour with Charles would live with Gladys for the remainder of her life. The whole broad band of a lifetime of human emotions was contained within those few moments.

As the door opened, Charles rushed into Gladys' arms and immediately Gladys was put at ease by his enthusiasm and innocent loving greeting. Later, she would reflect that it was exactly the way he welcomed his father and the way that Charles would greet Gladys on her weekend visits in the future. They went into the front room while Charles' nan busied herself making drinks and providing a slice of home-made cake. In a private moment together, Charles' nan revealed that he had been quiet and withdrawn over the past couple of days.

After drinks and cake, Gladys sat on the floor next to Charles helping him build a house with coloured toy bricks. Gladys began by saying that Daddy had had an accident at work but before she could complete the sentence, Charles interrupted saying that he knew that Daddy was dead.

"The policeman said so and Mummy cried a lot," he said.

Gladys was astounded, as they had presumed, he had not heard or understood. Charles turned to Gladys and a tear dropped down his cheek, those once-twinkling eyes now dull and withdrawn. Gladys held him tight as they cried together, locked in each other's arms.

But it was the next moment that was to amaze Gladys and to realise that this infant child was someone very special indeed. It was Charles who recovered first and said, "Dead means that we will not see Daddy again but that he is happy and safe living with Jesus in heaven."

Over the years, Gladys thought a great deal about that moment and those words. The apparent maturity of someone so young, trying to think through such strong feelings. The quietness and yet the seriousness of his voice. Gladys later wondered and asked herself, was this the first sign of a calling to a vocation, a life of faith? Or, even more incredibly, was this young infant offering comfort and care to his adult aunt?

Gladys knew that Albert and Evelyn had continued taking Charles to chapel after his christening and that he had recently begun attending Junior Church. Charles was a bright, young lad and listened intently to the recent Easter stories of Jesus dying and then rising up to heaven. Still, she was amazed that

Charles had thought through such a deep process. Charles explained that on Easter Sunday, he had drawn a picture of heaven as a beautiful garden full of red and blue flowers.

"Daddy will be happy in such a lovely place," he said.

Encouraged by Charles, Gladys blundered on explaining that his mother had also had an accident and slipped and fallen on the same building site when she went to visit the place Charles' daddy died. It was too painful. It tipped Charles over the top. He collapsed in absolute grief. He screamed, his small body heaving with deep and profound sobs. Gladys held him in her arms, cuddling him, trying to soothe him with kind words, promising him that she and his grandparents would always be there with him. But Charles had gone. Lost in a mire of tears and desolation.

As Gladys sat on the floor with Charles in her arms, sobbing uncontrollably, she realised now it was too much. She had been too hasty, too direct. It was too soon for a young child to be able to cope with even more bad news. Gladys felt awful. Why did she not have the foresight to realise how Charles would respond? Maybe the truth was too much for such a small four-year-old after all? Should she have lied to protect Charles, or at least, not mentioned his mother's accident? And as Charles continued to express his distress, it dawned on Gladys that Charles had spent virtually every minute of his life with his mummy.

From his birth, breast-feeding him, finishing work to be at home with him, playing games, reading stories, beginning to teach him the letters of the alphabet, counting up to ten with him. Charles loved his daddy but he had spent his daily life so far with his mummy. Their relationship of mother and first-born son was so close and loving, it should have been obvious to Gladys that Charles would be heart-broken.

Gladys resolved, with tears running down her face, that she would dedicate her life to trying to lessen Charles' pain and grief. This little bundle of love had already incurred a lifetime of suffering in such a short period and she would try to ensure he grew up in a loving home. In that moment, Gladys gave her life to Charles. Her only child would be him and around his needs, she would shape her life.

Eventually, Charles quietened and Gladys explained that his mummy had not died but her accident had made her very poorly and that she needed special care. Charles would be able to visit his mother but not for some time and Mummy would be very different because of her accident. Charles nodded and cuddled closer into the arms of Gladys, seeking love and reassurance.

Gladys explained to Charles that for the moment, he would remain at his nan's and at weekends go with her to Grandma and Grandad's home near the seaside. As Gladys spoke quietly and lovingly with Charles wrapped in her arms, his eyes became heavy and he fell asleep, exhausted by the turmoil of emotions. His world had been turned upside down and would never be the same again.

A spark of light had been extinguished in his four-year old life. The sleep came as a defence mechanism to protect him from any more pain and anguish. As he entered his darkness, the gloom of the late afternoon descended outside. The streetlights began to flicker on, to offer some hope for the future.

Albert's funeral would take place the following week at their local chapel followed by interment in a double plot, at the local council cemetery nearby. Gladys had taken annual leave that was overdue from her job with the Co-operative Society, so that she could be with Charles during these difficult days. After that initial distressing and emotional time with Charles, Gladys was encouraged by Charles and how he was trying so hard to cope. Maybe, she thought, that being honest and upfront with Charles had, after all, not been so disastrous as she had first imagined.

As they sat together on the floor in his nan's front room, playing trains with his special red and blue engine the next afternoon, Gladys explained to Charles how, when someone died, family and friends came together to have a special service to say goodbye before laying their loved one to rest in the ground. Gladys explained how Daddy would be placed in a box called a coffin, so he would be comfortable and protected and how there would be some special red and blue flowers on top of the coffin to make it look beautiful. Everyone would say prayers for Daddy and they would sing Daddy's favourite hymns and someone would say nice things about his father.

Charles had stopped playing with his trains around the track and was holding in his little hands his special red and blue engine, that his daddy had made for him. He had been listening intently to Aunty Gladys' words and after a moment's thought, he said, "Can I put my picture of heaven in Daddy's box so that he can look at it and be happy?" Gladys burst into tears and blubbered, "That is a lovely idea and I'm sure Daddy would love to have your special picture with him for ever." And again, it was Charles who led, coming forward to give his Aunty a hug and comfort.

The funeral took place the following Wednesday. It had been decided by grandparents that Charles was too young to attend, although Gladys disagreed. The chapel was packed with family, friends and chapel members. Gladys stood up and spoke about her brother and their shared childhood and of his love for Evelyn and their son, Charles. The minister led prayers and they sang, 'All things bright and beautiful' and 'Jerusalem', Albert's favourite hymns. Afterwards, the family journeyed to the cemetery and laid him to rest. A wake was held later in the chapel hall with sandwiches and tea.

Later, Gladys went to see Charles who had stayed at his nan's home and took him to the graveside, telling Charles all about the loving service that had taken place. Gladys promised Charles that they would come every year on Daddy's birthday and bring some special red and blue flowers to put on the ground next to where he lay. Charles nodded but he welled up with tears and there was a far-away look in his eyes.

Two months later, the Coroner's Inquest took place in the Town Hall in Gattingford. Gladys attended and heard the foreman on the building site give false evidence stating that he had tried to persuade Albert from going up on the scaffolding due to the high winds on that day. The builder spoke of the excellent quality of Albert's workmanship and how highly Albert was thought of in the trade, expressing his sorrow at such a tragic loss of a talented life. A local police inspector spoke of the building firm's good safety precautions and record. After a couple of hours of listening to evidence, the coroner pronounced his judgement that Albert's death was 'accidental'. Later that same day the coroner, the police inspector and the builder met at one of their Lodge Meetings and shared a pre-dinner drink together.

At around the same time, Gladys went to visit Evelyn who had now been transferred from the hospital to the North Midland Counties Home for Incurables in Gattingford. The home was in an old, red-brick, nineteenth century building that housed severe mentally and physically disabled patients.

The home was run by the local Health Board and the stark, wooden floors reflected its purely functional state as a bare, cold, holding base for the under-privileged disabled in society. The decor of chocolate and cream colours was dull and uninspiring with the furniture being sparse, old, iron beds. There were two corridor-style wards, one each for women and for men, containing twenty beds crammed into the limited space, giving little or no privacy. All the patients were bed-bound, many held by thick leather straps to restrain them. Gladys was escorted by a nurse to a chair placed next to Evelyn's bed. Gladys was grateful for the nurse's guidance as she would have found it difficult to recognise her best-friend in this setting.

Half of Evelyn's head was shaved and scarred from the injuries she had suffered. Her eyes looked wild and fearful, moving rapidly and darting from one side to another. Her tongue lolled out of the side of her mouth and she dribbled constantly. Evelyn made sudden jerking motions with her arms and legs and shouted loud, guttural noises that emitted from deep within her. To Gladys, the utterances sounded like screams of frustration with Evelyn locked into her living hell.

Gladys spoke softly but soon realised that Evelyn was unable to communicate or comprehend anything that Gladys said. However, Gladys persevered and talked of the family, explaining that Charles was well and living with his nan in Sheddingworth during the week, while at weekends going with Gladys to her parent's home. Gladys spoke of the happy times they shared together in their early days working at the Co-Op store. But it was all to no avail. There was no reaction, not even to Charles' name. Evelyn was in a totally different world, the damage to her brain so severe that she existed in another reality. Her mind, history and memory were seemingly completely empty. Tears ran down Gladys' cheeks.

As Gladys walked back through the dark, dingy corridors of the home to the exit, she realised that it would be too much for Charles to visit his mother. He would not cope with such a picture of his much-loved mummy. He had enough to deal with — this could take him over a line that would break him completely.

Gladys must become his mother.

2.6 Charles' childhood

Gradually, Charles' life settled into a familiar routine. From Sunday evening through to Friday afternoon his home was in Sheddingworth with his nan. All of his toys and clothes were brought from Gattingford and a fuss was made of his 'special' bedroom with his train track set up winding its way around the legs of his bed. His nan loved having Charles in the house and doted on him. For her it was a re-birth and discovery of the parenting that she had missed out on with her own children, due to the atmosphere of fear created by her late husband's domineering and cruel manner. She was now released to spend time with Charles playing in the park, reading books to him and joining in endless games — none of which she could do with her own children because her husband demanded her sole attention.

On Friday afternoon, Charles' nan would help him pack his bag for his weekend trip to Grandma's and Granddad's home by the sea. Each Friday morning, Charles would wake and feel the surge of excitement looking towards the weekend. Eagerly he awaited the knock on the door that was to signal the arrival of Aunty Gladys to transport him to his other home. In the early days, it was a coach trip from the Bus Station in town to Pinton-on-Sea and then a local bus to the village, five miles away where Grandma and Granddad lived. Later on, as Gladys' career evolved, it was by her newly-bought car.

Charles loved the weekends by the sea, watching the waves gently breaking upon the sand, or with the wind blowing and at high tide, seeing the waves crashing onto the rocks and experiencing the spray being flung high into the air. Energy and passion in the driving of water against earth. Listening to Aunty Gladys explaining how the cliffs had been moulded and shaped over thousands of years by the constant back and forth movement of these forces of nature. Charles was spellbound by the sea and would sit for hours on the rocks, watching the deep rhythms of life unfold before him.

Initially, Charles' grandparents had moved to this area and lived in a small park of mobile homes. Once established in the area, they had looked for a small home and after a year or so had found a small cottage on the outskirts of the village of Grange-next-to-Sea. It was about five miles from Pinton-on-Sea and ten miles from the county market town of Tuxbury. It was at this cottage, that Aunty Gladys and Charles spent their weekends in those early months after his father's and mother's accidents.

Charles was surrounded by a loving family, who in different ways tried their best to minimise the devastating loss he had suffered. For his grandparents, this meant trying to keep him occupied all day — always finding new things for him to do and places to visit. Keeping Charles on the move, filling every moment so there would be little time for him to sit and think, avoiding getting in touch with inner feelings.

They didn't talk to Charles about his parents or former home-life — but tried to draw a curtain around the past and just move on. His grandad had set up a workshop in the shed at the bottom of the garden, initially to continue to make small furniture to sell at the local market in order to supplement their retirement income. Charles was allowed to join him in the workshop at the weekends if the weather was inclement and help put together the stools or coffee tables his Grandad was constructing. It was one way to keep Charles occupied and not dwelling on what had gone before.

Aunty Gladys differed in her approach as to what was best for Charles. She felt his parents should not be forgotten but that, softly and gently, they should be brought into conversations and remembered. Gladys would try each week to visit Evelyn at the home and on the journey to his grandparents, would tell Charles of her time with his mother and what she had talked to her about. Charles listened to his aunt's words and gradually over the months, began to find words to ask his questions which reflected his concerns regarding his mother.

On one hand, Charles continued to have a stable, loving family supporting him. He enjoyed his days with his nan, playing and listening to stories. He particularly enjoyed learning all the old nursery rhymes that Nan sang to him and was very quick to pick up the words and join in. The weekends were also a child's dreamworld, with the sea and beach within yards of his grandparent's home. Days combing the shoreline, fishing the rock pools, climbing the short cliff face with an aunty who was always alongside him, offering cuddles and love whenever things got a little difficult.

But there was the other side as well.

The dark moments. Those times after being tucked up in bed and before sleep came. The minutes when no-one was there. All had gone away. Charles, lost in his loneliness. Deserted. And the deeper he slid under the blankets to get away from the isolation, the darker it became. From deep in his bed, he would call out but no-one heard. No-one came. Just him, alone. And through the long hours of the night when sleep finally came, also came a recurring nightmare. Lying in bed, the ceiling became black and then all crinkly, slowly lowering itself towards him, inch by inch, until it was only just above his face. Trapped and entombed in a dark place, he would wake, screaming in terror, as his nan or his Aunty rushed into his room, observing him pushing upwards with his arms in total panic. This nightmare would return, time and time again during his childhood, sometimes more often than at other times, dependent upon his changing emotional state.

On the first anniversary of Charles' father's death, Gladys took Charles to the graveside. A gravestone had been erected in the meantime and included the words, 'A loving husband to Evelyn and a special daddy to Charles'.

On the way, they had picked wild red and blue flowers in the local woods and Charles placed them in an urn upon the grave. Charles stood next to Gladys, holding tightly her hand as his aunty said a prayer out loud, thanking her brother for his life and love. Tears poured down Charles' face and he turned inwards to Gladys and hugged her.

As they went back to his nan's home, Gladys talked about the funny times she had shared with her brother. The moments that they had laughed together. She recounted some of the adventures that they got up to during the summer holidays. How, on one occasion, she had dared Albert to cross a field where they knew a bull was grazing. Albert got half way across before being spotted by the bull who then gave chase. Gladys could see her brother's face, full of surprise at how fast the bull could run and he only just made it to the other side of the field, quickly jumping the gate as the bull screeched to a halt, puffing and blowing in anger. Unfortunately, when Albert landed on the other side of the gate, he fell into a recently deposited cow-pat. Charles laughed and laughed with his Aunty at the thought of his daddy running full-pelt from the bull and then rolling in cow muck.

Aged five, Charles began his schooldays at the local church school in Sheddingworth, in the same building that his mother had attended. He took to school immediately and loved the lessons, quickly learning to read and write. He rapidly finished the set reading books and his teacher soon realised that he was an exceptional pupil and encouraged him in his studies, giving him individual tuition. She set up a special reading programme for Charles to extend his knowledge in all fields of learning. At the age of six, his teacher began introducing Charles to foreign languages, teaching him some basic phrases.

Charles loved the learning — he was genuinely excited by discovering the world around him. He read widely and devoured books well above the level which would have been considered the norm for his age. He loved the natural world of animals and plants and would quickly learn the names of flowers and trees. He was happiest alone in his world of knowledge, sitting in a corner with a book in hand, or listening to his teacher explaining how plants grow and animals breed. His nan bought him a pair of binoculars for his sixth birthday and he would wander off to the local woods and sit quietly on his own, observing the birds and other wildlife. From the library, he obtained a book identifying the size and colouring of British birds which he used to record his sightings in the woods. The first time he recognised a Kestrel in the woods, he raced home, full of excitement, to share the moment with his nan.

But not all was straightforward in those early school days.

Charles loved his nan, the songs they sang together, the games they played and the trips they went out on but it was so hard for Charles going to and from school. Virtually all the other smaller children arrived at the school gate, holding their mother's hand and being kissed goodbye by their mums. At the end of the school day, the children ran across the playground to jump into a loving hug from their mum or dad who had come to meet them. At the end of one school day, Charles walked slowly across the playground to his waiting nan with tears pouring down his face. Charles could not verbalise his distress to his nan, so she hugged him and took him home via the sweetshop, to buy some aniseed balls.

During the day at school, Charles thrived in the classroom, lapping up the range and variety of the lessons. One week his favourite was history, the next - sums, the next - reading and writing. His appetite for learning was insatiable. But it was outside the formal setting of the classroom that Charles struggled. He was constantly teased about being so clever and taunted continually as 'the teacher's pet'. The other boys would always play football and exclude him from their game, leaving Charles to wander aimlessly around the playground on his own. The loneliness of being parent-less, permeated through Charles' life.

It was on one of their Friday evening journeys to his grandparents that Charles found words to express the difficulties he found at school. It had been a particularly hard week, where some of the older boys had taunted and bullied Charles with jibes about his lack of parents, physically shoving and pushing him to the ground. Gladys had been prewarned by

Charles' nan, explaining that he had been more tearful than usual this past week, having had several nightmares. Gladys asked how school had been and Charles burst into tears. Slowly and falteringly, Charles said how hard it was to see all the other children's mums bringing and collecting their children at the school gate. He really missed his mum and dad so much at those moments and to make matters worse, some of the children teased him about not having parents.

Gladys listened quietly to the now seven-year-old and hugged him and speaking softly, she said that she could never replace his mummy and daddy but that he was still much loved by her and his grandparents. Then, from the heart, Gladys asked Charles if he would like to go and see his mother. It took a long time for Charles to reply. He knew from Gladys' visits that his mother was very poorly, unable to speak, walk or even recognise Gladys when she visited. Eventually, after a seemingly long pause, Charles replied that he would love to see his mummy.

It was a month or so later, when Gladys picked up Charles on the Friday afternoon, that she explained that they could visit his mother today. The Home for Incurables was on the other side of Gattingford from Sheddingworth and would take about half an hour through the Friday afternoon traffic. As they drove along, Gladys reminded Charles about his mother's condition and what to expect.

Charles had mixed feelings as they drove into the grounds of the home. What would his mother really look like? Would she know him? Would he recognise her after such a long time? And yet, he was also excited. He felt a tremor running through him as he opened the car door. This was a moment he had thought about a lot, especially since Gladys had asked him about visiting his mother. Over the last month, he had tried really hard to remember his old home and the visits to the park and the games he played at night with his parents. Sometimes the memories appeared vivid to him but at other times, the memories were dim and mixed up.

As they walked across the car park, Charles realised that he was frightened. He was shaking as he grasped hold of Gladys' hand. She stopped and knelt down beside him, giving Charles a cuddle and reassuring him that he just had to talk to Mummy about his school and the lessons he loved, his time with Nan and his weekends and holiday time with Granddad and Grandma at the seaside. Gladys explained that his mummy may not understand anything but we really don't know how much she comprehends.

Gladys had prearranged with one of the members of staff at the home, whom she had got on well with, to have Evelyn moved to a side room for their visit and to have Evelyn's hair done and to be made as presentable as possible. Gladys hoped, by avoiding a full ward of severely mentally and physically disabled women, that the time with Charles' mother would be easier for him to cope with.

As they entered the building via the main doors, Charles was struck by the long, dark corridor ahead that seemed to go on endlessly. As they walked, their shoes made a loud noise upon the polished, wooden floor which echoed off the dark chocolate and cream brick-painted walls.

Half-way down the corridor, a nurse stood waiting for them by a door. She greeted Gladys and Charles, leading them into the room. In the centre of the room was a bed with two chairs by its side. On the bed was a woman whose arms and legs were constantly jerking back and forth. At first, Charles wondered who this woman was and then, as he drew closer, guided by Gladys, Charles realised that it was his mother. Over the years, her hair had grown again and most of the scars were hidden beneath. The home's hairdresser had been asked to style Evelyn's hair according to an old photograph and had done a good job.

Charles sat down by the bedside. In some ways, Charles had been prepared by his aunty concerning his mother's arms and legs thrashing about and the fact that her tongue hung and dribbled outside of her mouth. But the hardest thing for Charles was the noise that erupted from his mummy every few moments. A deep, guttural shout, which on the first few occasions, made Charles jump. To Charles, it sounded like a shout of agony, someone trying to burst out of the body from deep within.

But Charles felt and knew it was his mother and prompted by Gladys, he began telling his mother all about his favourite subjects at school and about his life. They spent about half-an-hour at her bedside, then Gladys said they had to leave in order to travel on to Granddad and Grandma's for the weekend.

As they got up to leave, Charles asked Gladys if he could kiss his mummy goodbye. Gladys held him close to his mother and Charles kissed Evelyn lightly upon the cheek, as he had done so many times in the past. There was an instant reaction. Although Evelyn's arms and legs still moved, it was not the thrashing about of before. Most noticeably there were no shouts of that pent-up agony emerging from deep within her. Just a calmness and quietness. On the twisted and hurt face, a slight smile emerged on Evelyn's lips. A tear slid down Gladys' cheek as she realised that at some inner-level Evelyn knew that her son was there and was well. The frustrated utterances had been for her son, Charles. His kiss of love had been recognised by Evelyn and now, finally, peace came to her.

Later that night, towards dawn, Evelyn died in her sleep with that same smile on her lips. Reassured.

On the journey to his grandparent's that Friday, Charles was a lot quieter than usual. Normally, he would tell Gladys about his week at school and share with her the new knowledge he had enjoyed learning. But this journey was different. There were long periods of silence as Gladys realised that Charles needed the space and time to process what he had experienced. Towards the end of the journey, Charles turned to Gladys and said, "I wish Mummy could die and be happy with Daddy in heaven."

Gladys took a moment to absorb what Charles had shared with her. And again, she was amazed at his insight, his depth of feelings and his maturity in expressing his thoughts and emotions. Gladys replied by saying that one day Charles, mummy would be with Daddy again and their love for one another would never die. Gladys encouraged Charles to talk about his impressions of the visit to his mother and discovered that they were a mixture of sadness and yet, also of happiness that he had seen his mother again, even if it was in such a very strange setting. He thanked Aunty Gladys for taking him and being with him. "I love my mummy and would like to go and see her again in the future".

It was the following day, Charles' nan rang through to tell them that the Home for Incurables had contacted her to say that Evelyn had 'fallen asleep' peacefully, during the early hours of Saturday morning. Gladys went to Charles' room to share the news with him but this time, after their conversation on the journey, with less trepidation. As Gladys spoke, Charles listened intently as he pictured his mother in that room in her bed. Tears trickled down his face but he was also smiling at the thought of his mummy and daddy cuddling and kissing one another again. He remembered times in his early childhood when he would push in between them as they kissed and held each other, demanding to be a part of the family hugs. Gladys reminded Charles of those last few moments with his mummy and how quiet and happy she had become after he had kissed her goodbye.

It was later, in the loneliness of his night-time bed, that the 'other' thoughts came to him. Gladys had gone back to Sheddingworth to help Charles' nan begin to make some initial arrangements, leaving Charles to return later with his granddad and grandma for the funeral. Charles felt more alone than ever. He felt desolate, at a depth which he had never experienced before. He felt totally on his own in the world. He really missed both his mummy and daddy and today's events brought a flood of memories of family occasions spent together, such happiness, which he now finally realised would never be lived again.

He was now officially an orphan, parentless, different from most other children, an oddity. Endless tears wet his pillow as Charles recalled the moments of fun and laughter from his earlier life. Then a dreadful thought struck him. Was it his fault that his mother died? His wish that his mummy could die and be with his daddy? Was it he who had killed his mother? This deep thought was so terrifying that he immediately buried it within him, vowing that he would never ever share this fear with anyone, including Aunty Gladys, until a much later time. His tears turned into sobs until after what seemingly felt like hours, finally, he fell asleep in a turmoil of emotional exhaustion.

The nightmare returned that night, waiting to greet him. The rippled, black ceiling descended slowly upon him. He cried out but no-one came. He felt so very alone. Gladys was away and his grandparents' hearing aids not engaged, so his calls were met with nothingness. His solitary existence was confirmed. No one to reach out to, no one there in moments of despair. Isolated, a solitary soul. He rolled out of the bed to sleep on the floor, cold and shivering.

Evelyn's funeral took place the following Friday at the chapel in Gattingford. Again, the chapel was full and again, Gladys spoke, this time of her friend. Talking of Evelyn's love for her brother, Albert and for their son, Charles. Gladys also mentioned the fun that she and Evelyn had in their working life at the Co-Op store in town. Charles had not heard the stories before that Gladys shared with everyone and he laughed along at the tricks and antics his mummy and aunty had got up to at work. They sang Evelyn's favourite hymn, 'Morning has broken' and Charles' grandma read a passage about love from Paul's letter to the Church at Corinth, on behalf of Charles' nan, Evelyn's mother. Then towards the end of the service, Charles was invited by the Minister to come forward and say some words he had written about his mummy.

It had been Gladys who had asked Charles whether he would like to write a few words about his mummy and it was Gladys who now led him forward to stand next to his mother's coffin. Charles had written his words on a piece of paper and together with Gladys, had practised speaking them in a loud voice.

Holding Gladys' hand with one hand and with the other his piece of paper, Charles began,

"I love my mummy and always will, she was always there for me, especially when I was ill."

He continued his rhyming couplets all through the lovely things Charles said about his mummy until the final words,

"I hope that my daddy is now very happy, as he has my mummy with him once again to cuddle; but *I* miss them both ever such a lot."

There was no rhyming couplet in that final sentence, no soft finish, just the reality and starkness of an ending of love that he could no longer reach out and touch.

There was stunned admiration at Charles' words and a wonder at how such a young person could express such incredible thoughts with such mature feelings. Unheard of before in chapel worship, applause broke out spontaneously from the whole congregation and there was not a dry eye in the building. The Minister fought to compose himself in time to continue the service with the words, "Let us pray."

After the service, the family journeyed to the graveside and laid Evelyn to rest with her husband, Albert. Gladys had already arranged for a copy of Charles' words to be placed in his mummy's coffin. Then, after Evelyn was lowered into the grave, they all threw red and blue flowers in. Charles hung on to Gladys for support and to say his goodbyes. He was amazed at the depth of the grave and worried for years afterwards as to whether his mummy and daddy would find each other in such a huge space. After the wake, Charles returned to his granddad and grandma's home for the weekend, with Gladys and his nan accompanying him as well.

For the next few years, Charles' life continued in the same routine of dividing his week between grandparents with Aunty Gladys, a constant source of love and encouragement. Charles loved the school holidays and getting away from the busy and noisy town of Sheddingworth into the peace and solitude of the countryside. It also took him away from the endless baiting and bullying that was ongoing at school.

Granddad and Grandma's cottage was at the very edge of the small village and each morning he could walk out of the back door into the wonder of the surrounding natural life. Armed with his binoculars and guidebooks, he discovered an entrancing world of beauty. One day, when nine years of age, he was sat on the rocks overlooking the sea when he spotted a Sea Eagle swooping down. Later that year he discovered a badger's sett and observed, after many patient hours of watching, the young cubs playing near the entrance.

In some ways, life for Charles seemed idyllic. Love, security, warm homes and the beauty of the world around him. But beneath the surface, there were also moments of deep loneliness and despair. At school he had no friends. The culture of his school was not about learning and knowledge but about football and fighting. A working-class environment where education was not valued or thought important. Charles was labelled as an outcast, a misfit, outside the norm, a bookworm, someone to be ridiculed and tormented.

By the sea, his grandparent's village consisted of only a dozen or so homes, mostly occupied by elderly couples who had moved to the area in retirement. There were no other children in the local neighbourhood. Occasionally, some of the village families had grandchildren come for the holidays and Charles played with them quite happily, joining in the games and scouring the local beaches together. But the relationships never lasted, the other children moved on and Charles never established any lasting peer friendships.

Later in his life, Charles began to recognise this failure to engage deeply with others as a defence against being hurt and left alone again. The inner pain of his parents' deaths had become a barrier that prevented Charles from ever making any real friendships. The loss of such parental love had hurt him; so, unconsciously he now stood back, hesitant and withdrew into a more solitary world, unable to commit and trust himself fully in any loving relationships with others, for fear of being rejected. This was all within Charles and the only outward sign of this inner pain was the occasional dullness of those once sparkling eyes, looking vaguely into nowhere.

One of the highlights of Charles' weekends and holidays at Grange-next-to-Sea was going to church in the nearby larger village of Somerberly. When they moved into their cottage, Charles' granddad and grandma discovered that there was no local chapel nearby and so decided to go along to the nearest Church of England church instead. They were encouraged to do so by the visit of the local Vicar, Paul, during the first week in their new home. He was warm and accepting of their chapel tradition, simply offering a full welcome if they wished to attend at any time. The following Sunday they went along and soon became regular members of the congregation, making lots of friends in their new environment.

Charles loved the Vicar, Paul. He was married to Pat and they had four children, living in the large old vicarage next to the church. Paul was always full of fun and involved the children in the services. Before they started, Paul would get the children to come and light the candles and help give out the books. On other occasions, he would get the children to help with prayers and laying out the table with the bread and wine. He played the guitar and taught everyone new songs where the children went out to the front and did actions to the words. In the middle of the service, the children went into a side-room with his wife, Pat and had a story and activity time. Pat used to say that this was much more fun than listening to Paul's sermons and then she would laugh, with the loudest laugh that Charles had ever heard. Everyone knew when Pat was in the room because of her laughter.

Paul also had special services for families including a Pet Service, where everyone took along and talked about their favourite pet to the congregation. Charles was in a bit of a dilemma — he did not have a pet. He loved seeing the animals and birds in their natural setting but he could hardly take along a badger or fox. On the day of the Pet Service, Charles was watching the frenetic activity of a Red Admiral butterfly in the garden, flitting from flower to flower. He got his net, caught the butterfly and placed it in a large, glass jar with some greenery from the garden. He quickly read up about the butterfly from one of his nature books and went along to the afternoon service. When it was his turn, Charles, encouraged by Paul, went forward to show and talk about his butterfly.

Paul was very much aware of Charles' background and the loss of his parents, as his grandparents had spoken to him about their grandson. He had warmed to Charles, seeing within him a real potential and depth of character in the way Charles seemed to have coped with so much tragedy in his short life. Without favouring him above others, Paul still found time and space to nurture and pour special attention on Charles.

In return, Charles always felt safe and secure with Paul. He seemed to have this natural gift of being alongside people, encouraging and affirming everyone in their lives. He was a person who people had confidence in and one whom you could easily go to and talk about life's problems, knowing that Paul listened quietly and non-judgementally, offering advice only if it was sought. Although Charles was not consciously aware of it, Paul was like a father-figure to him. Later, as Charles' vocation began to emerge more fully, it would be Paul's way of ministry that would be a role model for Charles, one to which he would often refer back to, time and time again.

When Charles was ten years of age, his nan in Sheddingworth became ill with severe back pain. She had to go into hospital for a series of tests which eventually confirmed that she had a degenerative illness of the spine and would soon need special full-time nursing care. Although Charles' nan could still stay in her own home for a while, it was now impossible for her to look after him for five days of the week. Aunty Gladys explained to Charles that because of his nan's health issues, he would have to go and live with Grandma and Grandad in Grange-next-to-Sea.

For Charles this news was greeted with mixed emotions. On one hand, he was pleased that he would be away from the urban grime of the mining town of Sheddingworth, with its lack of green spaces and nature. Away from the taunting by other boys at school and their calling him names and on occasions, hurting him with their 'Chinese Burns' on his arms. But he was also sad about not being able to live with his nan. He had grown to love her very much over the six years he had been with her during the school weeks. She had always been kind, spoiling him with treats such as iced buns and his favourite sweets: aniseed balls. Aunty Gladys reassured Charles, that on some weekends, she would bring his nan to stay at Grandma and Granddad's. However, it was another loss in Charles' young life.

Charles was in the last year of his primary schooling when the move came to leave Sheddingworth. He would now attend the nearest local primary school to his other grandparents in the village of Somerberly. His Sheddingworth school had over two hundred children, while his new school had only thirty-five children, organised into two classes. Charles was in the older children's class with the Headteacher, Miss Crosby, who quickly recognised Charles' advanced academic standard. Miss Crosby set up extra lessons to coach Charles, with two other children, Emily and Jane in preparation for the Eleven Plus examination. Charles was invigorated by the small school and the individual attention he received which contrasted starkly with his old school, where he was one in a class of forty children competing for the teacher's attention.

All three children were successful in the examination that took place just after Charles' eleventh birthday. The marks that Charles achieved were some of the highest recorded nationally in that year's entry. Miss Crosby was notified by the Examining Board of the high level of Charles' attainment and was determined in the next six months to enjoy teaching the brightest pupil she had known in her thirty-year teaching career.

In the next few months, Charles was introduced to a whole new world with trips into algebra, geometry, biology and chemistry, Roman history, Shakespeare, classical music, poetry and much more. Charles loved it and being the eldest in the school meant there was no one to intimidate or threaten him. He could just focus on his love of learning without any worrying distractions. At weekends, Charles had the woods to explore behind his grandparents' cottage, with the beach and sea a mere hundred yards further on over the small hill.

In September, Charles changed his short trousers for long ones as he began his secondary education. The Grammar School bus arrived in the village of Grange-next-to-Sea at 7.30 a.m. each morning, on its journey through local villages eventually reaching Tuxbury by 8.45 a.m. Charles boarded the bus on that first day, kitted out in his new uniform, with school jacket and cap, his satchel around his shoulder. Nervously, he entered the bus and journeyed into a new world of academia.

His grammar school was steeped in history and traditions that went back hundreds of years to its founder in the 1500s. It valued the importance of knowledge, learning and the pursuit of excellence. All of the staff were highly qualified with Oxbridge backgrounds and had huge expectations for their students to achieve at the very highest level in society. It counted Archbishops, Prime Ministers, leaders in industry, commerce, medicine, science and the arts, amongst its past pupils. The school was set in grounds on the banks of the River Tux near the edge of the market county town. Parts of the buildings dated from the sixteenth century, although there had been extensive additions in early Georgian times.

For the next six years, it was to be an academic honing ground for Charles, which he loved. The school ethos was of extending the pupils to acquire knowledge, combined with a sense of responsibility and self-confidence being foremost in its approach. The curriculum was fashioned for the brightest of children and Charles entered the world of classics alongside other traditional subjects. A rigorous, but fair system of rules and guidance was clearly spelled out to pupils in those early days and everyone was expected to follow the school's way of life. The day was full of learning with a minimum of two hours homework each evening and six hours at the weekends. For

Charles, this meant a day that began at 6.30 a.m., not finishing until homework was complete at 8.30 p.m.

In his first few months at the school, Charles was held captive and exhausted by this new experience in his life, with the endless stream of facts and figures that the enthusiastic staff poured into him, stimulating him to research deeper into new ideas and thoughts. After homework was complete, Charles spent many extra hours at weekends and in school holidays reading around numerous subjects. Each night Charles would fall into bed, tired from the cerebral strain of so much learning. Too exhausted even to think about the past or to have that nightmare. Charles was fully immersed in something he loved and it filled his mind and time, leaving little energy to ponder difficult or more challenging life issues.

However, towards the end of his third year at the grammar school, Charles' nan died of pneumonia. She had spent the past two years in a nursing home, unable to walk and mainly confined to bed. It meant a trip back to Sheddingworth and a rather dull and uninspiring church service in the local parish church, followed by a burial in the churchyard. Charles' nan had asked to be buried at the other end of the churchyard from her husband. The vicar taking the service seemed to be in a hurry and said only a few words about Charles' nan before rushing through a set liturgy that held little meaning for those present. At the graveside, he recited the Prayer of Committal and then abruptly left the family without words of condolence or a gesture of comfort. Afterwards, Gladys was scathing about the incumbent, saying that he had done too many funeral services and based around her newly acquired management skills, suggested he needed to attend a re-training course.

The funeral and the return to Sheddingworth reawakened

unhealed scars in Charles' psyche. At the service, he cried tears for the past as well for his nan. The desperate feelings of emptiness and loneliness re-surfaced as Charles visited his parent's grave in Gattingford later in the day. That night, the nightmare returned causing him to wake, crying out loudly at the enclosing terror of the darkened, crimpled ceiling. The next day, Charles was quiet and withdrawn, avoiding eye contact and conversation with others. It was his Aunty Gladys who came to him, recognising his distress and gave him a hug and words of reassurance.

On return to Grange-next-to-Sea, Charles retreated deeper into his despair, spending hours in his room, gazing endlessly into a vacuum of nothingness. He missed the final week of the summer term and spent the first part of holidays isolated within his family and home. At one level, Charles understood his emotions were a result of his childhood losses but he could not understand the deeper issues of grief and bereavement — the anger he sometimes felt, the inability to express his feelings, burying everything within him.

It was Emily who helped Charles cope with the mire of his tangled emotions.

On that nervous first day travelling to grammar school three years ago, Charles saw the familiar face of Emily from his primary school on the bus and sat next to her. Each day was the same and over the next few years they developed a friendship, sharing their new experiences of grammar school life. Emily attended the nearby Grammar School for Girls and lived with her father in the nearby village of Somerberly. She never spoke of her mother, so Charles had never asked.

It was in the second week of the Summer holiday that Emily called at Charles' home. He was ensconced in his bedroom, lying listlessly on his bed when his grandma called him. They went for a ride on their bikes and after an hour or so, they stopped and sat on the banks of a small river as it slowly wound its way down towards the sea. Sitting side-by-side, Emily suddenly blurted out, "My mum died seven years ago. She had breast cancer. I'm sorry about your nan dying." It was the first time Emily had mentioned her mother to Charles. He turned to her and noticed a small tear in the corner of her left eye which slowly moved down her cheek. Charles placed his hand upon her hand and squeezed slightly. She moved closer to Charles and hugged him, holding him tightly.

It was a strange mixture of emotions that flowed through Charles during that long embrace. On the one hand, there was a genuine experience of someone else who was alongside him in his sadness and despair, a kindred spirit and then secondly, and most oddly, the very closeness of this encounter brought with it for Charles sexual overtones. Charles could feel Emily's breasts against his arm and after a few moments, felt uneasy at the near proximity of their bodies. He became flushed and confused, withdrawing from the arms of Emily.

Later, in times together during that holiday, both Charles and Emily spoke of the deaths of Charles' nan and Emily's mother but Charles was unable to go further and speak of his parents' deaths. Charles liked Emily a great deal but after that first hug, he was confused and worried by his variety of feelings. At home in the secrecy of his bedroom, he touched himself as he thought about her but avoided any physical contact with Emily on their trips together. He could only give so much of himself but gradually with Emily's companionship, Charles slowly began to emerge from his solitary self and return to academic study.

Charles' earlier love of the natural world had moved on, so by the time he approached school external examinations, he was more interested in human life and thought, which now fascinated him. Charles started to read more literature, theology, philosophy and psychology, finding time to question his teachers about abstract ideas and theories. Charles had a special relationship with the English teacher at his school and often sought him out at lunchtime to engage him in conversation about some dark theme, such as the anti-Semitism running through Shakespeare's Merchant of Venice play or about D. H. Lawrence's working-class background as portrayed in his novel, 'Sons and Lovers'.

Charles also spent a great deal of time with Paul, his local vicar, discussing the Bible and spiritual life. Paul had some very unconventional ideas for a vicar in the early 1960s and viewed the Holy Bible as a source of thought and guidance rather than the absolute word of God. These opinions were in direct contrast to Charles' grammar school chaplain, a low churchman, who followed a very strict and traditional establishment line, totally against any 'liberal' views, seeing them as twentieth century heresy.

The worship that the chaplain led in the school chapel reflected his very conservative stance and to Charles, was rigid and boring, unlike Paul's more modern approach to services in his village church. Charles was fascinated by Paul's theory that most of the stories in the Bible were just simply stories, created to illustrate an important point that the writer was trying to put across. Paul claimed it was the Jewish way of writing not only in the Old Testament but also present in the Gospels as well.

Paul shared with Charles his difficulty of holding such controversial views and not being able to share them with his congregation, for fear of upsetting them with the consequences of bringing down the church establishment's disapproval on himself. Paul, half-laughingly, talked of an Arch-dragon whom the church appointed to police wayward clergy, commissioned to bringing them to heel. It was a dilemma which Paul would wrestle with for many years, until eventually his conscience would no longer allow him to be a part of a church faith that often hid behind a woolly sentimentality, ignoring what was to Paul the deeper truth. So, Paul eventually left ministry to move into social work with the local authority.

In his fourth year at the grammar school, Charles was entered for his GCE O-Levels a year earlier than usual. He achieved the highest grades in all subjects and a year later he completed two Advanced level subjects, with a further three the following year later. He again achieved the highest grades in all five A levels.

At seventeen years of age, he had received an unconditional place to read Theology at Oxford.

In that final summer before leaving his grandparent's home, Charles spent time with Emily, who still had another year at school to complete. They would often visit each other's homes and play records on Charles' Dansette record player. It was the time of the mid-sixties boom in 'pop' music when The Beatles and the Rolling Stones were topping the charts. Charles had a wide range of music that he enjoyed listening to, including classical composers such as Rachmaninov, Bach and Handel, as well as some of the modern pop groups, while Emily loved folk music and some female vocalists. Emily also played the guitar and sang her favourite folk songs.

Charles and Emily's relationship had not changed much

over the years. They were friends who had shared school experiences and some sad family bereavements with each other but the relationship remained at a reserved level, not deepening or intensifying with the years. With both enjoying literature, they often talked about different books and authors. Both loved Shakespeare and had been on a couple of combined school trips to Stratford-upon-Avon to watch Romeo and Juliet and A Midsummer Night's Dream.

They had now both matured physically and Charles had started to grow a 'Mexican-style moustache' since finishing school in June. Emily was a little overweight and seemed to lack confidence in herself, often following Charles, rather than leading. The only change in their physical relationship was that this summer they had taken to kissing one another on the cheek when greeting or leaving each other's company.

One hot, sultry afternoon in late August they were both lying on the floor in Charles' bedroom listening to records. The music was playing loudly as Charles' grandparents were out at the local Pensioners' Club Whist Drive and Tea. Charles was wearing a pair of shorts and t-shirt while Emily wore a mini-skirt and loose-fitting top. On a couple of occasions during the afternoon, Charles had noticed Emily lean over and her ample breasts were visible to him, encased in a white, lacy bra. A little later, as she moved and sat cross-legged, Charles could see her white knickers, transparent enough to depict a darkness underneath.

With one of Emily's favourite romantic songs playing, Emily suddenly rolled over and came close to Charles. She took his hand and placed it on her right breast and began moving his hand inside her garment. Charles could feel Emily becoming excited and she began to moan softly. Charles was hot and confused. He became flushed and yet, he felt deep urges overwhelming him as an erection pushed against his tight shorts. Charles slid his fingers inside Emily's knickers and into her. She gasped and cried out. Charles continued and within moments, Emily's body tightened in a stiff paralysis of an orgasm. Charles' fingers seemed trapped within her, lost to himself. Gradually as Emily's body relaxed, Charles withdrew his fingers.

Emily started to encourage Charles to enter her, reaching towards him but Charles could go no further. It was too much to give all of himself. Later, he rationalised his holding back as being sensible and not taking the risk of getting Emily pregnant. But, within him, he wondered why he could not make that final commitment and move into a deeper relationship.

They met a couple more times in that summer but the opportunity to continue their liaison never arose with grandparents being at home. It never occurred to Charles that he always invited Emily over on Tuesday afternoons, when his grandparents were always in. Charles never talked to Emily about that one afternoon and never mentioned it to anyone else. Emily returned to school and her final year, while Charles prepared for his time at Oxford by reading widely around his chosen subject of Theology.

Charles' grandparents were now aging and spent more and more time at the doctors and on hospital visits at the General in Tuxbury. His grandad had long-term diabetes type-two and was beginning to get complications with eyesight difficulties, foot ulcers and breathing. His grandma had ongoing painful arthritis in her hand joints and most weeks, one or the other had an appointment or treatment to attend. Charles' Aunty

Gladys still came most weekends and had been the constant support throughout his childhood but in the last year, their relationship had begun to change.

Gladys' career with the Co-Operative Society had progressed. She was now based at an office in Central London and was the Senior Buyer for the clothes section of their stores. Her job involved travel and she journeyed across the world, visiting manufacturers and suppliers in countries as far away as India and the Far East. It meant that sometimes she was out of the country and unable to visit at the weekend. However, her high-powered job also meant that she was able to provide Charles with free samples, including up-to-date fashions for young men, often ahead of the Carnaby Street fashions hitting the market.

There was also another reason that Gladys' visits became less frequent. At her office, Gladys had met someone who worked in the firm's finance department and they had started dating. Their romance had blossomed quickly and within a couple of months, they were living together in Gladys' small flat in Richmond.

It was not Gladys' first sexual encounter as she had known two other men in short-term relationships in the past. However, with Alan, this was a different and new experience; a closeness that she had avoided before because of her deep commitment to Charles. Gladys found herself: wanting to be with Alan all the time, longing for the moment he would walk through the door, sharing in intimate pillow-talk after making love, laughing at life shared together and holding hands in the back row at the pictures. Just having someone to share her daily life with, loving and being loved. Gladys' body clock was also ticking on as she was now in her late thirties and if she was to have a family, it must be soon.

Gladys was also aware that her relationship had changed with Charles over the last eighteen months or so. He seemed more assured and was extremely focussed on his studies and, now in the summer of 1966, was preparing to go up to university becoming even less reliant upon her. She felt that she had been faithful to her pledge to care and nurture him after the death of his parents, fulfilling that task. However, she did still worry, for there were times when she caught Charles looking into nowhere, still a lost and lonely child, apparently vulnerable.

In early September, Gladys visited for the weekend and on Saturday afternoon went with Charles for a walk along the nearby beach. It was a warm, late summer's day, with clear blue skies and a calm, tranquil sea lapped the shore. As they walked, they talked about Charles' preparations for university and the reading he had been asked to do before arriving at the college in Oxford.

Half-way along the beach they stopped and sat upon a collection of rocks to watch the endless rolling of the waves upon the sand. The tide was turning and as it ebbed slowly away, it seemed to leave them even more isolated on their rocky seat. Gladys was nervous of how Charles would react to her news but she knew she must be honest about her new life with Alan; truthful, as she had always been with Charles. Gladys talked of how life changes over time and that Charles was now about to begin another stage in his life. This time, he would be away from his family and it was the beginning of him building his own life out in the wider world. Gladys said to Charles, "In some ways, moving on can feel a little frightening and daunting. How do you feel about this next step in your life?"

Charles thought for a long moment and then to Gladys' surprise said, "Is your life about to change, Aunty?" It was another of those moments Gladys had experienced in her times with Charles, when his perception and empathy were almost beyond belief. Maybe it was the slight tremor in her voice or the edge of her nervousness that Charles recognised. "Yes," she replied, "I have met a wonderful man called Alan, whom I want to spend the rest of my life with."

Charles was genuinely pleased for his aunty and her future. He had understood how much she had given up for him and the love she had tried to give in attempting to replace his parents. Charles had appreciated the time and conversations they shared and the many cuddles and hugs Aunty Gladys had given him, always first to recognise when he was in a dark time.

The following weekend, Gladys arrived with Alan. He was a tall, slim man in his mid-thirties with bouncy, brown hair and kindly eyes. It was obvious to Charles and to his grandparents that Gladys and Alan were both deeply in love with one another, always close and discreetly touching each other tenderly. Alan had taken a course in Business Studies at college and had progressed in his career to higher management within the Co-Operative Society and was now one of their Senior Accountants. He had parents living in North London and an older sister who had emigrated to Australia on a £10 ticket scheme. Alan appeared to be a quiet, content and happy person, who enjoyed being with people.

On a walk through the nearby woods on Sunday morning, Gladys asked Charles what he thought of Alan. Charles was aware that Gladys wanted, maybe even needed, his approval to ease her concern that she was moving on and assurance that he would be content with the situation. Charles reassured his aunty that he thought Alan was a lovely person and that he hoped they would be very happy together. Gladys turned to Charles with tears in her eyes and gave him a big hug and a kiss on his cheek. "Thank you," she said.

After Sunday lunch, Gladys and Alan left to journey back to London to their flat and work for the week. That night, Charles had his nightmare again. The closing in upon him, the helplessness of his situation to stop the dark, crinkled ceiling crushing him. He woke sweating, yet cold, confused as to why this nightmare should return.

Later in the day, Charles thought of Alan and his brown hair and how similar that was to his father's. Had Gladys, unconsciously, chosen someone who reminded her of her late brother? Sub-consciously, was Charles' nightmare a reminder of his hidden and suppressed grief? Had it awakened deep within him, a picture of his father? Or was the nightmare the desperate fear of soon to be totally alone in the world now that Gladys had a new love and a fresh beginning with someone else? Left again, deserted, lost, just like when his parents had died so many years ago. Charles spent the next few days cocooned in his room, reading the recommended theology books ready for his time at university, finding comfort in another world and time.

Two weeks later, the day arrived for Charles to take his place at his Oxford college. Gladys had taken a day-off from work to transport him and his cases, which were mainly laden with books. There were sad goodbyes with his grandparents at the door of their cottage, as both they and Charles, acknowledged in tears a moving on. Charles had been the centre of their lives for the past seven years and his leaving would mean a huge gap in their daily routines. They knew that he would return in the holidays but it would never be the same again and soon, he would make his own life and return only occasionally.

As Gladys and Charles drove away, Charles was quiet and withdrawn, feeling sadness at leaving behind his secure and loving grandparent's home and nervous of what the future held, frightened of being even more alone in a strange world.

Gladys sensed his unease and nervousness and reminded him of all the wonderful memories of the last few years at Grange-next-to-Sea. The woods, the sea, the wild animals, his schools and the fun that they had had together at the weekends. Charles recognised Gladys' attempts to raise his spirits and joined in, sharing together hours of laughter at the times that they had enjoyed in the past.

2.7 Oxford

Charles entered the ancient college through an impressive gateway with a prominent notice attached, declaring to all students that the gates would be locked at 11.30 p.m. every night. Through the gateway was a large quadrant of well-maintained lawn surrounded by an immaculate border of flowers, with rose bushes most prominent. In the centre of the grass area was an ancient oak tree, whose history matched the length of the college's past. The tree had become, over time, a part of the college's tradition as a gathering place for students to sit under on summer days.

On the right-hand side of the square was a doorway that led up worn, stone stairs to the second-floor rooms that were to be Charles' accommodation. Inside there was a sitting-room with a study-desk next to the window overlooking the quadrant and a settee that could double as a bed for an invited guest to stay overnight. In the corner of the sitting-room, there was a kitchenette where light meals could be prepared. Charles' grandma had provided a large bag of supplies for the first few days including his favourite home-made fruit cake and oatmeal biscuits. The sitting room led through to a bedroom with a double bed and a wardrobe. The shared bathroom was next door to his rooms.

Charles soon felt at home in the academic ethos of his Oxford College. His professors were some of the world's most eminent voices in theology. He hungrily sat at their feet, satiating himself on their knowledge and expertise in the many different areas of theology. The Old and New Testament scholars, Doctrine, Ethics, Liturgy and Church History were all within his reach in the colleges of Oxford.

For Charles it was an academic heaven laid at his door. His enthusiasm was boundless as he visited the colleges to listen to visiting professors lecture on a myriad of theological issues. He welcomed his one-to-one tutorials where he could pick the brains of such learned people and the seminars with group discussions.

The early 1960s had seen the publication of Bishop John Robinson's book, 'Honest to God' calling for the church to adapt and modernise in the late twentieth century. His premise was that the Church of England was losing touch with modern life and becoming irrelevant to today's society. It created a storm of reaction from traditionalists and heated discussions ensued over the following years. There was to be a full debate at the Oxford Union on the motion, 'This House believes that the church must modernise or it will die'. Two professors were to propose and oppose the motion and two students to second, either supporting or opposing. Charles was chosen by the theology student body to second the proposal. It was a recognition of the talent, insight and the knowledge he had already shown in his first few months at the university.

All who attended the debate were agreed on one thing, that Charles was by far the most convincing and informed speaker. He had prepared meticulously and had mastered the arguments supporting (and opposing) the motion. He was third to speak and began by taking apart the Opposers' principle speaker's comments and then he built his own logical case based upon the premise that religion must relate to the culture it is in or it becomes irrelevant. One example that Charles gave was the changing role of women in modern society, indicating the need for the church to recognise this movement to equality and to ordain women as priests and bishops. He spoke of the spiritual life of women in that they were not just there to clean the church and arrange the flowers. This brought enormous cheers and got the majority of women present on his side immediately.

Charles also focussed on the need for liturgy to be in a language that was understandable to the people of the present day. He proposed that language used in the seventeenth century-created 'Book of Common Prayer' may well be seen as beautiful by some but to many in the late twentieth century, it was incomprehensible and out-dated. As he sat down there was thunderous applause. After the last speaker spoke, a huge majority supported the motion and it was carried. Charles had made his mark and his outstanding ability and intellect was recognised by fellow peers and teachers. It was the beginning of his vision.

Among the audience that night was the editor of the national Church of England newspaper. In the following week's edition, there was a centre-page article concerning the debate. In the account, the editor made special mention and praise with regard to Charles' contribution, finishing with the comment, 'that here was someone to watch out for in the future'. Also present in the hall that night was the Chair of the Church of England Liturgical Commission, who was so impressed by Charles' analysis of liturgy that he invited Charles to become a student member of the national committee. So began what was to become one of Charles' special interests; in contributing to modernising church worship.

Charles loved the study, the new ideas, the research, the discovering and analysis of different concepts. The vast libraries in which to spend endless hours reading ancient manuscripts in Greek and Latin, losing himself in this academic wonderland.

But in other areas of university life, he felt estranged. The unease he experienced at dinner each evening within the college with its formality and rituals. After the first few weeks he rarely attended, finding his own places to eat or just snacking in his rooms. He argued to himself that it took too many hours away from valuable study time.

Charles also felt out-of-place socially. The majority of students around him were from public schools, who at Oxford, formed their own social clubs with strange initiation ceremonies. They were exclusive and in their apparent arrogance looked down upon students with grammar school backgrounds. Conversations were cut short once they discovered you were a 'grammar school' chap!

Charles also found difficulty in establishing relationships with the opposite sex. There were very few women in the theology department, as the church hierarchy in the late 1960s was very male dominated. With the few women whom Charles came into contact, he enjoyed their passionate contributions to discussions in seminars. He also began to feel their real, sincerely-felt experiences of being on the outside, excluded because of their gender. They gave Charles the sense that there were feminine voices wanting to see the church change, for it to move into the twentieth century and maybe, that through the rise of women in society they may bring new hope for the church in the future.

In social situations, outside of the theological discussion and seminars, Charles struggled with 'small-talk' in his contact with women. There was one embarrassing moment in his first term when he invited Sarah, a member of his seminar group in Old Testament studies, for a drink. In a quiet corner of a local pub, the silence was heightened by periods when Charles struggled to keep any conversation going. Through awkwardness and in desperation, he resorted back to theology and talked non-stop about Harrison's assessment of the role of prophets in the development of the Jewish faith. Thankfully, the evening finally ended when Sarah politely excused herself as she had to complete an outstanding essay!

Charles, walking home alone was crestfallen, his cheeks still flushed with the failure and embarrassment of the evening. Much later in his life, Charles was to think back upon this 'first date' in Oxford, as one of those moments which reflected his inability to enter into meaningful relationships. On that night, he felt useless in making friendships, so Charles retreated to his academic world where he felt more confident and reassured.

Charles returned to his grandparent's home for the Christmas vacation and Gladys and Alan joined them for the week of Christmas and New Year. They all attended the Christmas morning service and then shared a traditional Christmas lunch together. After the meal was eaten, Gladys took out a little box and placed an engagement ring on her finger, happily announcing that Alan had proposed to her and they were to get married. There were hugs and kisses as the family expressed their delight at the news.

Later, in a quiet moment, Charles held his aunty tightly

and whispered in her ear, "Thank you for the past, now go and live your own life to the full." A tear glistened in Gladys' eyes as she fully realised that Charles had given her release from that life-time commitment to him. For Charles, it was a moment when he knew that he must begin to turn and face his reality alone.

Over traditional Christmas pudding and coffee there were further announcements by Gladys and Alan. Their marriage was to take place next week at a Registry Office in North London and they had booked a hotel nearby for a celebratory meal and for accommodation for them and the family to stay overnight.

The surprises continued as Gladys patted her tummy announcing that they were expecting a baby due in June and that Alan and herself both felt it was important to marry quickly and quietly. The family also knew that Alan was divorced from his first wife and that the Church of England would not marry divorced persons, so a Registry Office ceremony was the sensible option. Gladys' parents were a little taken aback and slower than Charles to show their delight at the news but they also recognised the love that their daughter had for Alan and within moments, Charles' grandma was talking about choosing knitting patterns for booties, gloves and hats for the baby.

On Boxing Day, Charles, Gladys and Alan went for a walk through the nearby woods and along the familiar beach. Alan spoke of his recent promotion at work and how they could now afford to buy their own home in North London. He spoke with such pride and joy about Gladys and the forthcoming baby that his love for Charles' aunty was crystal clear. It seemed to just bubble up within Alan and was expressed not only in words but also in the constant close contact towards each other and especially through the happiness in their eyes. It was amazing to Charles how a simple action such as the way they held hands as they walked along, could become an outward expression of a real love for each other. To Charles it appeared to represent their togetherness and happiness, linked to one another.

It was a lovely, sunny, crisp winter's day, with little wind, which brought a calmness to the scene before them. They sat together on the low rocks at the far end of the beach, gazing across to the endless roll of the waves upon the sand, with the seagulls circling overhead, expectant of sharing in a picnic.

Gladys turned to Charles and said there was one other announcement to make — this solely to Charles. She explained that when Charles was eight years old, a promotion at her work had given Gladys some extra money, which she invested in a ten-year bond for Charles. Gladys continued that as the years went by, she increased the amount deposited each month until his recent eighteenth birthday when the bond matured. Gladys handed Charles an envelope which contained a cheque and a note with the words:

'Thank you, Charles, for all the love, care and comfort we have shared over the years in our car journeys and weekends together. With all my love for your future life, Aunty Gladys'.

Charles turned to his aunty and said, "No Aunty, it is for me to thank you. You have been a wonderful mother and father to me. I will always try to love as you have loved and helped me through the good and dark times of my life. Thank you."

Charles placed this note in his wallet and it stayed there throughout his life as a constant reminder to him of the depth of love that people can share together, through a selfless giving of one to another. Later, in future moments of darkness and despair, he would take the note from his wallet and seek reassurance in its words.

The following week, everyone travelled down to North London to Gladys' and Alan's marriage ceremony. Gladys' father gave her away and both Gladys' parents acted as witnesses. On the walk back from the beach on Boxing Day, Alan had asked Charles to be his Best Man to which Charles happily agreed. Later, the celebrations continued with a family meal at the hotel, followed by short speeches at which Charles was Master of Ceremonies. It was a wonderfully happy time and reflected the love that Gladys and Alan had for one another.

In March, Alan and Gladys moved into their new home in Hanwell, North London and then, in late June, Gladys gave birth to a son whom she named Albert Charles. A year later, Albert Charles was joined by a sister, Katherine Evelyn; the family now complete. Charles visited his new cousins regularly over the years and Gladys rang him weekly to have a long chat and to share in Charles' life.

In the new year, Charles returned to Oxford and to his academic studies. His attendance at the Liturgical Commission meetings fuelled his growing interest in worship. He looked back at the history of words used in services throughout the life of the Christian Church, with his fascination for this subject to eventually become the basis of his thesis in the third year. In his second term, Charles met and became life-long friends with a student called Graham Sharp, together discovering a kindred spirit.

He, like Charles, loved the academic rigours of study and particularly of theology. Graham was to go on to become a much-respective professor and author of many influential books on the New Testament. Their friendship was centred around their respective studies and they would spend hours in discussion and debate, feeding off one another as they extended their knowledge through each other. It was not an intimate sharing of life or feelings but a friendship of exceptional minds, which acknowledged each other's insights and expertise.

Towards the end of his third term, Charles decided to use some of the money that Gladys had given him to rent a flat in a town house. This would be more spacious and give Charles the option of being able to spend more time in Oxford during the holidays, able to continue his research and studies. It also gave him space away from the social side of the college, which he found distracting and tiresome.

Eventually, a two-bedroom flat at the top of a town house, together with living room, kitchen and bathroom became available near the centre of Oxford. Charles invited Gladys to come and look over the prospective furnished flat and was encouraged enough by her comments to take the flat on a two-year contract. At the end of term, Charles moved into his new home and then, in the early summer of 1967 Charles began driving lessons, passing his test at the second attempt. He then purchased his first car, a second-hand Morris Minor Traveller with a 948cc engine, with which he proudly boasted could get from zero to fifty miles per hour in twenty-eight seconds! His solo long journey was to return to his grandparents for a fortnight's holiday at Grange-next-to-Sea.

His grandparents had both aged and were finding life difficult to cope with in such a small, isolated hamlet. In a quiet moment, Charles' grandad confided in him that they were seriously considering moving to the local market town and finding sheltered housing or a care home, in preparation for their final years.

Whilst out walking one day along the coastal path, Charles met Emily. They had not seen each other since Christmastime and had much news to share. Emily had achieved a place to read English at a northern university and was working at the local pub in Somerberly to raise some money to travel across Europe in August. Charles spoke of his studies, his new flat and car and in a moment of surprise to himself, invited Emily to come and stay in Oxford for a few days in late July. He quickly added that the flat had two bedrooms!

Charles met Emily at the railway station in Oxford and they walked through the streets to his third floor flat. The town was in the midst of a summer heatwave and the sun was beating down upon the pavements. Charles had left the windows open and two fans on to try to cool the flat as much as possible, with the small breeze that existed. He was wearing only shorts, t-shirt and sandals, while Emily had the briefest of tops and skirt on. As Charles followed Emily up the stairs, he noticed the bare skin of her inner thighs and caught brief glimpses of her cerise underwear. He felt that same stirring he had done the previous year at his grandparent's home and by the time they entered his flat, he was excited sexually.

The day before Emily arrived, Charles had been to the barbers for a haircut and whilst there, had purchased some contraceptives. He argued, rationally to himself, that it was socially responsible to be prepared if ever such an opportunity arose.

Once in the flat, Charles reached out to Emily and kissed her passionately. She could feel his excitement through their scant clothing and responded. While Charles fumbled and got into difficulties with bra-fastenings and putting on his contraceptive, it was Emily who took control. In the past year she had had several sexual partners and used that experience to lead Charles. After that first time together, in which Charles' embarrassment was compounded by coming to an orgasm before even entering Emily, they then enjoyed one another over the next couple of days, with Charles learning quickly how to exercise more control and to bring pleasure to Emily.

Charles and Emily also found time and space to see the sights of Oxford and to take in the collegiate atmosphere of this centre of academic excellence. Charles shared with Emily his new-found interest in liturgy and Emily confirmed Charles' belief that most young people experienced church worship as boring and totally out of touch with modern life.

After three days together, Charles walked Emily to the railway station. On the platform they said their goodbyes with a kiss on the cheek. Emily was off to Europe and then to a university life up north and Charles back to a summer of research and the preparing of a paper, to present to the Liturgical Commission on the pros and cons of the Book of Common Prayer in modern worship, with particular emphasis on how it is viewed by the younger generation.

For Charles, his time with Emily had been a voyage of discovery in sexuality but his feelings towards Emily had not changed from being someone that he liked; a friend. A new experience, enjoyable, fun, were words that came into Charles' mind when he reflected upon their lovemaking time together. A process learnt but he felt deep down that something else was absent, something he could not identify.

In September, Charles attended the three-day Liturgical

Commission Autumn Conference in London where he presented his paper to delegates. It created a storm which had half the members on their feet applauding, whilst the other half stuck fast to their seats in their opposition. Central to Charles' theme was the belief that the Book of Common Prayer, while containing some beautiful prose, was of no interest to most young people today. It did not make contact with them and its use of old English words was outside of their present-day diction. He used the phrase, 'Thou Hippy!' as an example of the polarity of the two words, from both traditional and modern languages.

Charles argued that the Common Prayer Book language indicated to young people nothing other than the past with its archaic words symbolic of out-of-date beliefs, only attractive and relevant to an older nostalgic generation. Controversially, Charles expressed the view that The Book of Common Prayer would disappear within fifty years. A new liturgy, using modern language was urgently needed to hold the attention of the younger generations; words that spoke of today's experiences. He proposed a working group to be set up to begin writing new services that should be trialled in churches across the land.

In the following weeks, Charles discovered another aspect of the Church of England that had not been apparent to him before. The supposedly 'broad' Anglican Church which prided itself in a diversity of opinions was, in reality, a deeply divided and occasionally bitter organisation with entrenched fundamentalist and traditionalist views held at either ends of the pole; evangelical at one and Anglo-Catholic at the other. In the middle ground were the more liberal thinkers who had supported Charles' presentation and ideas. This time his call for a new liturgy hit the front-page of the national church newspaper and created a bagful of correspondence over the next few weeks.

Many wrote in support of a new approach to try to halt falling attendance figures in churches but numerous hard-hitting traditionalists, wrote vehemently against any changes to the liturgy, claiming that it had served the church faithfully for just over three hundred years from its Cranmer origins in 1662. One letter to the church newspaper stated, 'What did a young, eighteen-year-old student know of the church, its heritage and its worship? It was time for this impertinent child to get his head down and do some proper studying'!

Most upsetting to Charles were the letters he received at his college on return to his second year in early October. Spiteful and threatening with abusive language, offering no logical arguments in return but just simple hatred, bigotry and resistance to change. It was Charles' first experience of ecclesiastical conflict but it was not to be his last.

In his distress and hurt, Charles turned to his friend Graham. They spent many hours, often late into the nights, with Charles trying to rationalise the reaction that his paper to the Liturgical Commission had brought upon him. Graham possessed a quiet character and made an excellent listener, a sounding-board for Charles to be able to express his angst. Occasionally, Graham might offer a suggestion, an idea, a thought, including the possibility that Charles had inadvertently stumbled across a hornet's nest and brought out into the open a debate that had been bubbling away under the surface.

Graham speculated that maybe Charles was being stung and held up as a scapegoat for people's inner fears, that their cherished and traditional institution was under threat by the modern age. He pointed out how John Robinson, after publication of his book, 'Honest to God', had been so heavily criticised by his own church that he had felt the need to leave his Assistant Bishop post and return to the less controversial world of academic study.

It was around the same time that Graham shared with Charles his own radical thoughts concerning the research he had undertaken during the summer vacation. Graham had made an early decision that his thesis and specialisation was upon the New Testament, particularly Matthew's Gospel. He explained to Charles that he was fascinated by the fact that the early New Testament writers were all Jewish and steeped in the traditions and ways of the chosen people.

Graham had come to believe that Matthew, Mark and Luke, the synoptic Gospel authors, naturally followed the Jewish way of writing through the tradition of story-telling. He illustrated his theory by referring to Matthew and the visit of the wise men. Here he propounded Matthew wished Jesus to be recognised as a person who came for all people, not just for the Jewish nation. So, Matthew introduces a story that is only found in his account, where important foreign leaders come to be with Jesus around the time of his birth. Matthew, Graham claimed, writing in the late 70s AD, was the first to mention anything about the birth of Jesus. Paul, in all his earlier letters, makes no reference to Jesus' early life.

Graham argued that all Jewish people reading this text from Matthew would recognise it solely as a 'story' to get across his important underlying message, not as an event that actually happened. It was only later, in the late first century, as the early Christian faith became dominated by non-Jewish people, the Gentiles, that the story was then taken literally under the Greco-Roman influence, being passed down through the generations as fact.

Throughout their second year, Charles and Graham spent many happy and earnest hours together in theological conversations. Going through Bible stories in Old and New Testament, searching out the important underlying messages of the text. For Charles it was a whole new world of discovering ways of how these vital messages could be incorporated into worship in church life rather than the stories that had been read as almost unbelievably literal, clouding the true Christian faith over the ages.

For both of them this was to be the basis of their lives' work and a lasting friendship of mind and intellect. For Graham, it was to be through academia and his writing and for Charles, by the building up of a vision of how the church could be relevant to a late twentieth century society, with a renewed liturgy and changed approach.

Charles continued through his second year with the same mixture of study and research combined with his increasing interest in the work of the Liturgical Commission. His paper suggesting the need to modernise the liturgy had gained ground and a working group had been set up to which Charles was a co-opted member. Charles found himself fully engaged in his studies and challenged in his learning by so many fresh theories and hypotheses.

It was in Charles' personal life that he continued to struggle. His nightmare had been largely absent in his first year at Oxford but reappeared briefly during the furore that his presentation to the Liturgical Commission created in the early October of his second year. His intensity of application to his academic work mainly cancelled out any social life but there were moments when he wondered why he studied so earnestly, giving so many hours to his research and so little time to socialising.

Charles did have an awareness of his inner being and on more than one occasion, he pondered upon his inadequacy in the social sphere. He understood that in casual relationships he came across as kind, loving and caring and that he possessed an innate ability to feel and have empathy with people at a deep level. However, he also began to realise that he always held back when that opportunity of a closer relationship presented itself and discovered that, for whatever reason, he could not make the whole commitment, resulting in him standing back.

This was illustrated in the summer of Charles' second year when he met Charlotte. They were working together on the sub-committee group to plan experimental new liturgy. Initially, their relationship was as colleagues but it gradually grew through friendship to a sexual one. Charlotte was several years older than Charles and was a church youth worker in London. She was sexually experienced and put a lot of enthusiasm into their lovemaking, on the one and only time they made love at her flat during a weekend workshop for the Planning Group.

After the lovemaking Charlotte began talking enthusiastically of their future together and Charles became alarmed at the depth of commitment Charlotte's intense character exuded. Charles retreated into himself, distraught at the negative feelings and emotions he felt at the possibility of being involved in such a deep relationship. He withdrew from the Planning Group citing the need to concentrate on his third-year thesis and did not answer her letters.

In the late summer of that year, Charles returned for the last time to Grange-next-to-Sea to help Gladys move his grandparents to retirement sheltered accommodation in the market town of Tuxbury. Their health had declined and they could no longer cope with the house and had decided it was now time to move to a more supported setting.

It was a major undertaking to help his grandparents downsize from their three-bedroomed home to a single bedroom flat with a lounge/dining area, kitchen and bathroom. A lifetime of possessions and memories had to be disposed of including his grandfather's precious carpentry tools in the garden shed. There were tears and heartache as their world shrank before their saddened eyes. During these two weeks of moving, the only joy was in Gladys' thoughtfulness in bringing her two children, Albert and Katherine, along for the doting grandparents to play with.

Despite the grandchildren, it was still a tearful final closing of the front door for his grandparents and for Charles as they realised a chapter in all their lives was ending. For Charles, it was an end to a loving home and on his journey back to Oxford, the realisation dawned that he no longer had a base to return to. Nowhere to call 'home'.

In the coming days, the darkness again descended as Charles felt the full force of his loneliness. He thought back to his own short memories of his parents. Tears welled up within him as he tried to remember the actual features of his father and mother. The colour of their eyes, their hair, their expressions, their clothes and especially, Charles recalled time and time again, that final moment at the Home for Incurables with his mother when he kissed her goodbye. He tried so hard to revisit the final words he spoke to his mother, to view in his mind's eye the room, the bedclothes, the nurse who greeted them, the colours on the walls. Charles tormented himself into a state, strenuously trying to recall his own personal base of love, so savagely torn away from him.

Mentally exhausted, Charles only survived by throwing himself back into his studies, working even longer hours to try to keep the demons at bay. He was totally absorbed in lectures, seminars and tutorials, yet also aware that within him he was still struggling with the past.

At the beginning of his third year, Charles' Personal Tutor spoke to him about his plans for the future. The Chair of the Liturgy Commission had been in touch hoping that Charles would go into the Ordained Ministry as he saw Charles as a potential future leader in the Church of England. Charles confirmed that he had considered exploring a vocation to the ministry and his tutor stated he would enthusiastically give his support.

At a further meeting, Charles' tutor outlined the process that the Church of England followed and the attendance at a three-day Selection Conference. If accepted, Charles would then have to seek out a place at a Theological College where further training would take place for two or three years.

It was March when Charles attended his Selection Conference at a Diocesan Retreat House in rural Warwickshire. There were twelve candidates present with three assessors discerning their potential callings through collective group work and three individual interviews, one with each of the assessors.

Charles quickly realised the assessing was continual, not only during set sessions and individual interviews but also over collective meals and informal discussions. He made a special effort to join in the small, social conversations over meals and coffee breaks, realising that the accessors were looking for characteristics that a clergyman would need in relating to people in everyday life.

His warmth of personality shone through and his innate ability to recognise underlying feelings was evident, particularly in one of the group sessions known as the 'ten-minute topic'. One candidate was asked to lead a discussion on an impossibly difficult subject and Charles was the first to recognise that the difficult planted topic was to see how others reacted in coming to the aid of the baffled candidate. It was Charles who prominently came to the other candidate's assistance and supported the discussion throughout. The accessors' pens were observed scribbling copious notes during that session.

Everything seemed to be going well for Charles until the last interview that focussed upon pastoral matters. This accessor was very incisive and probing, asking Charles' about his family life and how he had coped with the tragedies he had been through. The accessor explained that behind his questions was a concern that ministry was not only about the people one served but also about the deep understanding of one's own self. Charles was unsettled by this line of questioning and felt he was not very convincing in his replies.

Despite this, two weeks later, a letter arrived saying that Charles had been recommended and was invited to continue testing his vocation by attending theological college. Charles visited a nearby theological college and was accepted for a two-year training, which was reduced from the normal three years due to his theology degree at Oxford. Charles would have to be a resident at the college during term-time, as there was an emphasis upon being together in a community.

However, Charles needed a base to call home and so extended the renting of his flat for another two years so that he could have some continuity of accommodation but also, so that he could be a little more independent and continue to be close to research sources in holiday times.

In due course, Charles completed his third year and after presentation of his thesis, it was deemed to be of such a high standard that it was published by Oxford University Press. It was later revised to become a standard history of liturgy textbook for theology students at universities. It also had a wider and popular appeal in theology sections in mainstream bookshops and was reprinted several times over the next decade.

2.8 Ministry training — part one

The next part of Charles' preparation for ministry at theological college had a mixed effect upon him. Academically, Charles felt it was like going backwards, from high-level degree study and research at Oxford University to a standard that was comparable to his previous education at GCE A-level. The theological college was on the outskirts of the university town of Oxford and yet to Charles, academically, it could have been a thousand miles away. Old and New Testament, Ethics and Church History were all a poorer repetition of studies already completed.

But the subject that frustrated Charles the most was his specialisation: Liturgy. He sat through lectures, biting his tongue and squirming in embarrassment at the ignorance of an elderly tutor in this subject. His limited knowledge seemed to end twenty-five years ago and he appeared unaware and unread concerning more recent developments in liturgy.

The saving grace of these two years for Charles was in one subject and in the tutor, who had responsibility for Pastoral Studies. Rick was an off-the-wall type of character who differed from all the other staff: in his persona, approach and teaching techniques. He was always informally dressed, often wearing jeans and casual shirts and floppy jumpers. Rick was a loud, boisterous character, full of energy and enthusiasm, bounding along in gait as well as with ideas and thoughts. He had only recently arrived from being a vicar in an inner-city parish and was full of fresh experiences of having to deal with a wide variety of people and social issues. Rick stood out in sharp contrast to the other tutors who had not served in parishes for many years.

All the other staff gave lectures or seminars in formal settings with traditional content. Rick's sessions were deliberately unstructured with a questioning approach, inviting students to form their own conclusions. Never were facts and formal ideas presented but instead, Rick invited students to bring their own personalities into understanding of pastoral issues in ministry. He placed before students, case studies highlighting pastoral issues such as conflict, gender equality, race relations and class, which he claimed could only be effectively dealt with in parishes by a leader who had an understanding of themselves and of their and others' psychological make-up.

For Charles, Rick was a breath of fresh air. An original thinker with a real understanding of what being a minister was all about in a changing and modern society. A belief that to be effective in a parish, one had to be deeply aware of one's own strengths and weaknesses. Rick maintained that one had to have empathy for others, combined with the ability to know oneself inside out. For Charles, this was a huge personal challenge, indeed, a frightening one.

Despite Charles' admiration of Rick, many of the students viewed Rick differently. They wanted the pastoral studies tutor to teach them the practicalities such as: 'how to take a funeral', 'how to do sick/hospital visiting' or 'how to prepare couples for marriage'. The 'nuts and bolts' of the job. They wanted structure, facts, means of doing the work, not this mumbo-jumbo, psycho-stuff about 'how did that feel' or 'where we're at' sessions? For many students, Rick was asking too many difficult questions of them to cope with, so they defended their inner selves by labelling Rick as a lefty liberal with wishy-washy theories, not in the real 'down to earth world'.

At the first seminar with Charles' cell group, Rick spoke about their time at college as being in two stages. Firstly, to be broken down, asked to take time to ponder and think about oneself and then, secondly, about being built up again to be sent out as loving and whole priests into the world. Charles found that that was exactly what had happened to him in those two years. Exposed and vulnerable, recognising limitations of abilities as well as personality, before beginning to find a new confidence, partially healed.

In that first year, during the self-analysis sessions with Rick and his cell-group, Charles began to examine his own strengths and weaknesses in pastoral terms. He was uplifted by his ability to express warmth in human relationships and the innate awareness he possessed, in understanding deep underlying feelings in others. At other sessions, though, he plummeted back into the depths of depression by the realisation that after superficial contact with people, he was often unable to enter into a closer and more involved commitment.

Charles recognised this weakness in relationships with his own cell group. Over the first few months, members within the cell-group began making closer friendships, where they spent time together outside of formal sessions. Charles, although liked by all the group, found himself on his own. On the surface, everyone's friend but nobody's soulmate. There was

Alan and Roy, Brian and Adrian, Norman and Steve, Jeffrey and Maurice, Charles and… no-one.

Rick, as the Pastoral Studies tutor, was also responsible for providing students with two insights into practical ministry through placements out in the world. Charles was very much aware that the communal aspect of living together in a training community was outside of the real world's experiences. At times, Charles, found the theological college life to be an enclosed existence, false and apart from other normal peoples' lives. Some married students had not even been allowed to bring their family with them as insufficient family accommodation was available. So, for Charles, to spend two four-week periods in challenging, real-life surroundings was a break to the daily routine of college life. It was like breaking out of a claustrophobic bubble.

The first placement was in a parish where ten thousand people had been rehoused from east London into a concrete jungle on the outskirts of a Hampshire town. The new settlement was deliberately separated from the old town by a dual-carriage by-pass which served as a barrier, herding these new intruders away from the pleasant side of town. Charles worked alongside an incredibly dedicated priest who had no church and no vicarage but simply lived and worked alongside these people from his end-of-terrace council house. Henry was a very clever and intellectually astute priest with the rare ability, to also be able to relate to the working-class people he served. For Charles, it was an insight into the fact that ministry was most importantly about people and not about buildings, status and institutional power. In later times, Charles would recall the humanity and simplicity of this priest as an inspiration in his own ministry.

However, it was Charles' second placement that was to have a profound impact upon him. He was sent to work in a night shelter for young people in Soho, London. Each evening, homeless, young people would queue at an iron gate at the back of the shelter to be admitted for a night's food and bed. Some were allowed in but others were refused due to violent behaviour displayed on previous occasions. Across the road from the gate, 'pimps' waited to try to pick-up those who were turned away with false promises of drink, drugs and accommodation. Inside the shelter, a cooked meal was given and advice offered, before separate male and female dormitory-style bedrooms provided a safe space in which to sleep.

Some of the young people had mental health problems, others showed signs of alcohol or drug abuse. There was often violence and/or the threat of violence in the air. Their stories often followed a common theme, as Charles listened to their experiences over cups of tea. The main heart-breaking accounts given by these defenceless and vulnerable young people were about broken homes with parents separated; a violent step-father moving in who then forced the child out of the home through mental, physical or sexual abuse suffered by the young person. Many of them came from northern and midland cities and towns, drawn by the lights and false hopes of an apparently glamourous London West End.

Charles could identify with these children and their feelings. Their loss of families, their isolation and despair, combined with a lack of deep affection. Driven away from home to seek something elusive and having no one to help and love them. At one level he could feel the lack of love in their lives, the desperation in their faces and the sadness in their eyes and yet, at another personal level, Charles could give thanks for those who tried so hard to balance his life after his parents' deaths.

However, it left Charles with his emotions in turmoil. He acknowledged his own good fortune, whilst also being aware that his own parental losses, with the repercussions of the absence of that foundational love, gave him a special understanding and rapport with these young people. The carnage of life sat before him each evening in such young faces, where the lack of love was so visibly etched into their blighted, young lives.

Each morning at 7 a.m., the gates opened and the young people went out into a cold world trying to survive another day, alone and isolated to the dangers of a hardened exploitive society. Charles walked back to his digs each morning full of tears. Questions poured through his placement's final report back to college. Surely the church should be here to meet these youngsters on the streets? Why is the church not out amidst the young homeless providing money and resources for those with virtually nothing, instead of worrying about their leaky roofs with endless fund-raising appeals for the maintenance of historic churches?

After four weeks, Charles returned to theological college and to 'normal' life. That summer, the College was to launch an appeal to renovate its buildings and a letter would be sent out to present and past students inviting everyone to contribute to the one million pounds appeal. Charles sent nothing but instead, donated monthly to the Soho Night Shelter for the remainder of his life. Those four weeks had had a profound effect upon Charles and he was determined to awaken the church to its 'social Gospel' of helping those in need, as Jesus had done so many times in his life.

Another brick in his vision of building a church relevant to a modern society began to take shape in his thoughts. He decided to discover more about how the church could be at the forefront in being alongside those in poverty and to find a curacy in an urban setting to further this commitment.

That opportunity came just after the Christmas of 1970, when Charles was invited to explore the possibility of a curacy at the large, inner-urban Parish of St. Francis of Assisi in a northern industrial town. There had been a place of worship on this site since the late fourteenth century, when a small group of Franciscan friars arrived and built a community which included a friary and a church. In the sixteenth century, under Henry VIII, the original church was mainly destroyed, leaving a pile of stones. However, in the mid-nineteenth century the church was restored and the new building incorporated some of the old, stone pillars and walls from the ruins of the past.

When Charles arrived on an exploratory visit to the church on a crisp, snowy Friday morning in January, he was greeted by a chaotic site. Builders' vans, cement mixers, bricks and timber littered the grounds around the front entrance porch. As Charles stood, amazed at the scene before his eyes, a priest came rushing towards him.

Father Hugo was dressed in a black, flowing cassock, stained with splashes of mud from the church building site. He greeted Charles enthusiastically, apologising for being late. Hugo was a slightly-built man in his late forties, a bachelor, married to the church in his lifetime commitment to serve his people. Hugo explained that the congregation, after ten years of arguing, discussing, planning and fund-raising had decided to reorder the inside of the church so that it could be used throughout the week to provide facilities for their local community. Hence, the builders' mess and his dirty cassock and shoes!

Charles warmed to Hugo immediately. He had a vibrancy about him that shone in his eyes and through his personality. He had already spent fifteen years in the parish and saw it as his life's work. Hugo was much-loved by the local people, church attenders or not. He always had time to stop and talk to people in the streets and was always cheerful, with a good sense of humour. Hugo was a 'people-person' and someone who always left you feeling valued and listened to. Charles immediately thought back to Rick at college and his belief in the importance of knowing one's self in ministry.

They had a brief look inside the church but were unable to go in more than a couple of feet. The sight before Charles was incredible. The interior was completely gutted. Every normal structure in a church: the pulpit, the font, the screen, were all gone with the floor taken up for a new heating system to be installed. Hugo explained that the works would be completed by the summer but in the meantime, services were being held in the church hall next door.

Hugo, with his excitement overflowing, explained that the two side transepts of the church were going to be transformed into meeting rooms and include kitchen facilities where meals would be prepared providing lunch clubs for the elderly and homeless. The main part of the church would have moveable chairs so that children and youth group activities could take place in the large space, while the east end of the church would have an open chapel where all could find quietness and a place for prayer.

The other side of the church from the parish hall was the

vicarage, where Charles was to stay for the weekend with Hugo. Over the first of many pots of tea, Hugo explained that the parish was in a relatively poor area and struggled to balance its books financially. The re-ordering was only proceeding due to seventy-five percent of the money being acquired from different charities supporting community ventures in poor urban areas. There was no finance to purchase a curate's house, so if Charles decided to come to St Francis' Parish, he would have to share the vicarage with Hugo.

After an afternoon touring the parish, Hugo and Charles spent the evening talking and sharing a bottle (or two!) of red wine. Hugo was a bit of a wine buff and spent some time introducing each bottle that they drank over the weekend. He contended that the only wine worth drinking was from France, in particular the area around Bordeaux. Wines such as Pomerol, St. Emilion, St. Julien, Márgaux, St. Estephe and Pauillac were to the fore in his impressive racks of wine.

His pride and joy, was a bottle of Chateau Palmer, which he allowed Charles to hold in its dust-covered state for ten seconds, before returning the precious vintage to its prime place of storage. A wealthy member of the congregation had bought Hugo that wine and he was determined not to drink it until the day of his retirement. Hugo received many more bottles of his favourite wines at Christmas and on his birthday from his congregation, funeral directors, family and friends.

Just after midnight, Charles stumbled up the stairs and fell into bed, knowing that this was the place for his curacy. Before leaving college for this weekend's visit, he had spoken to Rick who advised him that one of the most important elements in choosing a parish was to be the relationship with the parish priest. Through the pleasant haze of alcohol, Charles was convinced that he could learn a great deal from Hugo. He had been honest with Charles concerning the difficulties of working in such a challenging, socially-deprived area and yet, he had also demonstrated a belief in the people he served. What impressed Charles most about Hugo, was that he possessed a clear way forward in terms of the ministry in this area. He had a vision.

Charles was also impressed that Hugo had spent a lot of the time listening to him during that first evening. Hugo was aware of Charles' academic achievements at Oxford and his expertise in the history and future of liturgy and encouraged Charles to speak of his experiences. Charles was relieved that Hugo did not feel threatened by Charles' expertise but quite the opposite, Hugo wanted Charles to develop his thoughts on liturgy in a practical parish setting. As Charles lay on the verge of sleep, he waxed positively upon the character of Hugo and the underlying confidence he exuded.

Charles' only doubt lay in Hugo's cooking! Their evening meal had been a collection of left-overs from the fridge that Hugo had thrown into the frying-pan with a few herbs, resulting in an interesting concoction! Suddenly, the vicarage phone rang and a few moments later, Hugo knocked on his door. It was nearly 1a.m.

Hugo explained that it was a call from the hospital as one of his congregation was in casualty after being beaten up. He was going to the hospital and would Charles like to come along? Charles quickly dressed and met Hugo outside next to his battered Ford Anglia car. As they sped through the mainly deserted streets to the City Hospital, Charles remembered that Hugo must have drunk at least a bottle of red wine over the course of the evening. When Charles mentioned this to Hugo, he was only slightly reassured by Hugo claiming that he knew all the local police by their first names and all would be well. They parked in one of the consultants' car parking spaces and made their way into the hospital.

Martha lay on the hospital bed in the casualty department. Her battered face broke into a painful smile when she saw Hugo approach her bedside. It was obvious that in the assault she had lost several teeth, as well as other injuries including a broken nose and a lump enclosing her left eye. There were also other minor cuts and scratches to her face and neck. As Hugo sat beside Martha's bed, holding her hand and comforting her through sobs and tears, the story of the attack upon her unravelled.

Martha was 'on the game'; working as a prostitute. With a drunken, unemployed husband, she struggled to provide for her five children. Since her husband's limited 'dole' money was mainly spent on his drinking, Martha resorted to raising money to feed her children by selling her body. This time though, it had gone wrong and her husband arrived home early having been thrown out of the pub before closing time. Caught in the act, the client made a speedy exit leaving Martha to take her husband's fury and aggression.

On the way back to the Vicarage at 3.30 a.m., Hugo explained that Martha was an occasional attender at the church but also one who often came to the vicarage door asking for food. Charles recalled his placement experiences at the night shelter and how these last few hours were similar in their call for the church to be with those who struggled in such dire socially-deprived circumstances. The die was cast and Charles decided that this was the place for him to try to live the social gospel.

The last six months of theological college life was spent preparing the students for their curacies. In Rick's cell group, this was about examining their strengths and building up confidence to face the difficulties they might encounter in their parishes. Rick encouraged them to recognise the skills they possessed and celebrate the positive gifts they would bring to helping others. Through role play, Rick highlighted the problems of dealing with awkward characters and reminding the group that sometimes the faults one saw in others could be a reflection of oneself.

Through those last few months, Charles had felt encouraged in his well-being. He had faced the realisation that his past did impinge upon his present self but now felt more at peace with being able to cope with these difficulties. Maybe, deep within him, he accepted that he might never be able to trust himself to enter fully into relationships at an intense level. However, with the help of Rick's obtuse teaching methods, Charles had many positive thoughts concerning his abilities and personality and felt the confidence to go forward in the knowledge that he could manage difficult times.

2.8 Ministry training — part two

Charles finished theological college in late May and returned to his flat in Oxford, where he again renewed his lease for a further period of time. He also visited Gladys and Alan in London for a few days, delighting in being with his cousins. They were a very happy, loving family but there were a few quieter moments when Charles drifted in his private thoughts to his own childhood and dwelled sadly upon what he had missed. It was a bitter-sweet time of reflection.

In mid-June, Charles moved his few personal belongings into his new home with Hugo. He still possessed his childhood train set with its red and blue engine which he unpacked, together with a few carriages and set it up on the shelf above the redundant fireplace in his room. The vicarage was a large rambling house built in the first decade of the twentieth century, with large spacious rooms that were now difficult and expensive to heat. In those early days, the vicar would have had servants and indeed, several rooms still had ropes dangling from the walls to call for attention, one of which still rang a bell in the scullery. In pre-world war days, the vicar's sizeable income came from a trust of industrialists who sponsored the parish in return for the clergy keeping the workers in order by espousing the protestant work ethic of hard graft being good for the soul.

The last Sunday of June was the celebration day of St.

Peter, known as Petertide. Charles' alarm shrilled out at 7 a.m. as he climbed out of bed onto the cold lino-covered floor of a guest room in the Convent of Our Lady Retreat Home. The building was set in countryside, just a couple of miles outside the cathedral city, where he was to be Ordained Deacon in a few hours' time. Charles, together with six other ordinands, had been on a three-day retreat to prepare for this moment of: pledging allegiance to the Queen as head of the church, taking vows of obedience to the Bishop of his Diocese and making his vows for the diaconate. The setting of the convent was austere and a disciplined programme had been followed during the retreat, to reflect the seriousness of the occasion.

As Charles washed at his functional, small sink in his room, he ruminated on the fact that as well as the surroundings being sparse and drab, so also was the food. A smile came to his face as he thought of the delights of Hugo's cooking!

It was a strange moment putting on his clerical shirt and 'dog' collar for the first time and then appearing at breakfast with the other candidates similarly attired. The ordination service took place in a packed cathedral and left Charles with mixed emotions. On one hand, he was aware that this was a defining moment in his life: a choice of lifestyle, a commitment to serve, a giving of oneself, a vocation, not just a job.

He was also uplifted by the presence of family around him, especially with Aunty Gladys, Alan, Granddad and Grandma sat nearby who had given him a lifetime of love and support. On the other hand, he found the service over-long being just a few minutes short of two hours. The liturgy was outdated in its language and designed to test the staying-awake powers of all present — which both cousins failed with Albert and Katherine, sleeping for a good hour in their parent's arms!

Most of all, for Charles, there was the tearful absence of his parents, not there at such a defining moment in his life. As he quietly cried inwardly, Gladys leaned across and squeezed his hand. She knew and understood his grief as she always had and once again, was there for him, alongside and comforting. He turned and smiled his thanks to her and noticed a tear in her eye. "Love you," she whispered.

Afterwards, Charles and the family returned with Hugo and the parishioners to the church hall for a buffet lunch, with wine of course, specially selected by Hugo. Food and drink were one of Hugo's most important mission methods of outreach, claiming that it brought more people to church and faith than a hundred street preachers. There were words of welcome for Charles spoken by one of the churchwardens and a gift of a black cloak for Charles to wear at future wet and cold gravesides.

The following Petertide, the day was repeated once more. The parish and family decamping to the cathedral. Vows again undertaken, another long and dreary service, followed by a party back at the church hall. However, on this second occasion there were one or two variations. Charles was no longer a deacon but now an ordained priest so on return to the parish, there was firstly a Holy Communion service presided over by Charles, before going on to the party in the hall. This second ordination now meant that Charles could also take sacramental services such as baptisms, marriages as well as Communion. The parish, who had warmed to Charles over the past twelve months, gave him a sick communion set for Charles to use whenever he took the blessed bread and wine out to those unable to attend church due to ill health.

The most important aspect of Charles' time in his curacy was being alongside Hugo, learning how everything worked in parish life. For Hugo, his mission centred on people; the very focus of his working life. In the first week, Hugo gave Charles a list of church members with a street map of the parish and tasked Charles to go and visit everyone over the first few months. Each week, they would meet on Monday morning and discuss the past week and the coming days as well. Charles would give an account of his visits and discuss church members' needs and concerns. Gradually a routine of working, living and praying together evolved. Charles had Friday as his day off and could, on occasions, stretch that from Thursday night to Saturday morning, giving him time to visit family or to return to his home in Oxford.

Charles enjoyed being with Hugo. As a leader of the church, Hugo had a wonderful, relaxed way with people. He had no interest in status or self-importance, treating all people in a down-to-earth, unassuming manner. In this working-class community, he fitted like a glove and was at ease with everyone. The town was greatly reliant upon the steel industry and had two massive foundries and many other factories and businesses linked to the production of the metal. At the time Charles arrived in the early 1970s, the import of cheaper steel from abroad was beginning to create problems for the town with many steel workers being laid off, resulting in the unemployment rate rising rapidly.

The church re-ordering had been completed and a group, led by Hugo, were beginning to plan how the facilities could be used during the week by the wider community. In their considerations was the worsening economic situation and the need for the church to provide facilities and assistance for those struggling to make ends meet.

As a first response, Hugo and Charles started by setting up a weekly breakfast brunch for unemployed people. Charles was charged by Hugo to organise and finance this venture. He set about building a team of church members to staff the buying, cooking and serving of food on a Wednesday morning. Together with the treasurer, Charles approached local businesses, charities and dignitaries to raise sponsorship to finance the project so that the meals could be offered free. It opened in the December of Charles' first year and served fifty-five Christmas brunches, all sponsored by the local butcher, a friend of Hugo's.

Charles was totally absorbed by the full-on involvement in the parish. He was amazed by the wide range of areas and skills required to be a clergyman in such a busy community-style church. In the space of just one day of ministry, Charles could be called upon to act as a social worker, a teacher, a counsellor, a leader of worship and much more. He had to do a quick, crash-course in the welfare benefits available to people who had just been made unemployed; to have knowledge of the appropriate resources for families struggling to pay their rent or mortgage and where the nearest housing shelters were located for those who did become homeless; to learn about alcohol, gambling and drug abuse in an area where desperate people seek an escape from the drabness of the poverty in their lives.

One of the most frightening moments of his first few weeks, was the time Charles attended his first school assembly. In a huge hall, just off the entrance foyer of the church school, Charles was faced with three hundred and fifty children aged between five and eleven years of age, sitting cross-legged and expectant. The headteacher introduced Charles and explained that 'Father Charles' had just arrived at St. Francis' Church and would be visiting the school on a regular basis. Suddenly, the headteacher turned to Charles and invited him to come forward to say a few words. A feeling of panic flooded through Charles as he had been under the impression that he was only attending the assembly and not speaking.

As he stood up, Charles' mind was in turmoil and searching for inspiration as to what to say to so many keen and enthusiastic bright faces looking at him. They were ready to hang on his every word, as fortunately, Charles suddenly remembered a funny story that Paul, the vicar at Somerberly, had used in a service for families. It was a Bible story that involved actions which everybody joined in with. Charles needed six helpers to lead with the actions and asked for volunteers. Immediately three hundred and fifty hands shot up in the air. After ten minutes of chaos and fun, Charles sat down to thunderous applause from staff and children. Charles breathed out a sigh of relief and felt that a lesson had been truly and scarily learnt by him about needing to be more prepared in the future!

There was one area of being a clergyman that Charles had had reservations about — the taking of funerals and dealing with grieving families. He had spoken to Hugo about this when he visited in March and the reasons for this being so. Hugo listened and counselled that it may help Charles if he just assisted at funerals in the first few months and slowly felt his way into this area of ministry.

In the first two months, Charles accompanied Hugo on numerous visits to bereaved families and attended the funerals, sitting at the back of the church or local crematorium. In conversations with Hugo after the funerals, Charles began to understand that a caring minister needed to be alongside the family at this time of bereavement and have empathy towards their feeling and emotions. Then, gradually, Charles also began to recognise that the family required someone to lead them through this time rather than someone mourning with them. As Hugo pointed out, it was of no use to a family if the minister at the front was in floods of tears.

Hugo encouraged Charles to realise that his personality and loving nature was enough to enable the bereaved family through this difficult time. In one sense, there was no need for Charles to enter into the deeper relationship with the family and thereby awaken his troubled past. Charles took on board Hugo's advice that for the minister it was important to be there and sympathise with the bereaved families, but it was also vital, to maintain a sense of detachment as well. Charles began taking funerals in the late September of that first year, initially accompanied by Hugo on the first few occasions.

All went well and Charles' confidence grew as he realised that he would be able to cope, indeed, he began to enjoy this ministry in the meeting of so many different people in their differing circumstances of life and death. However, there was one moment when the past reached out and touched Charles.

After Charles' ordination to the priesthood, Hugo went on a much-deserved holiday for a month to visit relatives in Australia, leaving Charles in charge. In the first week of Hugo's holiday, a local funeral director rang through asking Charles to take a funeral for a four-year old boy: John, who had died of leukaemia. Later that day, Charles contacted the family and speaking to the father, he arranged to visit the following morning. When Charles arrived at the house, the door was opened by the father who led Charles into the front room of the terraced house, where the mother was sat hunched on the settee.

The mother's name was Sue and she had not moved from the settee since the death of her son. The father, Frank, explained that John had died in his mother's arms, whilst they were cuddling together on the sofa. Sue was still in a state of shock and unable to speak more than a few words in her heightened grief. As Charles looked across at Sue's tear-stained cheeks, he suddenly saw his mother's face.

Overwhelming heart-ache buried within him suddenly flooded back as Charles remembered the heaving, uncontrolled sobbing of his mother, with tears pouring down her beautiful face as she sat on that love-drenched settee in their home, twenty-odd years ago. Charles was floundering, distracted but he knew that he had to be strong and professional, serving this family's needs and not being distracted by his own emotions and past. He returned to his role, listening to the family's words. A date and time were confirmed for the funeral and burial and then Charles arranged to return in a couple of days to sort out what the family would want included in the service, leaving them with some ideas to think upon. Charles felt the family needed time to grieve before they could focus on arranging the format of the funeral service. That night his nightmare returned, the first time for a long while.

The funeral of four-year old John, was a hugely intense and tearful occasion for the family. His parents, Sue and Frank, had known that even after eighteen months of treatment, John was going to die. Yet, despite being prepared for this ending, the moment of his death had been devastating for them. On

Charles' return to the family, he had begun to get to know the parents better and spent several hours encouraging the parents to recall the happy times of John's life. Amongst all their tears and heart-ache, the retelling of their son's life brought tears of a different sort, tears of laughter, as Sue and Frank recounted lots of funny times and stories of the mischief that John had got up to.

At the funeral, Charles read not from the Bible but from Revd Awdry's book about the steam train: Thomas, the tank engine, which was John's favourite book. They also sang 'All things bright and beautiful' and 'Morning has broken', before Charles spoke about John's life, sharing all the joy, laughter and happiness he had brought to his mum and dad. Charles focussed the service upon being one of thanksgiving and celebration for a wonderful, full, if short, life. There were tears but there was also laughter and afterwards, many people commented, including Sue and Frank, on how an uplifting service it had been for their little boy. A first very important step in the healing process for John's parents and for Charles.

Charles found it was the most exhausting of times. After the service, the burial and the wake, he retreated to the vicarage and was unable to do any other work that day, other than attempt to cook, unsuccessfully, a meal in the style of Hugo, finally giving up and visiting the local chippy. Charles was totally drained, washed out and emotionally emptied and took time out with a bottle of Hugo's wine, which his mentor had left for him. Strangely though, he was also elated and inside, his being felt deeply contented. Somehow, he had re-visited the past and come through, strengthened with the knowledge that he had coped with some of the demons of his childhood. For Charles, it was an important step forward.

As time went by in the parish, the effect of the re-ordering of the church became a more prominent feature of church life. An elderly person's lunch club began, a mental health support group started, a distribution centre of tinned food for the needy was set-up, a youth club emerged on a Friday night and added to the breakfast brunch was a Job Club, provided and run by professionals, offering advice and help to the unemployed. The knock-on effect was more people attending, not only in the hours that the church was opened and used but also an increase in the Sunday congregation, as local people began again to see the church at the centre of a caring community life. Not just a building for Sundays and worship but also as a place for ordinary people to be cared and loved in practical ways.

Charles was involved in all of these groups: helping serve lunches, sitting listening to people struggling with mental health problems and handing out bags of food to mothers trying to feed their families on their husband's sparse unemployment benefits. He would act as DJ on the record player for the noisy, boisterous and sometimes violent youth club. He liaised with other churches, coordinating the use of their buildings to provide overnight shelter for the growing number of homeless people. Charles was working a minimum of sixty hours each week, leaving little time for any personal negative thoughts. The problems of others provided Charles with a cloak for his own dark moments.

Hugo encouraged Charles to continue his involvement with the Liturgical Commission throughout the three years of his curacy. Charles was heavily involved in the 1970s, firstly helping produce Series One, Two and Three of the Holy Communion Service and then, most importantly, his work on the new prayer book that was to supplement the old Book of

Common Prayer.

The endless meetings and discussions concerning what was to become The Alternative Service Book greatly frustrated Charles. He wanted the new liturgy to go much further and be more varied, encouraging flexibility for people to create their own variations of liturgy suitable for their specific occasions and localities. He pointed out that the language and culture of a town in stockbroker Surrey was hugely different from an urban, northern mining community. Charles argued that the church needed worship to match the people, 'where they were', not a bland, impersonal, middle-class script for all.

Charles also wanted the role of women in the modern world to be more represented in the church's liturgy. As a supporter of the movement for women to be ordained priests, Charles strenuously pushed for the liturgy in the new Prayer Book to be more inclusive, for the feminine aspect of God to be acknowledged. Charles wished to see an end to the male dominance that existed in every facet of the life of the Church of England. However, Charles faced the full force of conservative thinking within the Anglican community and his best efforts at trying to persuade the church to modernise its approach towards gender issues fell on stony ground.

In his own parish, Hugo was amazing in allowing Charles to experiment with new liturgy in their church. This was against official church rules and regulations and could have seen Hugo disciplined by the church authorities, usually by the Archdeacon, whose duties included being the overseer of clergy behaviour. At his first celebration of Holy Communion after his priesting, Charles wrote his own service, leaning on many alternative influences such as liturgy from the Iona Community, including their use of inclusive language. Charles also created lots of informal, modern family services which he had published as a resource for other churches to be able to use across Christian communities.

In the Spring of his third year at St. Francis', Charles received a phone call from the Principal of a Cambridge Theological College asking if Charles would come and talk to his students concerning the new liturgy being planned by the Liturgical Commission. After careful thought, Charles rang back the following day and accepted the invitation.

The Principal, Harry, had set a day aside for Charles to work with the whole community of students and staff. On arrival at the college, Charles was ushered into the Principal's study to be greeted by Harry leaping up from behind his desk and warmly grasping Charles' hand in a firm and lengthy handshake. He was a large man in his late fifties, who exuded warmth and certainty in his manner. There was also a real twinkle of mischief in his eyes and he possessed a raucous laugh which came from deep within him. Later, Charles would spend many happy hours with Harry, stretching each other's intellects in long theological debate.

The day's event was to take place in the library and they joined the rest of the community at nine o'clock. Harry introduced Charles and then sat back expecting a series of talks throughout the day by his visiting speaker on the planned, proposed new liturgy. Charles though, had other ideas. In his planning for the day, Charles recalled the methods of group involvement as a way of learning that Rick had used at his training college. In addition, after that first assembly at the local church school nearly three years ago, Charles had spent time as an apprentice observing and shadowing one of the members of staff in the school. For half a term he did a crash course in teaching techniques, including the process of how to encourage the learning process through questioning, involving the pupils in finding the answers for themselves. Charles drew upon both these experiences in his presentation.

He stood up and explained that today, *they* would be writing the liturgy and through an intense first hour of questions, Charles extracted from the community what constituted the content necessary for an act of worship. He then divided the community into eight groups of six, including staff and the Principal and tasked them to go away for the rest of the morning and write a Holy Communion service.

Each group was given a different setting for their service; a rural community, a suburban parish, an inner city, a mining town, a sea-side resort and a university city. After lunch, each group would then present their liturgy and invite discussion and comments. In the concluding session of the afternoon, Charles would draw together all the discovered themes and relate them to the progress made so far by the Liturgical Commission.

The day was a huge success with some thought-provoking discussion, debate and argument, bringing out both radical and conservative approaches to creating new liturgy. In his closing comments, Charles drew upon the different approaches revealed by the community and reflected that this was very similar to the problems being experienced by the Liturgical Commission in putting together new services. At the end of the day, Charles was thanked by a representative of the student body who enthused that the day had been one of the most stimulating in his two years at the College.

That evening, over dinner with the Principal, Charles' host said how extremely pleased he was with the way the day had gone and particularly impressed with how Charles had structured the day, involving everyone and creating liturgy through people's own experiences and cultures. Harry then revealed that there was an underlying motive in his invitation to ask Charles to lead the day on Liturgy. He wanted to offer Charles the post of Liturgy Lecturer at the college.

Harry explained that the present holder had retired due to ill-health and the appointment, if Charles accepted, would be from September of this year for an initial five-year period. Charles was surprised by the position as he was only twenty-five years of age and responded by asking if he could have time to think about the offer. Harry continued to explain that accommodation would be provided within the college grounds and that outside of term-time, Charles would be able to continue his own research, study and writing as well as his important work with the Liturgical Commission. It was agreed at the end of the evening that Charles would let Harry know his decision by the weekend.

As Charles drove back up north from Cambridge, he spent the whole journey weighing up this appointment to return to academia, trying to balance this future against remaining at the coal-face of the social gospel in an urban parish of his own. He was aware that a new curate had visited the parish and would be joining Hugo in June, so Charles knew he had to move on this summer. But the dilemma facing him now was to where? He had loved the three years with Hugo and the incredible work with the people and the projects they had set up, ministering to the whole needs of their community. The experience had opened his eyes to how much the church needed to change and become more relevant to a rapidly changing world. To get off its lofty perch and to come alongside the 'common' people.

Charles drove into the vicarage forecourt and getting out, he closed the car door and knew, deep down, what his decision was to be. Hugo and some other clergy were doing heroic work in communities but their efforts were hardly acknowledged by the institution of the church, or by those who influenced policy and the overall direction of the church. No, if Charles wanted to bring about a reformation of the church, moving people on from set historical structures and ways, he would need to speak out to a much wider audience and try to bring about a revolution of thoughts in people's minds. The Cambridge Theological College appointment would be a base to share his ways with future clerics and also give him time to write publications and books with the opportunity to express new ideas in liturgy and in other areas where reform was so necessary.

Later that evening, over a bottle of wine, Charles sat down with Hugo sharing his thoughts and feelings about his future. Hugo, as always, listened intently to Charles' analysis of his situation. When eventually Hugo spoke, he asked Charles a question. "How well do you think you can cope with conflict?"

Charles was a little baffled by Hugo's response and asked Hugo what was his thinking behind such a question. Hugo pointed out that Charles needed to consider seriously the consequences of his radical theology and the 'taking on' of the church's very conservative establishment, who were heavily opposed to any change. Hugo reassured Charles that he was supportive of Charles' ideals but concerned that he would be hurt by the bitter criticism he would encounter on such a journey. Hugo also pointed out that any change would take many years of campaigning and would require patience and determination from Charles to move the church onwards.

Charles slept uneasily that night. Hugo had identified his naivety and lack of experience in how the Church of England's hierarchy operated. It would take years to gain people's trust and support and to work alongside and within the present church order. Charles would have to influence others, build relationships, gain friends, create and build a group of like-minded people around him, a theological 'think-tank'. His arguments would have to be unrolled over a lengthy period of time, giving others the opportunity to absorb a new way of thinking, a modern way of 'being church' in the late twentieth and early twenty-first centuries.

Over the next forty-eight hours, Hugo's question came back constantly to the forefront of his thoughts. How would he cope, if and when relationships got feisty and there was anger aimed towards him? He had seen instances in the local deanery where one clergyman was forced to leave his parish by a group of parishioners who opposed his proposal to remove the historic screen that divided the chancel from the nave. Windows at the vicarage were broken in the middle of the night, his car was scratched and damaged and his family verbally abused by supposedly caring, loving members of the church family.

At one meeting of local clergy, the vicar of this parish was in tears and within weeks, he had left his church and all ministry. Charles wondered if and how, he would survive similar levels of opposition? Could he come through being isolated, 'sent to Coventry', ignored and maybe, even abused? Was he strong enough? Would this rejection by others trigger past losses, bringing back loneliness and times of depression and withdrawal? Would it not be easier to keep one's head down and bury his principles for a quiet life?

On Friday, Charles rang the Principal, Harry and accepted the post.

In mid-June, Charles left the parish of St. Francis, saying a fond farewell to Hugo and the people he had served for the past three years. There were lots of memories for Charles to take with him, some happy, with others more difficult to cope with. Hugo was very much at the centre of Charles' good times, recalling with lots of laughter, some of the extraordinary meals that Hugo had created. Hugo had the gift of transforming a few ingredients from an almost empty fridge into producing a banquet, admittedly with questionable flavours! Jesus' five loaves and two fishes were constantly beaten by Hugo's efforts. Hugo always claimed that it was the bottle of wine accompanying the meal that made the difference.

There were many other good times that Charles had of the people he worked with and those whom he helped. Seeing Sue and Frank through the loss of their young one, John. Being alongside them for over twelve months and witnessing their strength and love grow for each other as they came to terms with their shared grief. A death and resurrection experience. Charles also had fond recollections of Don, the churchwarden, who welcomed him to the Parish on his first day and who worked tirelessly in support of Hugo, Charles and the church. A holy man, yet totally unassuming and down-to-earth and a true example of a Christian living for others.

But there were other more painful memories for Charles to take forward with him. In the midst of his second year in the parish, an incident occurred when visiting a middle-aged woman regarding the death of her partner through alcoholism.

When Charles arrived to meet the widow prior to the funeral, she opened the door with only a towel wrapped around her body. It became obvious to Charles that the lady had been drinking heavily and within minutes, she made sexual approaches to him, dropping the towel and exposing her complete nudity. Charles fled for the door with the rejected widow shouting obscenities at him.

A day later, Hugo received a phone call from the Archdeacon of the diocese stating that a complaint had been made about Charles, alleging sexual misconduct. Charles found himself in the midst of a full disciplinary inquiry, led by an officious Archdeacon, seemingly lacking any pastoral care of the clergy in his diocese.

Charles went through some extremely dark and depressing months of enquiry, where he came up against the set institutional structures of the established church. Eventually, Hugo intervened and visited the widow and persuaded her to withdraw her complaint. However, it left an indelible mark on Charles' mind about archdeacons and their confusing and conflicting role of pastoral care alongside that of disciplining their fellow clergy.

During the summer break, Charles had spent time with his friend, Graham Sharp, joining him on a walking tour in the Dordogne area of France. They spent many happy, sun-drenched hours hiking and talking, with Graham waxing lyrically about the new book he was in the process of writing challenging orthodox views about the nature of Jesus' miracles. Charles, once again, re-discovered the listening ear of Graham that he had experienced in the past, pouring out the events of his curacy, including the horrendous treatment that he had experienced at the Archdeacon's hands over the sexual assault allegation. They both concluded that the pastoral care of the clergy was woeful. On a lighter note, they visited several vineyards in the area, which gave Charles the opportunity of sharing the knowledge he had acquired from living with Hugo.

On return from France, a letter was waiting from his Aunty Gladys which invited him to join their family for a two-week holiday at a cottage in Norfolk. Charles decided to accept but only for a week. He felt the kindness of the offer to include him in their summer break but was also sensitive to the fact that the family would benefit from time together without outsiders.

It was a lovely week in a homely cottage that had a special bedroom in the roof of the bungalow which the children enjoyed, accessing their room by a ladder. Albert and Katherine were now both at school and loved being with Charles. Although Charles was their cousin, they had always called him 'Uncle Charles'. To Charles they seemed to be growing up so quickly. Albert was similar to his Mum, Gladys, in character and personality. He was always on the go, full of life and active with a mischievous twinkle in his eyes. Katherine, was the opposite and more like her father, Alan. She was less boisterous and more reserved with a quiet nature. One a 'doer', the other a 'thinker'. Charles loved them both but he did have a special feeling for Katherine, being able to identify her with his own mother.

Most mornings, Charles would take the two children for a walk, either through the woods or to go beachcombing with them, searching through rock-pools and under stones for crabs and other sea-life. The mornings reminded Charles of his own childhood at his grandparent's home at Grange-next-to-Sea and he shared with Albert and Katherine some of the knowledge he had acquired about wild-life and sea creatures.

This gave Gladys and Alan some precious time together, as well as an opportunity for Charles to be alone with his cousins. One day, they returned a little earlier than usual, due to inclement weather, to interrupt Gladys and Alan who were definitely enjoying some time together! As Charles entered the house with the children, he could clearly hear the noise of bed-springs and some loud groaning from Gladys and Alan's downstairs bedroom. He quickly shouted out a greeting in a loud voice and the noises stopped abruptly. A few moments later, Gladys appeared in her dressing gown with a rather flushed face. Later that evening, after the children had gone to bed, the adults were relaxing together with a bottle of wine that Charles had brought back from France, when Alan joked about them being nearly caught with their pants down!

After that first week Charles left Gladys, Alan and the children to enjoy their own time together while heading back to Oxford to prepare himself for the packing and moving on to his new life in Cambridge.

2.9 Cambridge, Charles and Penelope

The Theological College was on the edge of the university town of Cambridge set in its own grounds of twenty acres. It had formerly been a Manor House where a local landowner's family had lived for generations. Its origins went back to the seventeenth century but following a fire in the early nineteenth century, the house had been almost completely rebuilt. The family line had come to an end in 1924 and the Church of England purchased the house, out-dwellings and grounds to set up a Training College for clergy. After modernisation, the college began its new life in 1926 and for the past fifty years, had produced a line of clerics to serve in parishes.

There were various cottages scattered around the grounds of the college and Charles had been allocated the one furthest away from the main building in a quiet part of the grounds. Although the college was within walking distance of the noise and bustle of the centre of town, when Charles awoke each morning and opened the curtains of his bedroom, he espied a beautiful view of the surrounding countryside, with rolling, sheep-occupied fields, rising in a gradual slope to a gentle, tree-laden hill. It was an idyllic setting and one that Charles would enjoy for nearly ten years.

Charles arrived in mid-August giving himself a month to settle in before the academic year began. Since the middle of

June, he had returned to his flat in Oxford and arranged to terminate the lease at the end of August, moving on to a new beginning and home in Cambridge. He had enjoyed his flat and become attached to his bolthole, where he had found some solitude and space from the business of parish life over the past three years.

In mid-September, forty students arrived, together with five members of staff. With the community assembled, the new term commenced with a Holy Communion service presided over by Harry, the College Principal. In his address, Harry welcomed new students and staff and laid out the daily routine of college life. The day began at 7.30 a.m. in the chapel with Morning Prayer followed by a communal breakfast. At 9 a.m. lectures commenced until a Midday Said Eucharist preceding lunch. The afternoon was for private study and reflection time with group seminars on Mondays. Evening prayer was at 6 p.m. followed by college dinner, then night prayer at 9 p.m.

Through the year there were three, twelve-week terms. Students had their own rooms which served as a bedroom and study. At the end of each term, students returned home to their families. Half of the student body were married men and they were allowed two weekends during each term to return home to visit family. No women were allowed to stay overnight at the college.

The ethos was based loosely upon a monastic style and encouraged time to focus upon the spirit of one's calling to vocation. The forty students were organised into five groups of eight, with two of the groups being over thirty, mostly married men, whilst the other three groups were mainly unmarried younger men, often fresh from university. Each student group was responsible for leading worship for two weeks every term, with the Book of Common Prayer the main source of liturgy. Each group were allotted a tutor to guide them in all matters, meeting once a week. In his first year, Charles was to lead one of the two newly-arrived, older groups.

It was into this environment and structure that in September 1974, Charles started this new stage of his life. He immediately had misgivings over several issues in college life: for married men to be taken away from their wives and children, then suddenly re-appearing, only to vanish again after two days, was not a good recipe for maintaining marriages or ideal for the emotional welfare of young children. Charles also questioned the value of mimicking the monastic way of life in the preparation of priests going out into the secular world. As Charles pondered upon these and many other aspects of college life, he recalled Hugo's words of wisdom concerning moving slowly, building relationships, gaining allies and introducing new concepts over a period of time. Charles resolved to spend that first-year listening, thinking, praying and building friendships with colleagues and students.

Charles loved the teaching of his subject: Liturgy. He was so enthusiastic about its importance in the life of the future well-being of the church, that his energy and vitality shone through his lectures and seminars. Each of the college groups followed a particular topic each week alternating: Old or New Testament studies, Ethics, Church History, Pastoral Theology and Liturgy. Charles would have one of the groups for five mornings of that week and offered a variety of approaches in his teaching methods. Formal lectures one day, followed by experimental liturgy the next. Somehow, Charles succeeded in bringing the subject alive, stimulating students to grasp the importance of how vital relevant words and actions within worship were, to the future existence of the church.

His passionate drive to attempt to arrest the trend of declining numbers attending Church of England services on Sundays by making worship meaningful, was to the fore in his work. Charles was so inspiring in his teaching that on one occasion, a student turned up dressed as a miner with coal hat and light included. His task had been to imagine what the words of the Nicene Creed meant to a pit worker in a mining village. The student took on the role completely, including a northern accent, saying about the creed, "'Ah, I don't know what thou art talking 'bout in them funny words. Born of virgin, how's that then and wots this 'ere resurrection business mean?" With such imaginative teaching, Charles began to awaken future clergy to the need to make church worship more understandable to their congregation.

Gradually, Charles began to settle to the rhythms of college life. The day was so structured that, with the exception of Monday afternoon, he was free to spend time after lunch with his own research and writing. Alongside his ongoing commitment to the work of the Liturgical Commission, Charles was beginning fact-finding for the writing of a book on Eastern Orthodox Church liturgy, commissioned by a religious-based publisher. On occasions, he became so absorbed in his work that he might miss Evening Prayer and dinner in order to continue his own study.

It was in Charles' relationships with others that he revisited the wisdom and forethought of Hugo's question to him about coping with conflict. Hugo realised that Charles may face some hard times in the future having witnessed how difficult Charles had found the complaint against him and his struggle, with the challenging attitude of the Archdeacon. For the majority of staff and students, Charles came across as an open, caring person who had that ability to understand feelings and emotions within others. A sensitive character, complete with a quick, dry sense of humour, that was also combined with a generous spirit of tolerance, understanding and an innate ability to come alongside people.

However, Charles was viewed very differently by one or two others. Stephen Howard was the Church History and Ethics tutor and had been in post at the college for over twenty years. He was firmly established in the very fabric of the place and was well set in his opinions with regard to church traditions and worship. Stephen would oppose anything and everything that Charles suggested in the yearly staff review week. Their relationship would at times be extremely tense and fractious, creating for Charles, many sleepless nights as he questioned his own motivation in seeking change.

He would ask himself time and time again, why did he need to be loved by everyone? Why did he require that comforting smile and reassurance that he was accepted by all? Surely, he could accept that some people would not warm to him and that his ideas would be questioned as being too challenging for others to agree with? He found his confidence would ebb away under the onslaught of conflict and would begin to feel the frailty of his being, struggling when under attack from colleagues. He often faltered and bridled at the impossibility of the task he was setting himself, as it weighed heavily on his shoulders. Maybe his vision was an impossible utopia and unattainable; just an ego trip to get noticed.

Likewise, there was one member in his first year Monday

afternoon group, who was in a similar mould to Stephen. Frank Sheffield was from a very evangelical church and saw everything in black and white terms. For Frank, the Bible was sacrosanct and every phrase was the true word of God. Creation was a six-day wonder and the search for Noah's Ark would one day be successful.

When Frank arrived in the lounge of Charles' cottage at the group meeting on the first Monday of the academic year, he sat down and from his battered leather briefcase he took out his Bible, placing it upon his knees where it remained. Whenever Frank opened his large Bible, virtually every heavily thumbed page had phrases which were either highlighted or underlined.

Again, Charles struggled. Frank was totally closed to consider any view other than his own fundamental approach. On a whole range of topics, he quoted chapter and verse to support his narrow, bigoted opinions. On homosexuality, he condemned its practise quoting the Book of Leviticus and the fact that, all 'faggots', as he disrespectfully called them, would be cast out into the fires of hell for their sins. When Charles asked him how his opinion reflected a God of love and forgiveness, Frank dismissed Charles as a wishy-washy Liberal who ignored the hard bits of the Bible.

Within weeks, Frank had upset most of the group with his views and Charles found that he was in the midst of managing a group conflict. He spent time with Harry, the Principal, seeking his advice and wisdom. Together they decided on a plan to continually question Frank's statements and to challenge his right to condemn people, asking him to give references from Jesus' teaching to substantiate his opinions. Over time, this approach began to soften Frank's thoughts and he became less quick to judge and write-off people. By the second year in Charles' group, he began to join in discussions, asking more and more open questions. He no longer brought his 'comfort' Bible to every session.

It was, however, slow, hard work and the conflict situations during that first year drained a lot out of Charles. He had to admit that he did find it exhausting and during holidays, returned to Hugo for a confidence-boosting time and a special bottle of his red wine! As Hugo pointed out, Charles had survived and although hard, he had come through and in the case of Frank, had seen some positive results beginning to emerge. The situation with fellow tutor, Stephen, though would take a lot longer.

Charles had spent time with his fellow tutors through the year inviting them for evening meals at the weekends. He had become particularly friendly with Brian Jones, the Pastoral Studies tutor, who had a passionate interest in the work and life of Jean Andre Leige, a Benedictine French monk, who devoted his working life in the twentieth century, to exhorting the church to apply theology to the modern world, through cooperation with the social sciences of the day such as psychology, philosophy and sociology. Leige claimed that not do so, would leave theology in the past and would not be relevant to people's lives in the modern culture of today.

From Leige's inspirational work, Brian wanted the church training at theological colleges to give ordinands an insight into the social sciences and their importance to the future growth of the church in a modern society. To this end, Brian campaigned wholeheartedly at the yearly annual review week for the inclusion of social sciences into the college curriculum.

Charles, meanwhile, despite opposition from Stephen, the

Church History and Ethics tutor, brought changes to the Liturgy, arguing successfully for there to be a wider experience for the students to discover different styles of worship. The Book of Common Prayer was now used for one term only in the chapel, whilst one term was given over to the new liturgy soon to arrive in The Alternative Service Book and the third term to be a selection of other liturgies used in other Christian settings, including Franciscan, Contemplative communities and fellow Christian groups, such as the Methodists and Quakers.

The latter group's worship was thoroughly enjoyed by students as Quakers Meeting for Worship consists of silence in a community of stillness. A listening to God, instead of talking at one's maker. Charles added to this by reading occasional sentences from the section, Advices and Queries, in the Quakers Book of Faith and Practice. The students responded to the alternative liturgies positively and enjoyed the variety of worship placed before them, some of which they had never experienced before.

In the second year, together with his old friend, Graham Sharpe and now, Brian Jones, Charles began the formation of a like-minded group of academics committed to a new way forward for the Christian Church. Over the next few years, the group expanded in numbers and together with visitors, such as a radical American Bishop from the United States of America, spent time in shared thought and in exchange of ideas. Pamphlets were written and conferences arranged as the group grew in strength and confidence.

It was not all plain sailing for Charles in his vision for the future of the church. Despite his best efforts at the Liturgical Commission, Charles was heavily outnumbered by dye-in-the-wool theologians and conservative-minded lay people. His attempts to bring modern inclusive text to the planned new Prayer Book were floundering on the traditional rocks of those who were opposed to change. They argued that with the already proposed changes for the new Prayer Book, some church members had indicated that they would stop going to church and withdraw their financial support, unless they did not have the old Book of Common Prayer at the majority of services. To go further with inclusive language, they claimed by referring to God as 'she', or without any gender, would result in protests across the country in the Established Church.

They also pointed out that the Queen, as Head of the Church, would never countenance such a change in the liturgy of her traditional worshipping body. Charles argued back, saying that it was God's church and that it was incumbent upon the commission to move worship into the future, with a mission to appeal to the missing younger generations. His arguments fell on closed ears and minds.

There were times when Charles came back from the Liturgical Commission meetings in utter dejection and despair, wondering whether the church would ever move into the twentieth century, let alone the coming twenty-first one.

To bring himself out of depression on his return train journey to Cambridge from the meeting at Church House, London, Charles would remember Hugo's words, 'Bit by bit, step by step,' and smile at the memories of Hugo's culinary inventions. On those desolate journeys home, as the train trundled through the crowded, dirty and bustling London suburbs, it eventually reached out into fresh, green and straw-coloured fields of the rural countryside, reminding Charles of his journey in life through times of suffering to moments of hope. Charles would take out of his wallet the note from his Aunty Gladys and remind himself about her love for him and that such love, could and often did overcome difficult periods in life. It brought to Charles a warm feeling of reassurance and comfort to counter-balance the coldness of his lonely and isolated distress.

Life continued for Charles with his college work, steadily helping to introduce new ideas and concepts into college life. In May 1979 Malcolm, a member of his tutorial group, knocked on Charles' cottage door late one evening with the news that his marriage had collapsed. With Malcolm away at college, his wife, Maureen, had found it increasingly difficult to cope with life and her two small children. She had turned to Malcolm's younger, unmarried brother for help and comfort. Gradually, over several months their relationship deepened and became sexual. When Malcolm discovered that his brother had moved into his home and bed, he was devastated and distraught, unable to focus or concentrate on his studies. In his despair, he had arrived at Charles' door, pouring out his heart in a tearful and angry tirade.

Charles listened to Malcolm's story, desperately trying to recall the training he had undergone in his curacy with CRUSE Bereavement Care and their Counselling Skills course. He allowed Malcolm to vent his anger and frustration, not only at his wife and brother but also at the college for its policy of excluding wives and families. Eventually, through the evening and into the early hours of the morning, Malcolm became calmer and moved onto practical problems he faced concerning access to his children and the upcoming curacy he was about to commence in July. At about three o'clock, Malcolm thanked Charles for his help and returned to his room in the main house of the college, having arranged to meet with Charles again the following evening.

Later that same day, Malcolm walked along the railway line straight into the London to East Coast Express train and to instant death. His body, like his world, smashed and battered into pieces.

The college community were devastated and mystified as to why Malcolm should take his own life. Some had known and been alongside him, for nearly two years in study and discussions and had had no idea that he was so troubled. At Morning Prayer, the following day, Charles gave students and staff a brief explanation of Malcolm's state of mind in the aftermath of his marriage breakdown which had only come to light two days before. The Principal, Harry, informed the community that in such circumstances, courses would be cancelled for the remainder of the week and that students could visit their family homes, if they so wished, during this period of reflection and mourning.

For Charles, the next few weeks and months were horrendous. He thought he had listened well, played emotions back to Malcolm, brought a little calm and a bit of balance to his troubled mind. But no, he had failed. Malcolm appeared not to have heard a word or moved out of his intense anger and grief at losing his wife and family. Charles' initial feelings of absolute shock were quickly superseded by blaming himself for his complete and utter failure to see the depth of seriousness in Malcolm's state of mind. Alongside this, he blamed himself for not working hard enough to bring change to such an uncaring policy of not giving married men and their families the option of coming to live together at college.

Over the next few days and weeks, Charles' despondency

intensified and deepened as the death of Malcolm brought back the dark moments of his early life. In recent times, Charles had been in control of these memories, pushing them away into the depths of his thoughts and mind, losing himself in the excitement and business of his college teaching, writing, research and liturgy work. One incident and Charles returned to struggle with the past. Asking the same questions, 'Was it my fault that Malcolm and my mother died?', 'Did I say something that drove them over the edge, gave them permission to die?' He began to retreat into his cottage and himself, spending hours awake at nights, fearful of the nightmare which always came when he did eventually fall asleep.

It was to his Aunty Gladys that he fled. Principal Harry, recognising the agony that Charles was going through, granted him permission to have two weeks off. After that time had expired, Charles contacted Harry to ask for an extension to his sick leave until the end of term, which was granted. Slowly, Charles began to recover a balance to his life. He spent time with Gladys talking through his feelings, occasionally joined by Alan, whom Charles found to be a very empathic listener.

The key to his gradual healing, though, was in the very innocent and wonderful love that the children brought and shared with Charles. Albert and Katherine loved him so much that Charles was overwhelmed by how they just accepted him as he was, not requesting anything special, just some time to sit and play board games and read stories to them. Their uncomplicated and innocent lives restored a balance to Charles' fractured one and helped the bad dreams become less frequent.

Charles was determined to return for the final week of

term, which was the Staff Review Week. At the meeting, Charles firmly proposed that during the next academic year, married men with children be allowed to return home every weekend and do their Sunday placements at parishes near to their homes as an interim measure. In the following year, Charles suggested that the college must build and provide married/family accommodation in the extensive grounds available and that the trustees be commissioned to use its extensive trust funds to put this in place immediately. They should be requested to draw up the necessary plans in order that Malcolm's situation would never be repeated again.

The resolution was passed unanimously, with even Stephen voting for the very first time in support of a motion proposed by Charles. That meant so much to Charles and he smiled at Stephen and whispered a 'thank you'. In return, Stephen smiled for the first time at Charles. Five years it had taken. Bit by bit, slowly, slowly, came into Charles' mind and lifted him in a huge surge of hope and love. Stephen never agreed with anything else Charles ever proposed but from that day, they became good friends.

It was in the autumn of this year, 1979, that Charles met Penelope. Charles' emotions were still raw from the after-effects of the suicide of Malcolm and the subsequent re-awakening of his childhood memories. Their first meeting was when Charles attended an evening archaeological lecture at one of the colleges in Cambridge. After the publication of his book on the liturgy of the Eastern Orthodox Church, Charles was asked by the same publisher, to write a follow-up book highlighting the similarities and differences of the liturgy of Eastern and Western branches of the Christian Church. This archaeology lecture was by a Professor who specialised in the excavations of ancient Middle East religious sites.

Charles arrived a few minutes late, just after the lecture had begun. Quietly, he slipped into the back row of the Lecture Hall, finding a vacant seat next to a rather tall lady. The lecture was moderately interesting to Charles who realised he was coming to the topic with a somewhat different approach to the majority of the audience. After half an hour or so, his concentration began to wander and Charles' attention turned to the lady next to him.

Firstly, he was struck by the length of her legs which seemed endless in her tailored trousers. He was fascinated when she moved slightly and uncurled her legs to a new position. For a surreal moment, Charles wondered what it would be like to journey, with his hand, up the length of her legs and even more weirdly, how long that would take. Charles guessed that she must be at least six foot two tall, which was disguised a little by the roundness of her shoulders in a slight stoop. Charles speculated as to whether this was due to being hunched over in study or whether she was very conscious of her height and had therefore compensated, over time, by subconsciously leaning forward in her upper torso.

The lecture ended and a question-time followed. The woman next to Charles stood and asked a question, giving Charles an opportunity to continue his viewing of her without having to turn in his seat. Penelope was no stunner but had a pleasant, tanned face, whose colour negated the need for much make-up. Charles imagined that she had probably spent a great deal of time outdoors in a hot climate, resulting in her almost Mediterranean appearance.

The tall lady spoke with a clearly middle-class, educated, English accent indicating that her birthplace was somewhere in the Home Counties and not from some exotic middle eastern country. She was of slim build and had small, almost non-existent breasts under a blouse and jacket top that matched her trousers. Her hair was fair and contrasted with the brown complexion of her skin, as did her blue eyes.

Somehow, Charles felt drawn to this woman. There was something about her appearance and manner that he wanted to get to know. Despite his initial fascination with her legs, Charles' interest in the tall lady was not sexually motivated but more about finding companionship. Within him and unrecognised by Charles, it was more about being distracted from the recent re-emergence of his early life experiences and the nightmares that still occasionally plagued his sleeping hours.

As she sat down from asking her question, Charles leaned towards her and said, "Good question," although in reality, he had been too consumed in observing her to listen to the Professor's reply. She turned to Charles and said, "Thank you." After further small talk and introduction of names, Charles invited Penelope for a drink at the pub around the corner from the lecture hall. She accepted and so began their relationship in the autumn of 1979.

Over the coming months and into the early part of 1980, they would meet weekly either for an evening meal at one of Cambridge's many restaurants or on a Saturday for a walk in the surrounding countryside and a pub lunch. Charles and Penelope enjoyed one another's company and shared a variety of common interests. Penelope had studied archaeology at Leicester University and now in her mid-thirties, was a Visiting Professor at Cambridge, specialising in the Middle East.

With Charles' research, work and books on subjects dating back two thousand years, there was an overlap of material and interest they shared. Both also loved classical music, often journeying together to concerts in London and elsewhere.

In those first six months there was no sexual relationship. Both seemed content just being in each other's company with shared intellectual stimulation, rather than a physical coming together. For Charles, the togetherness was a relief, a distraction in his world and he began to notice that the dark moments of the previous year were being replaced by happier and more light-hearted times.

Penelope was totally devoted and committed to her career in archaeology and had spent several years over the past decade or so at places in Mesopotamia, excavating a variety of ancient sites. Her base was in Cambridge where she lived in a three-bedroomed, three-floor, Regency, terraced house near the centre of the city. Penelope, when giving Charles a tour of the house, explained that she had bought the property from monies left in her wealthy, banker, father's will after his death ten years ago.

Occasionally, Charles would stay overnight if, on returning to Penelope's home for coffee and with the time entering the early hours of the morning, he would be offered one of the spare bedrooms. In the early summer, they had journeyed to London for the First Night of the Proms. The concert had been an incredible performance of Rachmaninov's Piano Concerto No. 3 which had thrilled them both. Afterwards, they only just managed to catch the last train back to Cambridge, arriving well after midnight. Penelope suggested a nightcap and together they enjoyed a good bottle of French red wine at her home. Penelope invited Charles to stay overnight which he gladly accepted, as the wine and music had made him soporific and tired.

Charles quickly fell asleep but was awakened by a movement of the blankets, as Penelope slipped between the sheets into his bed. He turned to face her and realised that she was naked. Charles' hand moved to Penelope's small breasts as he caressed her tenderly. As he stroked her body, Penelope stirred and murmured her pleasure. Charles' hand went down her nearest leg to her feet and then slowly, his hand travelled back up to her thigh, counting the seconds as he did so. Charles brushed over her light pubic area and then again journeyed down the other leg, maintaining the slow progress. This time though, on its return, he could sense Penelope's and his, heightened excitement. He estimated it took thirty seconds for the leg closest to him and twenty seconds for the second limb, due to their eagerness on the way back up to her intimate area. There was no need for more stimulus as he could sense Penelope was ready to make love.

As their bodies came together, Charles could hear Penelope humming the tune of Rachmaninov's Piano Concerto No. 3 until the moment they both climaxed. Within seconds, Penelope disengaged, jumped out of bed and washed herself between her legs in the adjoining bathroom, before returning to her own bed without a word.

As Charles lay alone in the bed, he reflected upon his relationship with Penelope. On a surface level, it appeared to Charles that they had drifted together in a friendship through a sharing of mutual interests. They enjoyed being with one another, talking about their work, going out for meals and walks and listening to music but up until this moment, they had had no apparent urge to develop that into a physical and sexual encounter. Indeed, in the past six months, they had only kissed each other on the cheek as a greeting or farewell gesture. They had never embraced, cuddled or shown any passionate intent towards one another.

As Charles thought back over the evening's love-making with Penelope, he recalled that they had not kissed on the lips. He had focussed upon kissing her small breasts, which he found fascinating and delightful after his only other experience of Emily's large, dominating breasts. On the one occasion, he had raised his head from her breasts to kiss her passionately on the lips but Penelope had moved her head to the side, Charles kissing her neck instead. It did not enter Charles' thoughts that this sexual coming together might in part, be his own need for comfort and reassurance after the recent black period he had experienced.

Meanwhile, Penelope lay sobbing in her bed. She was reflecting on that moment in their lovemaking, when Charles laying on top of her went to kiss her passionately on the mouth. It had reminded Penelope of the horror of an early adolescent experience which now tumbled back into her consciousness. The memory of her first and only, boyfriend, who, together with her was babysitting a little boy of five at a nearby neighbour's house while the parents were out at the Annual County Ball. Penelope was only sixteen years of age and inexperienced in life. During the evening, her boyfriend persuaded her to drink some whisky that he had brought along. Then, after a little while everything became hazy and confusing for Penelope.

All she could remember was his overbearing weight upon her, pinning her to the settee with his heavy, large and sweating body. His face, so close to her, with its odours of whisky and cigarettes. His tongue forcing itself into her small mouth, causing her to struggle for breath. His hands all over her tender, innocent, youthful body. And then, the next thing Penelope recalled, was retching over the toilet and feeling a terrible soreness between her legs. Her boyfriend had gone, leaving her alone. Deserted. Everything else was blacked out. Blocked from her mind. Buried within her. Locked away until now.

Penelope really liked Charles and enjoyed being with him. The music and the wine had relaxed her and she felt a deep need for his physical presence with her. He had been so loving, kind, almost mystically aware of the need to be slow and caring in his lovemaking. When he entered her, Penelope tried to relax by focussing on the tune of the Piano Concerto they had listened to earlier. She succeeded and climaxed as the music came towards its finale. Charles was the first man that she had had sex with since that scarring adolescent ordeal.

After that first sexual encounter between Charles and Penelope, in some unspoken way, they came to an arrangement of mutual comfort. Both unable to express their inner torments and yet, both content with their friendship and the occasional sexual coming together. They usually made love after returning from a concert and followed a similar pattern of intimacy. Whenever Charles attempted to introduce any other variations, he noticed Penelope immediately became tense and agitated. He realised that she never touched his member and recoiled at any attempted oral sexual activity. Penelope was not a touchy person and in those early days, whenever Charles came up behind her and put his arms around her, he felt her body tighten. She rarely cuddled up to Charles on a settee, preferring her own private area. Charles once reflected on the contrast between their relationship and that of Gladys and Alan, who were constantly touching each other. Charles tried hard to patiently accept Penelope's need for space and low level of physical contact.

Their relationship continued and eventually in the autumn of 1981, they drifted into a marriage with one another. Charles had worries about the conflict between his calling as a priest and the church's rules about sex outside of marriage. Penelope was often away at excavations in Syria during summer months from May to September and it was on her return in that year, after making love, that Charles suggested they might possibly marry. Penelope accepted and a provisional date was agreed.

Later, they began making arrangements for the wedding and Charles asked Penelope if she would consider marrying in the college chapel despite being an agnostic. Penelope, with tongue in cheek, reminded Charles that marriage was, historically, a civil arrangement which the church had hijacked in order to bolster their coffers in the twelfth century. It was later justified by the church when another Pope declared marriage to be a sacrament of the church. Penelope was well aware that Charles needed to marry in a religious service because of his priestly position and readily compromised her beliefs for Charles. Afterwards, she joked to Charles that she had crossed her fingers during the blessing part of the liturgy.

After their wedding, they lived in Charles' cottage in the grounds with its views of the countryside. However, Penelope would also spend time working from her town house as the cottage did not have enough physical space for her books or for her study desk. Often, this would mean she would sleep over at her town house, especially if she had an early morning lecture at the university. They were together, occasionally as a married couple and yet, also often living separate and individual lives. Something held back.

This arrangement was to change further in the following year with the segmented aspect of their marriage becoming more prominent. In the spring of 1982, Penelope was offered the post of Director of a new excavation in north-eastern Syria, a part of the ancient world previously known as Mesopotamia.

An important discovery had been made by an American-financed team of archaeologists, who, using an aerial survey had identified what was almost certainly a probable Neolithic settlement. Consequently, the team were now trying to recruit the very best archaeologists all on five-year contracts. To be a leader of such an enterprise was to realise a life-time's ambition for Penelope. This was her golden opportunity; the area and the period were the subject of books she had published and the lectures that she had delivered to her students for many years.

It was in her student days at Leicester, that Penelope had begun to be fascinated by the Neolithic civilisation. In the summer vacation at the end of her first year, Penelope signed up for a 'dig' in Iraq and became captivated by the region and its ancient history. She read widely about the work of the nineteenth century archaeologist, Claudius James Rich, who was financed by the Honourable East Indian Company. He excavated mounds in the Middle East, bringing back to Britain many ancient artefacts for display. Penelope was also inspired by the twentieth century work of Braidmore and Adams and their explorations of Iraq and Syria in the 1960s and 70s. This offer was the moment for Penelope to truly establish her reputation in the archaeological world, a dream come true for

Penelope.

Penelope explained to Charles the importance of this opportunity to be the Director of such a huge and prestigious project; to discover and uncover more hidden treasures about the way of life of these incredible Neolithic people. It would involve the writing of further books and include world lecture tours to share the gained knowledge with others. Penelope's voice almost trembled with the excitement as she joyfully shared the news with Charles. She enthused that in ten thousand years BC, the fertile land between the Rivers Tigris and Euphrates consisting of modern-day Turkey, Iraq and Syria, had been the home for the first ever-known farmers.

Unable to contain herself, Penelope excitedly continued that the Neolithic people were extraordinary in their advanced development, not only in that they planted the first crops but also that they had invented the wheel - which was possibly the most revolutionary of all discoveries in the history of the world. They were also responsible for creating writing through the cursive script and being the first in the fields of mathematics and astronomy.

Charles could feel the massive enthusiasm in Penelope's voice and body, as she spoke of the meeting that she had attended in London outlining the expedition. There was to be six months planning and recruiting of staff, including Syrian and Iraqi members of the team. In the coming months, Penelope would have to spend time out in Syria organising all the logistics necessary for such a project. Charles was really happy to see Penelope so vibrant and motivated but quietly worried about the effect that her absence might have on their marriage.

The five-year excavation meant that Penelope would be

away for periods of up to three months, only returning for occasional week-long breaks. Penelope pointed out that Charles could also come and visit and they would be able to spend time together in Syria. For Penelope, this was her life's vocation, so there was never any discussion as to whether she might seek or require Charles' agreement. He was aware of the importance of this venture in Penelope's life and had the presence of mind to silently concur to her wishes.

In early September, they decided to go on a walking holiday in the Yorkshire Dales staying at a friend's holiday cottage. They spent some very happy times together and Penelope's growing excitement at the prospect of the expedition to Syria seemed to lighten her personality. She held Charles' hand occasionally on walks, laughed and just seemed more joyful and relaxed. In bed they made love more often and on one Saturday evening, after listening to the Last Night on the Proms on the radio and drinking wine, Penelope was more intimate with Charles than she had ever been before, caressing him and bringing him to fulfilment.

On return to Cambridge, Penelope packed and Charles drove her to the airport for her flight to Damascus with several other members of the team. They kissed lightly on the lips, with a goodbye hug, before the Penelope that Charles had known disappeared into the airport and into a different life.

A new college term began with a fresh tutorial group for Charles to get to know and to begin their training. Since the provision of accommodation for married Ordinands, the proportion of older students had increased in ratio to the younger ones straight from university. Charles soon became absorbed in college life and found himself working even harder to compensate for the loss of Penelope.

Charles had now been nominated by the Liturgical Commission to be one of their representatives serving on the Church of England's General Synod, which met three times a year for a week's session at each sitting. Charles, together with many like-minded academics and friends, still met for discussions which provided Charles with much stimuli and many thoughts on about how the church might move forward. Charles often spoke eloquently and knowledgably in debates, so much so, that he soon began to be noticed for his insight and vision. Particularly on discussions concerning liturgy, Charles often lit up the chamber with his ideas and enthusiasm, igniting fiercely-held opinions both in support or in opposition to his well-expressed views.

However, it was over his enthusiastic campaigning for the Ordination of Women to the Priesthood that Charles encountered the most persistent and ferocious opposition. Charles could not believe that the church would be so backward and reactionary regarding its refusal to give equality to women in ministry. In the early 1980s, Charles argued and convinced the college authorities to accept and treat women equally, in full-time training in their role to become Deacons alongside male counterparts. The role of deacons was about service and from the beginning of the Christian church had been accepted as a suitable role for both men and women.

Charles now became a leading voice in the campaign to recognise that women might be called to a vocation to be priests too. He rejected the idea that because Jesus and his apostles were men, that only the male gender would ever be called by God to celebrate the sacraments of the church. Charles became an ardent protagonist for the Ordination of Women to the Priesthood, speaking at many events and writing letters and articles to church and national newspapers. Gradually, his name and reputation were becoming recognised across the church and country, as a voice calling for 'a new way forward'.

Charles was aware that his views were contentious but he was staggered by the vehement response elicited. He even received some letters threatening him with physical violence. Most troubling to Charles, were the abusive anonymous letters with language that shocked him to the core. What upset Charles most was not just the four-letter words directed at him but the appalling sexist language denigrating women as a gender.

He could understand arguments that Jesus only chose male apostles, which he could counter with the view that this was just an example of a patriarchal cultural society that existed two thousand years ago. However, he was utterly revolted and despondent when in some letters, women in today's supposedly educated society in the late twentieth century were referred to as 'inferior', 'emotionally unstable', 'only good for cleaning, arranging the flowers', or even more appallingly, 'only useful for lying with their legs apart'.

He responded to letters responsibly, arguing against more rational objections by putting forward his alternative views. The 'other' letters he put aside to show Penelope when she returned, to share his amazement at such depravity.

Every couple of weeks, Penelope would write telling Charles about the progress made on the excavation. The site looked extremely promising and initial excavations indicated signs of a considerable settlement, almost certainly from the Neolithic period. Charles would reply, acknowledging the positive news and share some of his life at college and the other work he was involved with in the outside world.

It was a couple of days before Christmas when Penelope returned for the first time. She was full of the venture, so much so, that she returned to Syria within two weeks at the beginning of January. They shared Christmas at Gladys and Alan's new, larger house in Twickenham, where they now lived. Charles loved being with Albert and Katherine and seeing their excitement on Christmas Day opening all their presents. Charles had brought Albert an electric train set and helped him set in up in his bedroom while Christmas dinner was being cooked. Later, after the children had gone to bed, Gladys asked Charles if he still had his wooden train set. Tears came to his and Gladys' eyes when he affirmed it was in a box in one of the cupboards at his college home. The pain was still there, just below the surface.

Penelope found the two days at Gladys and Alan's home more difficult. She was an only child to a father who spent more time in the city, where he worked and lived during the week, than he did in the family home. Her mother was very much an important figure in the local community and spent a great deal of time out in society attending Bridge Clubs, Whist Drives, Sherry Parties and at the Golf Club. A succession of nannies was employed to look after Penelope, ferrying her to and from her Public School. At weekends her parents would often be out at charity functions, supporting and being seen at local fund-raising events. Family life for Penelope was a somewhat lonely and formal existence so she found it hard to cope with the noise, bustle and excitement of Albert and Katherine.

As usual, Gladys perceived Penelope's difficulty of coping with the children's exuberance and encouraged

Penelope to join her in the quieter kitchen, to help prepare the dinner over a couple of glasses of sherry. Gladys's easy-going nature helped Penelope to relax a little and by lunchtime she was more at ease in the family setting. Also, Alan had taken part in some archaeological digs in his younger days, so was able to draw Penelope into explaining the Syrian expedition.

Charles and Penelope made love a couple of times in the ten days together before she returned to Syria. It was strange coming together again after so long apart and it took time to return to where they were beforehand. To remember what they both enjoyed, finding themselves and each other and what brought pleasure. They turned to their shared love of music and Charles played a recently purchased recording of Rachmaninov's Piano Concerto No.3, bringing back loving memories from the past.

After Penelope left and returned to her work, Charles wondered about their time together. He thought about the phrase 'absence makes the heart fonder' and was not convinced by that truism in his case. It had been really good to see Penelope again and renew their relationship but it felt to Charles, that in some way the Penelope of the past had moved on. Another world and life had opened up to her and he was not sure that he was a part of that existence. A doubt lodged at the back of his mind.

Their lives continued in this vein for the following two years. Penelope fully committed and absorbed by the excavation in Syria, returning for two weeks at Christmas and Easter, with Charles travelling to Syria for a month in the summer. Eight weeks together and forty-four apart. They kept in touch through their monthly letters, Penelope writing and Charles responding. It was a strange marriage of occasional intimacy and long-distance friendship, often more in the mode of pen-pals rather than husband and wife.

After two years at the site in Syria, Penelope excitedly wrote to say that some extensive and significant finds had been uncovered. It was becoming evident that the discovery was of a large, important settlement from the Neolithic era and would be a more extensive project than first thought. Extra funding was being sought and the time-scale of the excavation was doubled to at least ten years with more staff to be recruited, including a team of archaeologists from Germany. Charles responded in his letter to say how pleased he was for Penelope that the project was turning out so successfully. He kept his personal thoughts concerning their separation to himself, not wishing to dampen her happiness.

Meanwhile, Charles buried himself in the fulness of his varied ministry life. College, The Liturgical Commission and the General Synod, together with the campaign for the Ordination of Women to the Priesthood meant Charles had little time for reflection. He was heavily involved in the initial planning of another Prayer Book that was to replace the Alternative Service Book in the year 2000.

Charles continued to argue long and hard, not only for inclusive language to be used but also for more variety and choice in the liturgy, including composing a children's communion prayer for the commission to consider. In addition, Charles had brought together a group of liturgists and educationalists to create materials for young people in church settings, including the concept of Holiday Club booklets to enable churches to provide Christian education in an entertaining and enjoyable way for children during school holidays, by incorporating modern music, crafts and games into the learning process.

Despite all this activity, which included small amounts of progress, Charles sometimes felt despair and despondency at an institution so rooted in tradition and in the 'old ways', that any mention of moving forward just heralded louder voices of opposition. Shouts of 'we've always done it this way', 'we need to preserve the traditions of the church' and 'it is inappropriate to use church buildings to play games in', all resounded from the conservative majority of the established church.

All of this resistance to progressing on and changing to adapt to modern society, was despite the obvious statistics that church attendance was declining rapidly across the country. Charles was aware of one diocese, who in 1980 declared the next ten years as a 'Decade of Evangelism' where they would work to increase church membership by ten per cent. By 1983 it had been shelved and not mentioned again, as an audit had recorded a fifteen per cent decline in numbers in those first three years of the decade.

Charles was beginning to doubt that he had any power or influence to move the church on. He continued to question his own motivation and consider that, maybe, it was he who was out of touch with the real world, stuck in his academic ivory tower. Charles wondered if he should be considering a change and move back into front-line ministry? He still visited Hugo in his inner-city parish and spent time in discussion concerning ways to make the church more relevant to people in today's society. He always left Hugo's home uplifted and re-energised by Hugo's down-to-earth, common sense.

An answer to his question about returning to the front-line of ministry was answered two weeks later. One afternoon, as

Charles was working in his study in the cottage, the phone rang. The caller introduced himself as a Personal Private Secretary at 10 Downing Street and informed Charles that his name had been put forward to the Prime Minister as one of two people whom Mrs Thatcher could recommend to the Queen, to be the next Bishop in the diocese of Tuxbury where Charles had spent the later part of his childhood. "If appointed by Her Majesty the Queen," the official asked, "would you be prepared to accept the position?"

For a moment, Charles hesitated and then realised, firstly, he would never be selected as his well-known views were not of the establishment and secondly, he had openly criticised the Prime Minister's Government policies in a General Synod debate. He reassured himself that he had no chance, so he replied in the affirmative!

A month later, a rather grand envelope dropped through his letterbox onto his doormat. On opening the letter, Charles read that Her Majesty, Queen Elizabeth the Second wished to inform Reverend Charles Albert Moore MA that by Royal Appointment, he would take up the office of Bishop of the Tuxbury Diocese from the first day of October, in the year of Our Lord, one thousand nine hundred and eighty-five. Charles, now thirty-six years of age was about to become the youngest bishop in the country. He was staggered but as the letter had arrived in the first post, he had to leave it on his desk, immediately rushing out for morning prayer being led by his tutorial group in the college chapel. This was their last service together before leaving for placements in different locations around the country.

He sat in the chapel amongst the students and fellow tutors in a total daze. It was the summer term and the community were following alternative styles of worship. Charles had lots of time to think as the liturgy this month was based on Quaker Meeting for Worship, which involved forty-five minutes of stillness and quiet, listening to God. Charles smiled to himself at the irony of this morning's time of prayer. Selected to be a bishop in the traditional state church a few minutes ago, he now sat in a Religious Society of Friends style of prayer time. Quakers, with their very liberal philosophy, did not recognise hierarchies. Deacons, priests, archdeacons, bishops and archbishops, were an alien concept to Quakers who hold that all people were equal in the sight of God and that every member has the same rights to speak and lead. They have no ranks of importance or status.

At the beginning of the quiet-time, Charles' mind was racing and his heart thumping against his chest, finding stillness and peace impossible. Thoughts tumbled through his being. How did this happen? He had convinced himself that Mrs Thatcher would have ignored his name. Maybe there was more to her than he imagined, or did someone put pressure on her to accept him as the nomination to the Queen? How would he cope? Was he really up to the job? How could he move forward the almost unmoveable, the established Church of England? How would he deal with the opposition he would inevitably encounter? Was he really strong enough? Why not stay in the safe world of academia and just throw out ideas for others to act upon?

And then, after thirty minutes of struggle and conflict, came the deep resting in his God of love. Pictures came to him of those who had brought that love and reassurance to Charles in his life. His Aunty Gladys and all those years of walking alongside him, of holding his hand, with those uncountable numbers of hugs and cuddles, the crying of tears shared together. Of his grandparents and their providing of safe, warm and secure homes. Of Paul, the local vicar in Somerberly and his courage and liberal faith. Of Graham, his Oxford friend, with their shared academic research, pooling ideas and thoughts for the future. Of Rick at his Theological College with his unique style of thinking outside the box and making connections between faith and life today. Of Hugo and his simplicity, an ordinary, hard-working priest at the coal-face but also an incredibly special, humble and caring person. There were so many more whom God had worked through to inspire Charles.

Charles listened to God through these people and knew that, in the words of the thirteenth century mystic, Julian of Norwich, 'all would be well'. He felt within him that now was the opportunity being presented to him to live out his visions and to try to bring it into reality. The time was right to encourage a new reforming of a declining church, to try to drag it into a new era, relevant to modern times. By the end of the quietness in the Quaker morning prayer, Charles felt more at peace and accepting of his new role.

The same evening, Charles sat down and wrote to Penelope with the news, asking her to keep it secret until the official announcement was made. He also visited Harry, the Principal, to inform him of his pending departure. Harry was delighted for Charles and extremely pleased for the college's reputation as well.

That weekend, Charles had no college duties as his tutorial group were away on placements so he decided to visit Gladys and then Hugo, on Friday and Saturday nights respectively. Inevitably, Gladys burst into tears at the news but this time, they were tears of joy and pride in Charles' achievement. Gladys was doubly pleased that it was in Tuxbury where Charles would be bishop, as she was becoming increasingly concerned about the health of her parents and their well-being. It was reassuring for Gladys to know that a loving grandson would be living near to them.

The following day, after a long drive north, Charles arrived at St. Francis' Vicarage on Saturday evening where Hugo was happily cooking one of his special meals. On hearing of Charles' appointment to the See of Tuxbury, Hugo responded by taking out one of his very best bottles of wine, a 1970 St Emilion Grand Cru Classe, which they joyfully shared together.

Later on in the evening, when the mellow, fruity red wine was almost drunk and both men were relaxed, sitting in comfortable chairs by the glowing coal fire in the sitting room, Charles confided the doubts to Hugo about his suitability and worthiness for such a role. He was aware that many of his views and some of his theology was not of the mainstream.

Over the years, his thoughts about what God meant to him had developed considerably. That early picture of God as an old white, bearded man sat upon a throne, all powerful in an angelic heaven had long since dissipated. Often, Charles saw God more in people, in their eyes, with love shining forth. He recalled times when he was with Hugo as a curate and remembered moments, when he observed God: in the eyes of people struggling with poverty and despair, in the helpless and powerless of society, in the homeless and unloved young people in the inner city and in the prostitute giving her body and soul in order to provide food for her malnourished children.

Charles explained that he did not see Jesus as the only Son of God, neither was his image of God as being 'all powerful and mighty' but as vulnerable and at times, often characterised by the powerless, alongside the needy and weak, never seeking worldly importance and status. Surely this meant that Jesus was asking us to give our lives to be alongside those in need, rather than be in pomp and luxury sitting in a magnificent Palace located in acres of grounds. He had even recently begun to question whether God was a supernatural being 'on high', or more like a living force present within each and every person. Charles finally uttered the question that was haunting him, "How could I hold such opinions and be a bishop in the traditional and established Church of England?"

Hugo had sat quietly, gently swirling the wine around the half-full glass of wine in his hand, listening intently to the openness and honesty of Charles' thoughts. After a few moments of silence, Hugo responded by saying that Charles was exactly what a failing Church of England needed. A new energy and force with a well-thought-out, modern theology that would be more relevant to a younger generation living in the more rational and scientific culture of the late twentieth century. Hugo added that he very much hoped Charles might shake up the sleepy, out-of-date beliefs that had held the church back from moving forward. As the second bottle of wine was opened, Hugo light-heartedly remarked that maybe on arrival in Tuxbury, Charles should nail his theological beliefs to the door of the cathedral as someone else had done four and a half centuries before!

As Charles drove back to Cambridge from Hugo's northern parish, he stopped en route to visit his grandparents at their home in Tuxbury. It was a strange experience, driving into the town that he had known as a schoolboy and as a child living nearby at Grange-next-to-Sea. He would soon be installed as one of its prominent citizens, the Diocesan Bishop. A person of status and importance, a leading light of the church, a spokesperson for morals, ethics and good Christian standards of how to live one's life. A leader of the community to whom people would look to for guidance and direction.

After visiting his grandparents and finding them in relatively good spirits, Charles continued his journey south to Cambridge. Retrospectively, Charles could remember little of the process of driving, stopping, roundabouts, speed-limits; all were totally dealt with in a mechanical, dream-like state. Somehow, Charles arrived home safely despite his thoughts being focussed somewhere else. Journeying through Tuxbury had brought home to him the enormity of the task ahead of him as a bishop, especially one who wished to move the church to a different place.

So many things weighed upon him on that final part of the journey home. All the formality of that office, the paraphernalia and rigmarole associated with the traditions of being a bishop in the Church of England. The special clothes, the mitre and bishop's crook. The public duties expected, such as on Remembrance Day at the War Memorial in town and in the political arena, the certain conflict of Charles' social, gospel beliefs as opposed to the views of a local conservative populace. Then there were the unreal expectations of so many people looking for a standard Church of England, run of the mill, Diocesan Bishop at everyone's beck and call - a nice, compliant figurehead parading in funny, colourful clothes.

Charles arrived home to his cottage and opening the door, he smiled to himself. Soon, he would leave this homely, two-bedroomed abode of the last ten years to live in a spacious palace. Charles said out loud to himself, “That will be the first thing to change”. Although full of doubt and tentative about the future, Charles was also determined to work slowly and steadily to bring about change and reform. True to his resolution, during the summer Charles had a sign made for his new home, which read, ‘Bishop’s House’. The palace would be consigned to the past. It was a small step but a significant statement of what Charles hoped to bring to the Tuxbury Diocese.

In early Summer, Charles spent two weeks in Syria with Penelope where he met some of the German archaeologists who had recently joined the team and extended the work being undertaken. Penelope introduced Charles to Greta, one of the German personnel who Penelope had become friendly with. Penelope seemed happy for Charles on his new appointment and was interested in all the preparations that he had to make, including Charles’ amusing descriptions of the several appointments that he had had to attend with a very fussy tailor at the clerical outfitters specialising in garments for bishops. Penelope promised to ensure that she would come back in time to be by his side for the York Minister and Tuxbury Cathedral services.

It was in mid-September 1985 that Charles moved into the private quarters of his newly-named Bishop’s House. He had two weeks before his Consecration in York and then the following Sunday’s Installation and Welcome at the Cathedral in Tuxbury. The future facing Charles was exciting and yet fraught with anxiety as to what lay ahead. Theories, ideas, visions are fine but putting them into practise is quite a different challenge. Charles prayed that he would have the courage and resolve to deal with the next few years and that his sometimes-fragile personality, would hold in times of stress.

Part Three
The Bishop's House

3.1 Charles, Penelope and Elizabeth

Tuxbury had changed considerably in the twenty years that Charles had been away.

In the past, although officially a 'city' due to its historical past and cathedral, Tuxbury was more akin to the size of a 'market town'. However, with more recent expansion it now felt like a small city. In 1985 it was divided into two halves with the idyllic southern, old part containing its historic cathedral and ancient buildings, totally contrasting with the newer northern section with light engineering, warehouses and suburban 1960s / 70s housing estates. Exploring Tuxbury again during his first week, Charles discovered that modern progress had even engulfed his old grammar school, which in the past was on the very edge of Tuxbury but now in 1985, was surrounded on all sides by housing developments.

The southern part of Tuxbury where Charles was to live in Cathedral Close was unchanged and remained in the past. The impressive, fifteenth century cathedral was at the centre of the Close surrounded by beautifully manicured lawns. The River Tux continued its dreamy, languid way through the Close on the latter stages of its journey towards the sea. A historic and picturesque setting that attracted thousands of tourists each year.

Wealthy, important and powerful people also had their

homes here in the ancient houses of the Close, wielding enough influence to ensure that their habitat would remain untouched by modern progress. The Close only had two gates for car entrance, one in the northern section and a second in the west part. Residents in the Close had their own keys for the gates for use if arriving after the Close closed nightly at 11.30 p.m.

Charles' home was on the southern side of the Close, nearby to other diocesan buildings but at the rear, it was the only building to have its own drive in and out, giving direct access to the surrounding modern ring road that encircled the inner city. The home of the Diocesan Bishop was in a grand Georgian building, whose ground floor was the working space for Charles and included his study. Upstairs, Charles' living accommodation consisted of four bedrooms, three bathrooms, a dining room and a spacious lounge. Outside, at the rear of the Bishop's House, there was a beautiful, well-maintained and extensive, enclosed garden. This was to be Charles' home and work base for the coming years.

In the second week, Penelope arrived to join Charles at the Bishop's House and to prepare for the Consecration Service. She was excited and looking forward to the occasion. Penelope spent the first full day searching Tuxbury shops for appropriate attire to wear, in the clothes, hat, handbag and shoe shops.

On the second day, Charles took Penelope for a drive around the Tuxbury Diocese. It was an area of considerable contrasts. In the southern, central and western parts of the diocese, it was a beautiful, rural way of life with farming being the main occupation with a scattered population living in small villages. To the east, there were the seaside towns of the coastal area and they portrayed a totally different picture with the changing seasons. Busy, bustling resorts packed with crowds for some parts of the year, contrasted at other times with a starkness and emptiness of the cold, windy months of the off-season. The church's Sunday congregations reflected the seasons, three-quarters full in the summer, three-quarters empty in the winter.

The northern part of the dioceses reached up to urban, industrial coal-mining towns where a dirty and grimy environment reflected hard, working-class communities struggling to survive on low incomes. This was Arthur Scargill and the National Union of Mineworkers' territory. The endless terraced, smoke-stained workers' houses situated in towns with chimney smoke polluting the atmosphere was a world away from where Charles lived, in the Cathedral Close in his luxurious home.

The early 1980s had witnessed a brutal conflict between Mrs Thatcher's controlled police force and the striking miners and their trade unions. As the strike dragged on through a harsh winter, there was great poverty and hardship for the miners' families. Some isolated churches reacted and tried to provide soup kitchens with basic food supplies but from the hierarchy of the Tuxbury Diocese there was only silence. The dilemma between the state church holding the Government line or helping those in need, was starkly exposed. The resulting inaction of the church caused great resentment in the mining communities, with many families resolved never to set foot inside a church again.

Over dinner that evening, Charles shared with Penelope his thoughts about the diverse needs of his diocese. Penelope had never attended church and so in their conversation she came to the discussion with a fresh and helpfully naïve viewpoint. When Charles spoke of his vision, it was Penelope who interjected to say that it might require three visions due to vast differences in the three areas they had visited during the day.

The vivid contrast between the urban and rural situations in the diocese was particularly stark to both of them. It was also a political divide, as the north of the dioceses returned a Labour Member of Parliament, while in the remainder of the diocese there were Conservative members. Charles thought that the need to rebuild bridges with the mining communities was paramount and to demonstrate that the Christian faith was there, equally, for all people.

The Consecration of Bishops Service took place on the Friday of Charles' second week in Tuxbury at York Minister. The service was conducted by the Archbishop of York, as Tuxbury Diocese was in the Northern Province. Charles was joined by another new appointment to a neighbouring Diocese. Both new bishops had met the day before with the archbishop, to talk and walk through the service. Charles was particularly pleased that it was the Archbishop of York who was leading the proceedings as he had attended and spoken at one of the conferences Charles had organised in Cambridge, on new ways forward in the church. The archbishop held liberal and progressive views and it was his lobbying that was behind Charles' elevation to becoming a Diocesan Bishop.

The over-long service followed its formal procedure using The Book of Common Prayer liturgy. It was, however, enlivened by the archbishop's sermon which was very down-to-earth and amusing; diffusing the over-serious liturgy with a welcome lightness. The archbishop's main point was to stress that the new bishops were not being elevated in importance and status but instead, they were being called to be lowly servants of all the people in their dioceses. The archbishop continued his sermon by suggesting to the newly appointed, that the most important aspects of serving others was the grace of listening with humility.

After the ceremony, Charles and the family met for lunch at a nearby hotel. Gladys and Alan had travelled from London for the weekend, staying with Penelope and Charles at Bishop's House. Sadly, Charles' grandparents were too poorly to attend so Charles planned to visit them later in the day wearing his bishop's robes. Penelope had been amazed at the formality of the occasion and its age-old traditions but was pleased that Charles was being recognised for his abilities and insight.

Two days later, on Sunday morning, Charles was installed as Diocesan Bishop in the cathedral at Tuxbury. This time his grandparents were able to be present and sat in the front row, where Charles could witness the pride and joy they had in their grandson's achievement. Charles had had some involvement in the planning of the service and requested that his Aunty Gladys be allowed to take part and read the New Testament passage from 1 Corinthians 13. There was a more informal feel to this service and Penelope felt more at ease with Charles' choice of liturgy.

In his sermon, Charles' spoke of the importance of balancing two elements in a dioceses' life. Firstly, to uphold the traditions of the faith and its historic heritage but, secondly and equally as important, to have the courage to move that faith forward so that it is also appropriate to the culture of the day. Charles continued that the way to balance these two points of view was through the most vital message of Christ's teaching, the gospel of love, hence his choice of 1 Corinthians 13 for his Installation Service. Charles spoke of how love had changed him in his life and carried him through the dark times he had experienced. As he said these words, he looked across at his aunty and grandparents and silently mouthed a 'Thank you'. He concluded his sermon by calling for the diocese to be a 'community of love' and to overcome all differences, by being a loving and caring church with the love of God shining through all that they did and said. Thinking firstly of others and the future of the church before themselves.

Afterwards, Penelope commented to Charles that the two services she had attended, seemed hundreds of years apart in their language and content. To her, the York ceremony was fussy and formal with ceremony and legalities dominated by ancient words, while the Tuxbury occasion had been joyful and appealing to her as a non-church going person. Penelope said she could really relate to his sermon and how simply, yet inspiringly, he had proclaimed a message for all people to hear, regardless of their beliefs.

After the Tuxbury Service, there was a reception with a buffet below in the crypt of the cathedral. It was a time of briefly meeting with hundreds of people with lots of handshakes, greetings and welcomes. Charles enjoyed the warmth of the occasion but two particular moments remained with him.

As he circulated amongst the congregation, Charles came across a young lady who introduced herself as Elizabeth, a churchwarden at one of the churches in Tuxbury just a few hundred yards away from the cathedral. Amongst all the people gathered, Charles was more than a little unsettled and disturbed by this one meeting. Maybe it was her beautiful eyes that struck Charles, especially the varied emotions they appeared to contain. They sparkled at moments with a depth of love but at other times, were dulled with hurt and past emotional pain. Both feelings present in those mysterious and beguiling eyes.

The second moment was the non-meeting with Archdeacon Colin, who, as the next person in the hierarchy of Diocesan staff, would be expected to welcome the incoming bishop. He noticed him walk by in earnest conversation with another cleric but made no attempt to speak to Charles. As the crowds swarmed round the newly installed bishop, the lack of greeting by the Archdeacon was significant to Charles, who later wondered whether the sermon had been the reason for his non-welcome.

The next day, the Archdeacon did come knocking at the door. At 9 a.m., Charles was sat in his study outlining his plans on paper for the initial period of his ministry. He had decided that to move the church forward needed to be preceded by visiting all diocesan parishes and listening to the needs of the people in the pews. Charles also planned to spend a day a week dropping in informally on his clergy, spending time listening and getting to know his fellow clerics at a personal level. He wanted them onboard and supportive, so that when his vision began to take shape, it would have their enthusiastic backing. Slowly, slowly, he wrote in capital letters. Eighteen months to two years before producing a report and structure for discussion and then, hopefully, everyone moving forward together.

That was the idea at 9 a.m. At 10.30 a.m. that plan received its first challenge as Archdeacon Colin arrived with his agenda.

The first knock at the study door however, was that of his secretary, Miss Jenkins. Charles had briefly met Miss Jenkins last week and arranged to meet with her on Monday morning at 10 a.m. As the grandfather clock in the hall struck ten o'clock, Miss Jenkins' sharp rap on the study door was acknowledged by Charles. Miss Jenkins was in her late sixties and had served the previous bishop faithfully for over twenty-five years. She had agreed to stay on for six months to help the incoming bishop settle into the routines of his office, before retiring to the country.

Miss Jenkins was a very prim and proper spinster, suitably attired in a below the knee, tweed skirt and white blouse. Her hair was always immaculately permed and she used the minimum amount of make-up. She was always precise and extremely efficient in her duties. Miss Jenkins was always known as Miss Jenkins. No-one ever referred to her by her Christian name, indeed, most people had no idea what it was. Miss Jenkins had been very loyal to Charles' predecessor and was well-informed, seemingly knowing everyone in the diocese. Very few people got through to the previous bishop's study door, as Miss Jenkins felt it was her duty to protect the bishop from too much stress and too many people, particularly clergy, wasting the bishop's time.

Miss Jenkins had some misgivings about the new bishop that had been appointed. For a start, he was so young and inexperienced in parish life and secondly, he was known for his progressive opinions including supporting women's ordination to the priesthood, which Miss Jenkins fiercely opposed on traditional grounds.

On this first morning, Charles requested that they find an hour each day for the next two weeks so that Miss Jenkins could brief him upon certain aspects of Tuxbury Diocese. Tomorrow, Charles would like to spend the hour sorting out the immediate calls upon his diary. Miss Jenkins concurred and then informed Charles that the Archdeacon was waiting in the library and would like a few minutes with him.

From the first moment of meeting the Archdeacon, Charles knew that this was to be a relationship that would bring conflict and opposition. Although Archdeacon Colin said the words, "Welcome to Tuxbury, Bishop Charles," there was no feeling or genuine sincerity in his tone. It was a phrase spoken because it had to be said but it betrayed other negative feelings behind it. The meaningless greeting was not accompanied by an embrace or handshake. It was a cold and ominous beginning.

The Archdeacon was a small, rotund figure in his late fifties, with receding, black hair, leaving him bald on the top of his head. He had a ruddy, country-like complexion with small, narrow eyes which constantly moved, avoiding any lengthy eye contact. Charles could not feel any warmth emanating from his personality, indeed he only felt bristling tremors of hidden anger. Charles decided that here was someone he definitely would not trust his life with.

Archdeacon Colin had spent his whole ministry in the Tuxbury Diocese since leaving theological college in his mid-twenties. He was married to Marjorie who lived with him in the Archdeacon's residence in the Close. They had no children and that particular 'family' topic was never brought up by anyone, if they wished to stay in favour with the Archdeacon. He had been a vicar in the rural part of the diocese for many years before becoming Rural Dean. He used that office to become friendly with the previous Archdeacon so, on that cleric's retirement, he ensured that his name was put forward to the bishop to become the next archdeacon.

He had now been in post for over ten years as the sole Archdeacon in the diocese. Over time, he had manipulated power, wheeling and dealing across the church, using his authority to influence and coerce. In later years with the previous bishop looking to retirement and a quiet life, the Archdeacon had become the central figure in decision-making, while the elderly bishop was content to concentrate on the ceremonial aspects of his job.

Recently however, Archdeacon Colin was finding it more and more difficult to hide his frustration at being overlooked for further progression to a bishopric. He was convinced that his non-attendance at either Oxford or Cambridge Universities was the main reason for not being considered. He told himself that it was because he was not a part of the 'Public School Establishment Club'. Now, to add salt to his wounds, the new appointee bishop to Tuxbury was an Oxford-educated, young, high-flying whippersnapper, hardly out of short trousers!

In return to the Archdeacon's welcome, Charles replied, "Thank you, Archdeacon for the welcome, although in some ways, this is my return to Tuxbury as I attended the boys' grammar school here twenty years ago and lived at Grange-next-to-Sea for seven years." The Archdeacon had done his homework and was already aware of Bishop Charles' attendance at the highly acclaimed school and of his achievements in going up to Oxford at an earlier age than usual, having achieved outstanding academic grades. The Archdeacon ruefully reflected upon his own schooling through the small, rural, all-age school which he had attended from five to fourteen years of age. The way he had to battle his way up the ladder to his present position, contrasted starkly with the man in front of him wearing the purple shirt.

After a few moments of meaningless pleasantries, Archdeacon Colin came straight to the point. "Bishop, I thought your sermon was received in two ways relating to the two main elements it contained. With universal approval when you spoke about the importance of maintaining the church traditions and history but unfortunately, with total disapproval for your thoughts upon the need for the church to change, be relevant and a sop to modern life."

Charles took a moment before replying. Here in front of him was his first real test, a direct challenge to his authority and future progress to 'be church' in this place. But more importantly, the Archdeacon was testing the waters to see how Charles would respond. Was he weak? Could he be bullied? These were some of the hidden agendas behind the Archdeacon's statement.

Bishop Charles began positively. "Thank you, Archdeacon Colin. It is always good to get feedback from colleagues and I appreciate your compliments regarding the upholding of church traditions. Regarding the concerns that you have about change, may I ask you if you are aware of the average age of church attenders? Well, it is fifty-nine and rising each year. We need to speak out and be there for younger people, as well as the older generations, otherwise the church will decline, gradually closing its doors for ever. The world is constantly changing and so must we."

Charles went on to explain that he would spend the first two years talking and listening to both clergy and laity, before drawing up, in consultation with others, a way for the diocese to move on. He was quite clear that he was determined to encourage change as a positive force. To do nothing and stand still was, for Bishop Charles, simply to go backwards and he hoped the Archdeacon would be alongside him going forward into the future. Then, without taking a breath and allowing the Archdeacon time to respond, Charles thanked the Archdeacon for his welcome and comments and in ushering him to the door, informed Archdeacon Colin that he would be asking Miss Jenkins to find an hour-long meeting-time each month for them to come together, as he would value the Archdeacon's opinions and input.

Afterwards, as Charles reflected upon that first meeting, he realised that he had deliberately not left the Archdeacon any time to argue back. By doing so, he could possibly claim he had won the first round but in the shadow of that victory, he could sense that there would be many more rounds to come in this battle. The Archdeacon had been around for years and had numerous allies to call upon to disrupt any plans he did not approve of. At one level, Charles felt he had come across as strong and determined but deep within him, he was quivering and disturbed by the prospects of future conflict ahead. Doubts and a lack of confidence surfaced and dominated his thoughts and feelings.

That night, Charles expressed his anxiety in the sexual act with Penelope, being less tender than usual; instead, being more vigorous in the lovemaking. He asked himself if this was his anger, flooding out of him into her? Pushing into Penelope to ask her non-verbally to absorb his distress? Feeling insecure, deep within himself and seeking comfort, running away into the arms of his wife. Was it, yet again, a cry of desperately needing love and reassurance to replace what had been so tragically ripped away from him, when his father and mother died in his early childhood? Charles constantly asked himself, time and time again, 'Why do I need everyone to love me, to accept me?'

On a rational level he knew through his time as a curate and as a teacher at theological college, that many people accepted him and reciprocated his love and friendship. He admitted to himself that while most of these relationships were not deep friendships, but even so, he was well liked by many people. However, this logic was unable to relieve the underlying negative feelings within him which occurred and re-surfaced whenever he felt rejected.

The following day, Charles drove Penelope to the airport to catch her flight to Syria and to return to her work. She appeared quieter than usual and the two-hour journey passed mainly in silence. At the airport, Charles said his goodbyes with a kiss on Penelope's cheek as she averted her lips at the last moment. Walking through the barrier, without a backward glance, it seemed as if a veil had begun to fall between them, a moving apart, the beginning of an ending.

During the next few nights, Charles found it difficult to sleep. Over and over again he would relive the conversation with Archdeacon Colin. Should he have been more conciliatory, less concerned with trying to win a battle, more like Christ, humble and accepting? Question upon question followed, one after another, endlessly. He was unable to stop his mind returning time and again to the same ten minutes he had spent with the Archdeacon. If only he had said this, or expressed himself in a different way, or listened to the Archdeacon more fully. Sleep eventually arrived and dulled his senses until the following night.

On one occasion, Charles tried to distract himself by thinking of Penelope and their last lovemaking but then he became fretful that he may have upset her by being too forceful on that last time together. Maybe her quietness on the journey to the airport had been a statement of disapproval of Charles' abandonment of their normal pattern of relaxed lovemaking. Departing from initiating her arousal by stroking her, instead pursuing a more urgent and needy explosion of Charles' emotions. More sleepless hours followed in the emptiness and coldness of his solitary bed. Charles resolved to write to Penelope apologising for his thoughtlessness and explaining about how upset he had become after his meeting with the Archdeacon. Two weeks later, a brief letter arrived accepting his apology.

Over time, Charles became more settled, the exacting business of his role as bishop absorbed his attention away from his inner thoughts. Charles' day began at 9 a.m. with Morning Prayer in the chapel to which he invited all the staff at the Bishop's House to attend. Miss Jenkins attended punctually every day and enjoyed being asked to do a reading in the service. Charles also included ten minutes of quietness and reflection as a part of the worship, again to the approval of Miss Jenkins as it gave her time to plan out her day and to be calm. Afterwards, Charles would meet briefly with Miss Jenkins to deal with any matters that she thought important to him.

Each day was different, with church and civic duties to complete. As bishop of the diocese, he was automatically on a variety of committees, some of which he chaired and required detailed planning. In November, he attended and was involved in the Remembrance Day Parade with its service at the War Memorial in the centre of Tuxbury. He was appalled at the liturgy used and its omission of the word ‘Peace’. Consequently, before the Prayer of Blessing which was his only contribution that he was commissioned to give, Charles strayed from the set script of the service to include a prayer for peace and reconciliation, resolving afterwards to enter into discussions with the local British Legion branch concerning next year’s worship.

At their meeting in November the Archdeacon, who was also present at the Remembrance Day Service, wondered whether the local populace might be a little upset by the bishop straying from a liturgy that they had used for many years. He had heard whispers that the ‘peace stuff’ took away from the sacrifice of the fallen.

Again, Charles thanked the Archdeacon for passing on ‘the whispers’, fully knowing that it was just one more of the Archdeacon’s ways to try and hold the bishop to a more traditional and conservative line. A constant drip by drip technique to try to hold back any liberal or unconventional ideas that Charles might want to enforce on the Archdeacon’s orderly, conventional and structured world.

In those first few months, Charles found a lot of satisfaction in two particular aspects of his new life. Firstly, in his visits to the different parishes around the diocese. Acting on Charles’ request for a programme to be set-up, Miss Jenkins had arranged a variety of locations in the north, south and coastal areas of the diocese for the bishop to visit. In the first year, she had filled his available diary with weekend visits. Charles’ idea was to spend some time on the Saturday with lay groups and then preach and celebrate at the Communion

Service on the Sunday. His purpose was simple. He wanted to ask questions, not give answers. Charles wanted the people to think seriously and deeply about the future picture of what 'being church' would be like in their towns and villages. Often, clergy would invite Bishop Charles to stay overnight on the Saturday and this would give Charles the opportunity to meet clergy and their family in more informal settings. Charles always took along a good bottle of French wine to share, some flowers for the vicar's wife and sweets if the clergy couple had children.

Secondly, Charles found it hugely encouraging and interesting in making informal 'drop-in' visits to the clergy. He decided to begin with vicars he already knew as ex-students at the theological college where Charles taught. There was a dozen or so such priests, four of whom were in the northern, more urban part of the diocese. Charles would use his 'day-off' on Friday, to undertake these visits, trying to spend a couple of hours with each cleric. Sometimes, however, the two hours lasted all day.

This was especially so in the mining communities where clergy were desperately working to alleviate the poverty created, due to the effects of closing pits and trying to heal the damage to the church's reputation following the miner's strike. Most importantly for the clergy was the impact on them of having to cope with the rage and indignation at a church, which miners and their families felt had deserted them in their time of need.

One vicar, who had served his community for many years, told Charles of the violence he had witnessed by Mrs Thatcher's mounted police force as they charged and battered miners into hospitals. He described how, after one bloody day, he joined the miners on their picket line to try to use his authority and position to lessen the police aggression but it was all to no avail. Trying to defend a miner on the ground, the priest received a broken arm from a police truncheon. The next day, he was summoned to the Archdeacon's office and given a severe telling off for being involved in miners' violence. The story spread among the mining communities and with the exception of this priest's parish, the Church of England was 'blacklisted' in the area. Attendances fell dramatically and worshippers sought out other places of worship at non-conformist chapels and meeting rooms.

On visiting parishes in seaside towns, different issues faced the clergy. Overflowing churches in the summer, with the starkly contrasting three-quarters empty buildings in the winter. How do you minister to a small congregation in the quiet season and what happens to their needs when trying to provide for holidaymakers, who will only be with you for one or two Sundays and then return home? It was different again in the countryside. Here the clergy spoke about the problem of young people leaving home to go to towns for work or education and not returning, leaving an increasingly ageing church congregation. They expressed the resentment felt by small congregations being asked to join together with neighbouring villages and to share one vicar between them. That, after hundreds of years of traditionally having had their own clergyman as a part of the community and life of the village, there was now no one on hand to call upon. They felt deserted in a spiritual vacuum.

Charles felt enthused and energised by many of the visits to parishes and their clergy. He was encouraged in meeting so many people working so hard to try to make their church the beating heart of their community. Often, Charles returned home optimistic and hopeful for the future, determined to try to use this enthusiasm as a base for encouraging leadership to look at new ways forward. He was even more convinced that new ways of working had to be sought out urgently. Too often he found hard-working priests making no progress, indeed often being unable to halt the decline by staying within traditional and conventional methods of being church.

Of course, there were exceptions. At one urban church they had created a community church, similar to Father Hugo's, where the formal church was replaced with a hive of community groups supporting the needy. At a seaside church, they had begun a Mission Church on the beach, teaching the Christian faith in an entertaining way to young people by incorporating a Christian-style 'Punch and Judy Show'. In contrast, Charles also got a distinct feeling from some clergy that they were simply drifting along, especially so, in some of the rural churches. Clergy who were just accepting of the situation and not straining to revitalise a declining institution. Charles also encountered some of the Archdeacon's friends with their intransigent attitudes to any alteration to the traditional order. But overall, Charles felt that there was potential and opportunity to lead the church forward through the many willing clergy and lay people.

Privately, Charles was also pleased that he felt at ease in his more informal visits to the parishes and to the clergy. He discarded the pomp and ceremony of traditional bishops' visits and preferred to be alongside people. His humour and easy-going nature allowed everyone the space to express their opinions, without being overawed by the supposed authority and status of a Diocesan Bishop. This approach suited Charles' personality, in that he was extremely good at brief encounters, coming across as relaxed and informal and in return, people responded positively to his approachability.

Charles' teaching skills were in evidence as well, especially with young people. If he noticed children in the congregations, he would always invite them to join him at the front, getting some of them to wear his mitre and carry his crook. Parents loved to see their children involved and again, Charles made a huge, positive impression with his ability to relate informally to the younger generation, enabling them to feel a part of a modern, forward-looking church. Young people, not just tagging along with parents but as important members of the church community.

At Christmas, Charles was involved with services until Christmas Day lunchtime, so Gladys, in harmony with Penelope, organised the family celebration at the Bishop's House, inviting Gladys' parents to join everyone for lunch. After an early morning sharing of presents, Charles left to attend the main service at the cathedral where he was preaching. Gladys and Penelope set about cooking the dinner while Alan entertained his parents-in-law and the children. All eight members of the family enjoyed an excellent meal of roast cockerel with all the trimmings, followed by Christmas pudding. After a brief rest, the children demanded the traditional raucous family game of 'stations', with a few allowances made for the lack of speed by the grandparents!

This was to be the last time they would all play, laugh and be together.

Penelope had arrived two days before Christmas and was busy preparing to host Charles' family. On their first night together they made love, with Charles gently bringing

Penelope to a long and deep climax. Afterwards, Charles referred to their last lovemaking in October and his distress at upsetting Penelope by being too aggressive and again, he apologised. After a short pause, Penelope explained that she believed that her reaction to Charles vigorous lovemaking had to do with an incident in her adolescence which she had buried deep within her. Somehow, it had been awakened by Charles' actions and it had taken her weeks to settle again, hence her short and curt reply to his apology. Penelope spoke of her friend, Greta and how she had helped comfort her and encourage Penelope back to some normality.

In early January, Penelope returned to Syria and her life-fulfilling work. They had made love on her last night, again gently and satisfyingly for both. After using the bathroom, Penelope slid back into bed and spoke softly and warmly, thanking Charles for his love and care in being so kind to her in the sexual side of their life together. She was aware she had problems in reaching out passionately but Penelope reassured Charles that she enjoyed making love with him. This time at the airport check-in there was a kiss, a hug and a backward glance and wave, as Penelope disappeared from Charles' sight.

In February, Charles grandmother died. In January, she had a bad cold which worsened and developed into a chest infection. With the dark days of winter and the coldness of a particularly severe, snowy spell, her health deteriorated until eventually the warden at the complex where they lived called an ambulance. Pneumonia was diagnosed and slowly, hour by hour, life ebbed away from her and within a week, Charles' grandma was dead. Charles had cleared his diary, having sat for days together with Gladys, at her bedside. Charles' granddad visited but he found it too distressing and tiring to stay for very long. Charles' grandma died peacefully with Charles holding one hand and Gladys, her daughter, the other.

Charles was devastated. This was the first loss of a loved one he had experienced as an adult. A loving grandma who had shared her home and life to help nurture Charles back from the tragedies of his early life. Someone who had cuddled him in those dark nights when he awoke screaming from his nightmare. Someone who was always there for him, holding his hand as they walked through the woods and along the beach. Her laughter was still ringing in Charles' ears from the Christmas Day games the family had played. Charles was desolate at how quickly death had come, like an all-enveloping shroud, to extinguish such a beautiful life of love.

The small funeral took place a few days later in the chapel at Bishop's House and after cremation, Charles' grandma's ashes were taken back to Gattingford to be interred in the grave of Albert and Evelyn, her beloved son and daughter-in-law. Standing next to Gladys at the graveside, Charles could feel all the grief and trauma of his life racing back to haunt him again, overwhelming and drowning him in a sea of despair and emptiness. He could feel Gladys move closer to him and then felt her arm around him, hugging him. How could she tell? How did she know? Still there to hold him up after all these years. Surely, here was the Spirit of God, not some grey-haired, bearded, old man sitting on some far-distant cloud?

After a few days, Gladys and her family returned south to their home and Charles attempted to continue with his ministry. Miss Jenkins was a great support in diverting enquiries away and lightening the calls upon his diary. She had delayed handing in her notice for a further three months in order for Bishop Charles to have time to mourn and to continue in a stable environment without too much change. Despite her initial misgivings at working with such a young bishop, Miss Jenkins had warmed to her employer, respecting Charles' enthusiasm and integrity. She noted his kindness and genuine concern for all people, regardless of their influence and status.

Within a month of his grandma's funeral, the whole process was repeated a second time. One Monday morning just before morning prayer, the phone rang and the warden at his granddad's complex informed Charles that during the night, his grandfather had died. Mrs Jones explained that every morning she contacted each flat to ensure that all was well but did not receive a reply from his granddad. Together, with her assistant warden, they entered his flat to discover that Charles' granddad had passed away, peacefully in his sleep.

Charles' relationship with his granddad had been very different to the one with his grandma. He was not the cuddly-type who expressed emotions outwardly. He was brought up in an age where men were taught to be strong and reserved, just getting on with life, providing materially for the family, while the wife looked after the other emotional stuff. Despite this, Charles knew that his granddad had loved him very much. He was a practical man, a craftsman, who expressed himself through a solid, down-to-earth skill in his carpentry work. Charles had many hours of memories of the time he spent with his granddad in his shed at the bottom of the garden in Grange-next-to-Sea, working alongside him with wood and tools. This was how his granddad had expressed his love for Charles, inviting him to share life in his special workplace.

After a post-mortem confirmed the suspected heart attack, Charles pondered on the thought that it could have been a 'broken heart' from the inner grief of losing his lifetime love.

The funeral followed a similar pattern to his wife, with a service at the chapel in Bishop's House, followed by his ashes being buried in the family grave in Gattingford. This time at the graveside, it was Charles who was the comforter rather than the comforted. Gladys was distraught with the loss of both her parents within six weeks of each other. For the whole of her life, they had always been there, loving and encouraging her in her career and in her marriage. They had been special grandparents to her precious children. Now both her mother and father were dead. Gone, out of her life.

A lifetime of two special people disappeared in a few moments of time. Life finished, ended so quickly. As Alan cuddled the tearful grandchildren, Albert and Katherine, Charles held on to Gladys, her body racked with heaving sobs. As she began to recover, Charles whispered to her that the spirit of each of her parents were still very much alive for us all but also, together again; reunited for ever in the love that they had shared. Gladys, who was beyond words at that moment, simply nodded.

After the funeral, Alan returned with the children to Twickenham so that they could resume their schooling, while Gladys stayed with Charles to sort out her parent's possessions and clear the flat for new tenants. The deaths, so difficult to cope with, were added to by the painful activity of sorting and disposing of a lifetime collection of loved material goods. So many little items with so many powerful memories. Questions as to what to keep and which to throw away dominated their hours at the flat. Charles took away the couple of carpentry tools his granddad had kept and a brooch that he had given his grandma for a birthday, while Gladys chose her mother's jewellery and one of her father's caps that he loved wearing.

Everything else was bagged up, the clothes going to the local Salvation Army and the remainder of their two lives consigned to the municipal tip.

After a week or so, Charles returned to episcopal duties, visiting parishes at weekends, dropping in on clergy on Fridays and a myriad of church meetings and civic concerns to fill his days. Despite this almost frenzied activity, which Charles rationally explained to himself was justified in an attempt to catch up on the work missed over the six weeks of bereavement, there were moments when he could not escape the grief. Whilst driving across the county on visits, there were times when pictures and memories of his grandparents flooded back. The realisation that they were such good people, such love that they had shared together and given out to their family. Charles would often arrive at his destination with tears pouring down his cheeks. But the nights were the darkest times, the struggling to get to sleep, the ever-reoccurring nightmare pressing down upon him, followed by the dawning of another day, with the yawning gap left by his grandparents' absence.

Then just before Easter, Penelope wrote to say that the excavation was at a crucial stage and that she would not be able to come home until July. The loneliness deepened and his sense of isolation was profound, as he felt the shrinking away of a loving family around him. Even Gladys, his lifter of spirits, was lost in her own deep grief, trying to stay afloat just to be a good wife to Alan and a mother to her children.

Charles' confidence dipped and Archdeacon Colin seemed to sense a weakness at their monthly meeting in May and tried to press home his advantage. A female, New Zealand, Anglican priest who was on a visit to England in the autumn, had been invited by Bishop Charles to come and preach at the cathedral in September. The Archdeacon reported to Charles of the enormous amount of discontent that this had created in the diocese, especially among the clergy. "Would the bishop reconsider this decision?" he asked. Charles hesitated and weakly replied that he would, "Think about it."

At the end of May, Miss Jenkins gave in her three-month notice in order to finish at the annual late August Bank Holiday. Charles thanked her for staying on those extra months and for the wonderful help she had given in protecting him during his recent bereavements. Miss Jenkins was genuinely pleased that the bishop had recognised and appreciated her efforts to assist during that difficult period for him. Charles then asked Miss Jenkins if she would help concerning the appointment of her successor by drafting an outline of her role as she saw it, to be included in the application pack for the future applicants. Miss Jenkins was delighted to be asked to do so.

At the June meeting with the Archdeacon, Charles was informed by Colin that he knew of an excellent candidate to replace Miss Jenkins when she left. Charles smiled wryly to himself aware that the new appointment advertisement and procedure had not yet been made public. Charles thanked the Archdeacon and asked him to inform his contact that once the advertisement was placed in the church press, he would look forward to receiving her application.

Charles then raised two issues with the Archdeacon. With regard to the interviewing panel for Miss Jenkins' successor, Charles had intended to ask the Archdeacon to be one of three on the interviewing panel but now wondered whether it was appropriate for Colin to interview someone he knew well, his candidate. The Archdeacon blustered realising the bishop had outmanoeuvred him, eventually finding the words to assure the bishop that he would consider each applicant on an equal basis, giving no favours to anyone. Charles smiled and stated that the Archdeacon's reassurance was adequate and invited the Archdeacon to be involved in the interviews.

Secondly, Charles informed the Archdeacon that he was continuing with the invitation for the New Zealand woman priest to preach at the cathedral in September. "It is important," Charles said, "to have a full, open and informed debate on such important modern-day issues concerning the role of women in the life of the church." The nightmares had become less frequent, with sleep easier and the confidence was returning to Charles.

There were a dozen applications for the vacancy and together with the Lay Chairman of the Diocesan Synod, who was to be the third member of the interview panel, a shortlist of three was made and these invited to attend the following week. In reading through the applications, Charles noticed that one of the most original and impressive was by a young lady whose name was Elizabeth, who mentioned she was churchwarden at St. Cuthberts Church. For a fleeting moment his thoughts strayed back to the reception at his welcoming service and the churchwarden he'd met whose name was also Elizabeth; remembering those beautiful eyes.

Charles also included the Archdeacon's nominee in those to be interviewed but was very wary that he did not want a 'spy in the camp'. On the day of the interviews, Charles had invited the candidates to attend at 9 a.m. Morning Prayer, after which they were looked after by Miss Jenkins, who spent time with them explaining how she understood the role of Personal Assistant to the bishop. The interviews began at 10 a.m., each lasting forty-five minutes with a fifteen-minute break between the candidates.

The room was set out with the three interviewers sat behind a desk with a solitary chair in front for the candidate. The Archdeacon's nominee was first on the list. She was the wife of one of the clerics who the Archdeacon had brought into the diocese. Her only work experience was limited in recent years to part-time secretarial work in an architect's office. She obviously had an informed background of church matters through her husband's role but Charles felt she did little to put herself forward. At one point, it crossed Charles' thoughts that she gave the impression of only being present because pressure had been put on her by her husband or the Archdeacon, or both, to be here applying for this job. Her heart and enthusiasm did not appear to be fully engaged in the role she had applied for.

The second candidate was extremely nervous to the extent that she was unable to answer questions in any detail, offering only short one sentence replies. During the course of the interview, she increasingly lost her confidence and became more flustered and confused. At the end of the forty-five minutes, she was so upset at her inability to perform adequately, that she profusely apologised for wasting their time.

Finally, Elizabeth walked into the room. As Charles looked up from the paperwork in front of him their eyes met. Recognising those eyes, he knew immediately that this was the same Elizabeth he had met previously. There was somehow a subconscious meeting, a togetherness of spirit, that he could not rationally explain.

Elizabeth gave an account of her working experience as Senior Secretary, managing a team of assistants at the local firm of solicitors in Tuxbury. She came across as an excellent and confident candidate, full of original ideas and with a driven sense of purpose. The Archdeacon recognised Elizabeth as the main threat to his preferred choice and was decidedly more aggressive in his questions to her. Elizabeth dealt well with this unexpected approach from the Archdeacon, remaining firm and focussed.

In the discussions that followed the interviews, Elizabeth was first choice of both the Lay Chairman and Charles and was therefore offered the position in a letter the following week. As a consolation to the Archdeacon, Charles agreed that Colin's candidate would be the reserve candidate if Elizabeth declined the job.

In late August, a small reception was held at Bishop's House for Miss Jenkins' retirement. She was presented with an impressive grandfather clock for the hallway in her country cottage as well as a cheque. Charles had organised a collection across the diocese in recognition of Miss Jenkins' long and loyal service. He had also invited the previous retired bishop to attend, with Miss Jenkins thrilled by her former employers' presence as well as the gifts she received.

The following Tuesday morning, Elizabeth walked into Bishop's House and into Charles' life.

3.2 Elizabeth and Charles

The Bishop's Palace was set at the very heart of the Cathedral Close, surrounded by other ecclesiastical buildings, including the Diocesan Office, a Theological College with Library and the Archdeacon's residence, the Archdeaconry. Although Elizabeth knew the Bishop's residence as the Bishop's Palace, she noticed that on entering it had a new nameplate, 'Bishop's House'. As she walked up the drive, Elizabeth recalled that nearly a year ago in the local press, there had been several letters to the editor questioning the re-naming of such a historic and ancient building by the new incoming Bishop. Bishop Charles had replied to these letters explaining that in today's modern society, it was not appropriate for a servant of Christ and the people to live in a 'palace'. Eventually, this minor furore blew over.

Elizabeth's office was on the ground floor of the palace / house next to the Bishop's study and had beautiful views across the rear garden. The remainder of the ground floor included: a reception office for incoming phone calls and to welcome visitors, a library where those awaiting meetings with the Bishop could gather, a conference room and a chapel. The upper floor was the Bishop's private living accommodation. It was to this setting that Elizabeth arrived on her first working day.

There was a great deal for Elizabeth to absorb and

understand in those early weeks and months. She had, in the past, learnt the structure of a legal office and how that functioned. Elizabeth now began the much larger task of coming to terms with the history, tradition and oddities of the whole of the Church of England. It was a huge undertaking but Elizabeth applied her customary determination and enthusiasm to the task.

Elizabeth's specific role was to be organiser, supporter, prompter and much more for the Bishop's work. It was an immense, multi-faceted role requiring many different skills on Elizabeth's behalf. She was in control of his diary, consulting and planning many months ahead. There to help him decide upon his priorities, fitting everything important into his schedule. Also, there was the running of the office and the supervision of two other secretaries and their work, together with dealing with so many requests from people who wanted to be a part of the Bishop's life. Elizabeth, at times, felt that she was also his protector, his first line of defence. Elizabeth loved her new job and thrived in its challenging and varying role.

On her first morning, Elizabeth was sat at her desk when the Bishop knocked and came into her room. She looked up and immediately knew. Their eyes met and Elizabeth felt that same feeling she had experienced back at her interview. There was between them, some deep rapport and empathy, a kindred spirit and a togetherness of sadness, of unfulfilled life. Instantly, there was a unity between them, unspoken and somehow, a loving bond that nothing would or could ever take away.

Each day, Elizabeth would pass alongside the grey stone cathedral on her ten-minute walk to work. The partners at the solicitors had agreed that she could remain as tenant in the flat. She would arrive just after 8 a.m., although officially her working day did not start until 9 a.m. It gave her time to sort out the post and plan her day, ensuring that she was prepared and informed.

At 9 a.m., everyone joined in the chapel for Morning Prayer usually led by the Bishop which included a quiet time. Elizabeth met with the bishop at 9.30 a.m., briefing him on the day ahead, responding to the morning's letters and raising any other urgent issues. The day then unfolded with a variety of tasks including taking minutes at meetings, arranging clergy interviews, advertising vacancies in the diocese, booking weekend visits to local churches, dealing with press statements on controversial social issues and a myriad of other daily church business, including pastoral matters regarding clergy who were going through difficult times.

Elizabeth still held on to her lunch hour away from work and often visited her quiet, out-of-the way church of St Cuthbert's, where she was in charge during the interregnum that was taking place after Richard left. It was also a peaceful break from the intensity of her work. At the end of day, Elizabeth often took folders home with her as there was so much to learn in a short time and so many reports and policies to comprehend.

As Elizabeth grew in confidence, efficiently coping with the numerous demands of her work, her relationship with the Bishop also developed. In those early months, they spent many hours together. Initially, it was about Elizabeth learning the procedures and routines of life in a Bishop's office but later, they just enjoyed being in each other's company, with the Bishop interested in Elizabeth's fresh opinions and enthusiastic approach. Elizabeth loved being with him and listening to his thoughts and sharing his concerns. She also treasured those doleful eyes, his warm smile and his loving attitude to all people, whatever they thought of him. He was the kindest and most caring person Elizabeth had ever met.

As Christmas approached, Elizabeth was asked if she could organise buying and decorating a Christmas tree for visitors to the Bishop's House and a second one for his family who were coming to stay over Christmas. Elizabeth put aside an afternoon for this task and was in the process of decorating the trees when the Bishop returned from a long and tedious church meeting. For some light relief, after the rigours of the five-hour meeting, Charles offered to help Elizabeth by passing her the decorations.

Elizabeth listened to Charles' amusing account of the boring meeting as the tree began to light up the growing darkness of the late afternoon. As they worked alongside each other, Elizabeth was asked how she celebrated Christmas. Elizabeth inwardly blushed and faltered in her reply, turning to recent years and explaining about her church's celebrations, not wishing to be embarrassed by the fact that since living in Tuxbury, she had always spent Christmas Day on her own, either reading or watching television.

Then seemingly, out of the blue, Elizabeth received an invitation to share Christmas with Charles' family here at Bishop's House. Bishop Charles explained that his aunty Gladys and her husband, Alan and their two children, Albert and Katherine, would also be there whilst his wife, Penelope, would not be arriving back from the Middle East until after Christmas, therefore would not be with them for Christmas lunch.

Elizabeth initially replied that she couldn't possibly intrude into Charles' family time. However, Charles insisted so Elizabeth finally agreed. It was arranged that Elizabeth would come along after the morning service on Christmas Day in time for a 1 p.m. lunch. Later, as Elizabeth thought about the invitation, she realised that Bishop Charles had seen through her reply and understood that Christmas for Elizabeth was a lonely time without the love of a family to surround her.

Elizabeth spent the next few days and sleepless nights, worrying and in fear that she would do or say the wrong things. Concerned that she would not know the correct etiquette, the right way of being proper, of which fork or knife to eat with. Charles had been at the exclusive grammar school in Tuxbury and then went on to Oxford University. His aunty Gladys was now a high-flying executive with the Co-Operative Society working in London and abroad. Elizabeth had just lived her thirty-odd years in this small area, attended a secondary modern school and not even been to a foreign country, except Wales! She had had such a limited small-town experience of life.

Elizabeth was feeling totally out of her depth. What interesting conversation could she make? What opinions did she hold, say about Mrs Thatcher and politics and the social issues of the day? Her confidence plummeted to rock bottom and she became anxious and worried that she would look such a fool in such clever company. She determined to think of excuses to avoid going along: a distant aunt had died and she had to go and help make arrangements for the funeral, or she had a sickness bug and a migraine or, even more bizarrely, that she had won on the Littlewoods Pools and was going abroad! She floundered in her distress and the night before Christmas

Eve, her nightmare returned. Drowning in ever rising levels of the sea, unable to grasp her mother's fingers, slipping away again into the depths of despair.

Christmas Day arrived and Elizabeth got up, bathed and dressed. Applying her make-up, she had a queasy feeling in her stomach with trepidation flooding over her as to how the day would evolve. The morning was taken up with her duties at her church, greeting many unfamiliar faces who appeared on Christmas morning to sing some carols and get into the Christmas spirit.

After the service, the congregation were invited to remain for mince pies and mulled wine. Later, after helping the elderly lady volunteers with the washing up, everyone left wishing Elizabeth a happy Christmas. She quietly counted the collection, noting that the spirit of Christmas had not extended to gifts on the plate. Elizabeth then entered the details in the church register before locking away the monies and other valuables in the church safe. Once all her tasks were completed at St. Cuthberts, Elizabeth then made her nervous way to the Bishop's House.

Charles greeted her at the door, wishing her a 'Happy Christmas' with a kiss on her cheek. Elizabeth blushed slightly and likewise wished Charles seasonal greetings. There were introductions all round, although the children now in their late teens, rushed off to play on their new Amstrad computers. Elizabeth felt so nervous that she imagined she was almost shaking but it was Gladys who seemed to understand her anxiousness and took her off to help in the kitchen, while the men helped the children set up the computers. Elizabeth found Gladys so easy to talk to and so down to earth that she began to relax. With the help of one or two glasses of sherry,

Elizabeth started to grow a little in confidence.

Elizabeth was amazed at how easily she was accepted into Charles' family. She had bought Albert and Katherine presents, despite Charles saying not to bring gifts.

Elizabeth also brought an expensive bottle of French red wine as a contribution to the meal which pleased Charles especially, who extolled at length upon the merits of the bottle of Marqaux. Everyone was very happy and the meal was simple, yet delicious and Elizabeth began to realise that maybe her worries of the last few days were unfounded.

She particularly enjoyed the games with the children, although watching Charles playing it was difficult to decide who were the young people. On one occasion during a raucous game of racing around trying to sit on the spare chair, Elizabeth competed with Charles for the vacant seat and in her enthusiasm, pushed him out of the way resulting in Charles ending upon the floor, much to everyone's amusement, especially the children and to Elizabeth's embarrassment. It was compounded when she went forward to offer a hand to help Charles get up, when instead he suddenly pulled her down on the floor alongside him in a further attempt to unfairly pinch the vacant seat. She felt her face was glowing as she retreated to her chair, although the sherry and wine consumed may have been an influence on her rosy cheeks!

As the day drew to a close, after giving everyone a kiss goodnight including Elizabeth, the youngsters took their computers off to their bedrooms. As it was now past ten o'clock, Elizabeth decided it was time to go home, giving the remainder of the family some time for themselves. Elizabeth thanked everyone for their kindness and for the warm welcome in the sharing of their family Christmas with her.

As Elizabeth walked home, she was so pleased with herself that she had not run away and had had the courage to join in the day's celebrations. Elizabeth smiled as she remembered the game they called 'stations' and the rushing and pushing to grab the one empty chair. How Albert and Katherine laughed so long and loud as they saw their 'Uncle' Charles deposited on the floor by Elizabeth. As she neared her flat, Elizabeth laughed out loud as she recalled that with tears of laughter rolling down her cheeks; she had apologised and tried to pick Charles up off the floor, who in turn, then pulled Elizabeth down next to him and made a lunge for the spare chair, only to be foiled by Gladys who stood in his way, disqualifying Charles' attempt as 'foul play'. A couple walking by smiled as they saw so much joy and happiness in another on this festive day.

By the time Elizabeth reached her flat, she was still giggling out loud, her eyes were sparkling and her face radiant with contentment. That night, Elizabeth slept solidly for the first time in many years.

As Elizabeth awoke to a new day, another reality began to dawn.

It started when Elizabeth, lying alone under the covers of her bed on a cold, Boxing Day morning, thought about how kind Gladys had been to her. The way she had so naturally taken Elizabeth under her wing and been so inclusive of her in every aspect of the day. An hour in the kitchen with Gladys had relaxed Elizabeth and reassured her that she would be able to cope with the day. Strangely, it was Gladys' love and happiness that now upset Elizabeth.

How much her husband, Alan, loved her. How many times, Elizabeth recalled, did Alan pop into the kitchen, supposedly to see if any help was needed but in reality, just to be close to Gladys? Each visit he would touch her: a hand on her hip, an arm around her shoulder, a delicate and secret kiss on her neck. No one had ever been like that to Elizabeth.

And the fruits of Gladys and Alan's love, Albert and Katherine, were so happy and joyful, obviously secure and loved within a family unit. Both the children welcomed and accepted Elizabeth, showing her their presents and sincerely thanking Elizabeth for her gifts. Elizabeth had bought Katherine some make-up and they spent time together talking about beauty care and how it had changed over the years with Elizabeth talking about fashions in the late 1960s when she was Katherine's age.

The happiness of Christmas Day and of such a loving family was dissipating fast for Elizabeth, as she remembered the stark contrast of her own life experiences. In her childhood there were few presents, no family fun, laughter and games but just memories of darkness and despair with little love and joy. Thoughts of her father going out to the pub and returning drunk in a foul mood, greedily eating his Christmas dinner, then snoring loudly sprawled over the settee.

Over the next few days, Elizabeth rarely got out of bed, hiding away under the covers of a defensive, self-contained, lonely life. She had only survived and not really lived, hidden away in a little, enclosed world, protecting herself from the hurt of the past. Elizabeth became more despondent at the thought of the loneliness of so many wasted Christmas Days.

All the defence systems Elizabeth had put in place to avoid the reality of her isolation at Christmas seem to crumble away, after spending a few hours with Charles' family. The money she had saved from not having to buy endless cards and presents, the worry that she did not experience in having to please others, not having to be concerned as to who to spend Christmas with and hence upsetting others who would have liked Elizabeth to visit them. All the barriers Elizabeth had built to justify her lonely Christmases of the past just evaporated. The contrast was so vivid and stark. No family, no love, no laughter. Just emptiness; a vacuum.

After the New Year break, Elizabeth called upon her determination to be strong and try to seek a more loving and sharing life by breaking out of her restricted lifestyle and deep independence. Elizabeth had no idea or plan how this could be achieved but somehow, that wonderful experience on Christmas Day gave her new hope and encouragement. Maybe her healing would in some way be in her working relationship with Charles and be a base, or at least a starting point, to coming to terms with deeply buried problems.

In mid-January, Elizabeth knocked at Charles' study door and entered to find the Bishop in tears. She went over and put her arm around his shoulder to offer comfort to him. Eventually, he recovered his poise and explained that the Archdeacon was scheming behind his back over the new mission strategy, encouraging his cronies to oppose the Bishop's plans. He had just spoken to the Archdeacon and had had a heated conversation with him. Elizabeth sympathised and stated that she had never warmed to the Archdeacon and noticed that he was always very cool to her since being in post.

As he wiped away his tears, Charles explained that the Archdeacon had nominated a friend of his for Elizabeth's job and been angry that the Bishop had appointed Elizabeth. Charles surmised that he probably wanted someone on the inside so as to monitor what the new Bishop was about!

They spoke for a few minutes, with Charles holding onto her hand, as he explained that he got distressed by internal church politics and the constant bickering and self-importance some senior churchmen gave to themselves. He believed that the Archdeacon was an angry and frustrated man because he had never been offered the position of Bishop, being overlooked after ten years in his present post.

Over the weeks, their relationship deepened. They spent many hours in conversation, sharing with one another their thoughts and feelings. Charles spoke about his earlier childhood in a mining town in the North Midlands. He talked of his wife, Penelope, of where they met and their rather strange marriage lifestyle. Elizabeth had only once met Charles' wife, Penelope, a well-known, respected and published archaeologist. They seemed to live separate lives with Penelope often away working at an excavation site in the Middle East and only rarely appearing during rest times between digs. They had no children.

When Elizabeth arrived at her office at 8 a.m. she would quickly look through the daily post, placing the contents into two piles. The first group were the more important ones for the direct attention of the Bishop. The second bundle were the more routine and mundane letters that Elizabeth would deal with when time allowed. One morning in February, Elizabeth opened a letter from a Mr Hatfield and recognised immediately the seriousness of its content. Elizabeth placed the letter on the top of Charles' post for his immediate consideration after Morning Prayer.

Elizabeth was shocked by Charles' reaction to his reading of the letter. She had never seen him so angry and upset. It seemed Mr Hatfield's daughter had been sexually touched, molested, by a Reverend Toole and that his earlier complaint, which had been made to the Archdeacon, had been ignored. Charles immediately asked Elizabeth to bring Reverend Toole's personnel file, which he scanned briefly. His anger increased as he saw that Reverend Toole had attended the same theological college as the Archdeacon and at the same time. It was Archdeacon Colin who had invited and was instrumental, in Reverend Toole being appointed to his present rural parish.

Elizabeth was sent to arrange a time, that day if possible, for Charles to visit Mr Hatfield's family. Elizabeth was also instructed to summon Reverend Toole and the Archdeacon, saying that the Bishop wished to speak to them on an urgent matter at Bishop's House tomorrow. The two appointments to be made at separate times and neither to be informed of the other's appointment.

Elizabeth returned having successfully completed the tasks, arranging for Charles to visit the family that evening. Reverend Toole and the Archdeacon would attend Charles' office tomorrow morning at 10 a.m. and 11.30 a.m., respectively. Charles was now a little calmer and explained that on reading the letter, he had immediately thought of Glady's daughter, Katherine, who was only a few years older than the Hatfield's daughter. He was horrified that someone in such a trusted role had done such an evil act to an innocent young person. Charles further explained that his anger was also concerning the Archdeacon's inaction. He appeared to be trying to cover up a crucially important matter that should have been dealt with by prompt disciplinary action, in order to protect other children and maintain a safe environment for them within the church setting.

Elizabeth continued with her daily tasks but found herself

troubled by Reverend Toole, the Archdeacon and the Hatfield family situation. At lunchtime, Elizabeth spent her lunch hour at her local church, St Cuthbert's, where she sat in quiet thought, not even giving herself time to eat her sandwiches.

Later that afternoon, Elizabeth sought out Charles on his return from a Mothers' Union event and explained the fruits of her quiet time. Charles sat and listened intently, as his eyes widened with surprise at Elizabeth's considered thoughts in dealing with the Archdeacon's appalling behaviour.

The next day, as Elizabeth was working, Charles came into her office with a big smile on his face. The Archdeacon had left, slightly confused. Chided but also now with a major commitment to begin drawing up a Diocesan Policy for the Protection of Young People. Charles thanked Elizabeth for her insight and clear thinking at a time when he was too enraged to consider the best way forward. Elizabeth coloured slightly with embarrassment but was gratified that Charles had taken time to acknowledge her contribution. For Elizabeth, Charles' approval was becoming more and more important to her. Walking home that evening, Elizabeth felt good. It was almost as if she had a new, real friend.

On a Spring day, seven months after beginning to work for the Bishop, that friendship deepened when Elizabeth shared with Charles the sadness of the events of her early life. They were sat in his study in the late afternoon as the failing light began to darken the room. They were talking about the vision and in particular, the difficulties experienced by seaside parishes, when Charles remembered that Elizabeth lived her childhood at Pinton-on-Sea.

Elizabeth's memory immediately flashed back to the

negative images deep within her. The empty, desolate streets with the winter's gales battering the promenade and her dark, depressing home. Charles listened quietly to her description of her father's desertion, his subsequent life and death and of his abuse of her mother, resulting in her mother's lonely and depressive existence. The circumstances of her mother's suicide and its effect upon Elizabeth's life, leaving her unable to trust in relationships and only able to move on with her life by hiding away from the loveless past.

As she spoke, Elizabeth began to cry and Charles came and sat alongside her, holding her hand. Elizabeth felt the warmth of his presence, the softness of his touch and the love he expressed in his concern. As she slowly recovered her composure, Elizabeth rose to leave. Without thinking, she turned and spontaneously kissed him lightly on the cheek. In horror, she jumped back realising what she had done, blushing and apologising profusely for her moment of indiscretion. Charles smiled that wonderful, warm smile and reassured Elizabeth. He jokingly said it was nice to be kissed as it did not happen very often nowadays. And not for the first time, Elizabeth saw a shared sadness within Charles' eyes and life.

That night, Elizabeth lay in her warm, cosy bed and thought back over the day. She recalled the moment when she had turned and kissed Charles. She remembered his soft skin and as she did so, her hand moved and began opening the buttons of her pyjama jacket. She felt her breasts and circled around her increasingly erect nipples fantasising that it was Charles who was caressing her. In her mind's eye, Elizabeth felt a stirring below and her hand moved slowly down her body, easing off her pyjama trousers. Within moments, Elizabeth climaxed, crying out in pleasure with her body stiffening and arching in ecstasy.

Afterwards, Elizabeth lay awake, confused and bewildered. The climax had been the most intense that she had ever experienced. On occasions in the past when she had touched herself, it was mainly after reading a love scene in a novel or from watching a film with a particularly sensual sexual moment, where her imagination had run wild. But during those times, there was never the reaction that she had experienced tonight. It seemed to Elizabeth that her friendship had moved on in a dangerous and inappropriate way and she became worried and anxious.

Then, the guilt and disgust flooded through her body. Her confidence dropped and the doubts and questions poured into her being. This was her employer, a person in Holy Orders and a married man. What was she thinking of? How wanton was her behaviour in bringing such a good man into her sexual dreams and fantasies? How unclean she felt yet again. Elizabeth spoke severely to herself in a very scolding manner, telling herself that this must never be repeated and that she must maintain the highest professional standards in the future. Even so, Elizabeth could not deny the warm glow that reverberated within her.

The following day, Elizabeth avoided eye contact with Charles, adopting a very efficient, professional attitude in her meeting-time with him. For the next few days, she maintained this pose, trying to avoid more informal chat that had become a part of their relationship. It didn't last long as Elizabeth missed the small talk, the being together, the friendship and when Charles spoke about taking Elizabeth to visit her mother's grave, Elizabeth readily agreed.

It was a week later that Charles drove Elizabeth to her

mother's unmarked grave in Pinton-on-Sea. It was an overcast day with the threat of rain from the low-lying clouds. When Elizabeth eventually located the unmarked grave, she stood still looking at the unkept patch of ground. Around her there were many other graves without monuments to the dead, reflecting the poverty of the occupant's families.

Elizabeth suddenly felt a huge surge of sadness for her mother's life. How empty and broken it had been with no one, including Elizabeth, there to help to release her mother from the torment.

As these feelings flooded through Elizabeth she began to shudder with copious tears. Tears for her mother and for that cold and horrific night of her death. Tears for Elizabeth, for herself and her lost childhood. Tears for the resulting loneliness of her adult life, hiding herself away, afraid of being hurt and rejected by others. Frightened of being deserted again. Charles moved forward and took Elizabeth into his arms and held her tightly to him, speaking softly and tenderly in her ear. Elizabeth now noticed that the dark, gloomy, polluting gas towers had been removed and that above their heads, the grey clouds had parted with a patch of blue sky breaking through. In Charles' arms, Elizabeth felt a real sense of light, hope and peace surrounding her.

Charles had thoughtfully provided some flowers and Elizabeth placed them tenderly on her mother's grave, whispering the words, "Let us now forgive each other. I love you." On leaving the cemetery, Elizabeth was determined to return more regularly and to have a stone suitably inscribed, placed on her mother's grave.

That night in her review of the day, Elizabeth remembered the kindness of Charles in being with her and in lovingly providing some beautiful, red roses to place at her mother's resting place. Like Elizabeth, her mother had been alone for too long. Now Elizabeth felt that their healing was beginning and she was determined that this discovery of love should spread through into the depths of her being and to be shared with others. Charles' loving embrace was a part of her re-emergence into the beginnings of a new phase of her life.

Each month, a letter arrived addressed to Bishop Charles from his wife, Penelope. On the first occasion, back in September, Elizabeth had opened the letter not realising it was from Charles' wife. After apologising to Charles, Elizabeth kept a special look-out for Penelope's hand-written envelope and delivered it safely, unopened to Charles' desk. He recognised the letter's author and always put it to one side to open in the privacy of his apartment later in the day. Just before Holy Week in March, Penelope's monthly letter duly arrived.

The next morning, Elizabeth was surprised that Charles was not at Morning Prayer so she stood in to lead the shortened service. At 9.30 a.m., Elizabeth knocked on the Bishop's study door and entered to find he was not present and so returned to her own office, a little mystified and worried at his absence. Elizabeth knew from his diary that he had a busy schedule that day, including a Bishops' Council meeting and an important civic luncheon. Concerned, Elizabeth went upstairs to his apartment and knocked on the door to ensure herself that Charles was not ill. As Elizabeth knocked on the door, it drifted open and Elizabeth called out Charles' name. There was no reply so Elizabeth entered to discover clothes hastily thrown about as if Charles had overslept and left in a great hurry.

Throughout the day, Elizabeth was puzzled by Charles'

lack of presence that morning. She could not recall a similar happening. He was always prompt and well-organised in his daily routines. Although she continued with her work, her mind was elsewhere.

In the evening, back at her flat, Elizabeth began to realise that she was upset and disturbed by her reaction to Charles' absence. She wondered what had happened to him to change his usual morning rituals. Had he not slept and if not, what had caused such a disturbance to his normal life? As Elizabeth's thoughts wandered through a myriad of alternative scenarios, she eventually began to realise how much Charles now meant to her. He had become the most important person in her life and she had shared more with Charles than she had done with anyone else, including Richard. It dawned upon Elizabeth how vital Charles was to her and his Christmas kiss and graveside cuddle came rushing back to her.

The following day, Charles was sat in his usual seat for Morning Prayer but Elizabeth could see that something was not right. He looked tired, withdrawn and although he led the service, he somehow did not seem involved or committed. His usual enthusiasm and energy were totally absent. Elizabeth looked across the chapel at Charles and saw that sadness and dullness in his eyes which she had noticed once or twice in the past. It was almost as if the spark of life had been extinguished.

They met as usual at 9.30 a.m. for a planned extended meeting in an attempt to catch up with a great deal of paperwork that had accumulated. Charles looked broken and desperate, with his mind unable to concentrate or focus on what Elizabeth was placing before him. Elizabeth was now deeply concerned that Charles was going through a mental health breakdown and asked on two occasions if Charles was well enough to continue. Then, suddenly, Charles got up from his chair behind the desk and rushed out of the room, saying he had to go out. Elizabeth followed but Charles slammed the front door behind him, went to his car and drove off at a high and erratic speed.

Elizabeth was beside herself with worry, constantly leaving her office to check if Charles had returned. She looked in his study and in his apartment upstairs, at least once every hour. Finally, at around 9 p.m. the front door opened and Charles entered. Elizabeth came forward, noticing his crumpled clothing which seemed to represent Charles' state of mind at that moment. Elizabeth guided Charles to the library, sat him down on a comfortable sofa and went to make some tea and raid the office cake tin to give him some much-needed nourishment.

When Elizabeth returned to the library, Charles was in tears holding out a letter which he asked her to read. As Elizabeth quickly read the contents of the letter from Penelope, she instantly understood the cause of Charles' distress as the letter signalled the end of Charles' marriage. Immediately, Elizabeth sat next to Charles and held his hand, placing one arm around his shoulders. Through the tears, Charles shared with Elizabeth the difficulties of his long-distant marriage to Penelope and the problems that both had carried forward from their childhoods into their life together. For the first time, Charles spoke in more detail about the tragic deaths of his parents. Elizabeth had not realised how young Charles had been at the time and she felt a great wave of sympathy and love for Charles.

Elizabeth sat quietly and listened. Part of her listening was initially not knowing how to respond and what to say but also, she had recently read an article in the Woman magazine about counselling skills, by a lady psychotherapist in which the author wrote about the value of just 'being there' and facilitating by listening and not speaking, especially avoiding responding with glib cliché-type comments.

For over an hour, Elizabeth stayed with Charles, quietly encouraging him with her attention and presence. As she sat close to Charles, Elizabeth could feel the pain and anguish pouring out of him. Gradually, it began to dawn upon her that at the centre of Charles' tears was the loss of his mother and father, with the unresolved grief still within him.

Breaking her silence, Elizabeth turned towards Charles and asked him how old he was when his parents died? Charles hesitated, so Elizabeth followed up asking whether Charles could remember the last time he kissed and cuddled his parents? Charles was startled by her questions but slowly he answered that he was four and half years old when his father died and seven years of age when his mother finally passed away, after suffering severe head injuries resulting from the fall at the time of his father's death.

To Elizabeth's second question, Charles firstly recalled the goodnight kiss and story read by his daddy as he lay in bed the night before his father's accident and secondly, the visit to his mummy at the Home for Incurables with his aunty Gladys. There, he remembered the long corridor, the colours in the room, the iron bed, his mother's fits and that life-long, unforgettable, guttural sound issued from within her damaged body. Then finally, his kiss goodbye to his mother and Aunty Glady's tears when his mother smiled. As Elizabeth held Charles even tighter, she could feel the tears streaming down her own cheeks as she absorbed Charles' halting account of those last moments of love.

Over the next hour, Charles became calmer and more settled with fewer tears. Their togetherness returned to a two-way conversation with Elizabeth explaining how she had managed to deal with most of the work that they had intended to cover that morning. Charles apologised for his sudden earlier departure but felt he needed to just run away, unable to cope. Charles then turned to Elizabeth and lightly kissed away a remaining tear from her cheek and said, "thank you." Elizabeth coloured and then they both laughed as they realised that this was their third kiss, each a natural expression of love, given and received. Elizabeth left the Bishop's House at 11.15 p.m., walking the short distance to her flat mulling over in her mind the last few hours.

In her thoughts was not only Charles' pain and difficulties arising from his earlier life but also, Elizabeth's own reactions to the day's events. Her depth of worry, the affection that she now felt for Charles. It seemed to her that the bond of both being deprived of love in their childhood, was bringing them ever closer to one another. Something deep within them, searching along two winding, uphill pathways that appeared to be merging ever-closer together, into a single way forward.

Elizabeth kept a close eye on Charles over Holy week and Easter observing him operating in a mechanical manner, doing all the things required of him but without the usual zeal and commitment, half-heartedly completing the necessary tasks asked of him but also holding back part of himself. Elizabeth was aware that Charles had prepared a break after Easter and was to travel to Iona for a ten-day retreat. The Bishop's House office was closed for Easter week but Elizabeth dropped in daily to deal with any urgent issues in Charles' absence.

All through Charles' time away, Elizabeth found herself worrying about his state of mind. She was mightily relieved on his return to see his smile and a twinkling return to those eyes. At their first meeting, Elizabeth inquired if Charles had had a good relaxing time on Iona. Charles smiled that wonderful smile of his and replied, "It was interesting," and shared a little of his struggles and joys.

At the end of their meeting, Charles took from a drawer in his desk a small jewellery box which he handed to Elizabeth as a 'thank you' for listening and sharing with him a couple of weeks ago. Elizabeth nervously opened the box to reveal a beautiful silver chain and Celtic cross made on the Isle of Iona. As she tried to place it around her neck, Charles came around his desk to help with the clasp. As Charles' hands touched her skin, Elizabeth felt a shiver of excitement run through her and once the clasp was in place, quickly moved away and sat down, her face flushed.

It was the first gift that anyone had ever given Elizabeth in her adult life.

One Saturday, Elizabeth accompanied Charles on a journey to re-visit his past. After picking up three bunches of flowers, they travelled to the North Midlands to the desperately dreary, industrial towns of Sheddingworth and Gattingford where Charles had lived his early years. Firstly, they visited Sheddingworth where Charles had resided with his nan during the weekdays after his father's and mother's accidents. From his nan's house, on the way to the graveyard at the parish church, Charles pointed out the local primary school he attended, recalling painful times. It was now deserted and vandalised. At the graveside, next to

Sheddingworth Church, Charles placed flowers in memory of the love that his nan had given in caring for him. As he did so, Charles recalled the sweet shop where his nan spoilt him so often, trying so hard to replace lost love.

They then drove onto Gattingford and Charles showed Elizabeth his end of terrace home of birth and of his first four years of life. Charles struggled to remember much about those early years other than helping his father do woodwork in the garden shed and the cutting of his finger on a chisel. He also recalled his mother's traumatic sobbing and grief on hearing of his father's death, news brought to her by a rather cold, functional and detached, local policeman. At his parents and grandparents' graveside, Charles laid the second bunch of flowers. He seemed strangely at peace; smiling, not upset but holding her hand tightly.

On the return journey to Tuxbury they rerouted to visit Charles' other grandparents' old home where Charles had initially visited at weekends and school holidays until his nan, back in Sheddingworth, had become too ill to look after him during the weekdays. Charles explained that at the age of eleven he had moved permanently to Grange-next-to-Sea, before eventually going on to university at Oxford when he was seventeen years of age. They walked through his beloved woods behind the house, passed the old badger set, across the hilltop to the beach, sitting on the rocks watching the waves rolling in. By now it was early evening and the sun was beginning to set. As they sat together, Charles recalled many happy moments at this home, bird watching, badger spotting, with hours also spent beachcombing.

Later, they stopped for an evening meal at a local pub and on returning to the car, Charles gave the third bunch of flowers, the red roses to Elizabeth, thanking her for accompanying him on this important journey back in life. As Charles went to hand Elizabeth the roses, he leant forward to kiss her on the cheek but she moved slightly to look at the flowers, resulting in their lips brushing against each other by accident.

Over the next few weeks, Elizabeth spent more and more time in the company of Charles. Their morning meetings would go on a little longer, they began to share tea and cake in the late afternoon in her office whenever Charles was around and both drifted in and out of their respective office and study, to mention the most trivial of matters in an excuse just to be in the presence of one another.

Then in early June, on a beautiful sunny, warm day they were together in Charles' study. Elizabeth was taking Charles through how she had set out the initial first draft of the vision for the church's future. She was standing close beside him in her light, floral summer dress as a soft breeze drifted through the partially open French window doors.

In that moment of time, Elizabeth felt so close to Charles, a part of him, that when his hand touched her leg, it felt as if love was overcoming all the hurt, loneliness and pain of her past life. Finally, pure love was now reaching out to heal her fully and enable Elizabeth to be truly alive, deep within her…

3.3 Charles and Elizabeth

Charles got up that first morning with a strange air of anticipation and even more oddly, a tremor of excitement. As he bathed and shaved, Charles rationalised these feelings as one of looking forward to a new beginning with someone who would be working close to him on creating new ways forward. Elizabeth in her interview, had expressed her belief that the church must try to attract a younger congregation in order to grow and prosper with more involvement in local community activities. Within him, there was a feeling that Charles was unable to verbalise but he knew that there was something more to his gathering excitement. Those outward sparkling, yet inwardly reserved eyes fascinated Charles. They seemed to hold a lifetime of goodness and love and yet, were also bearers of many painful experiences, seemingly searching to express themselves in a life that was still stunted and held back in a haunted past.

As Charles knocked and walked into Elizabeth's office on that first day, he caught sight of those eyes and her beautiful smile, knowing that in his inner being, his life was to be turned upside-down.

In the first few weeks, Charles and Elizabeth had to spend a great deal of time together with Charles guiding Elizabeth through all the different aspects of her new role. They quickly relaxed into an easy working relationship and began to feel at ease in each other's company. As their friendship developed, they shared some of their life details with one another. Charles was surprised to learn that Elizabeth lived her childhood in Pinton-on-Sea, just a few miles away from Charles and his grandparent's home at Grange-next-to-Sea. It began to appear that Elizabeth's childhood was not a happy one as she described the bleakness of the resort in the off-season. As the months working together unfolded, they shared more details of their lives including their schooling and families.

In the meantime, especially after the appointment of Elizabeth, the relationship with the Archdeacon became more strained. At their monthly meeting, Archdeacon Colin was ever more aggressive in opposing Charles' initial thoughts about his future plans. Charles was soon to put these into a document for discussion and debate at Diocesan Synod. Charles had, by now visited, the majority of clergy and nearly two-thirds of the parishes and recognised a clear call from many that the church needed to move on in order to have a positive future. The timing felt right to Charles but the Archdeacon's behaviour implied a fear that he would be left behind, powerless, by the new Bishop's 'Vision for the Future'.

On one 'drop-in' call to a clergyman, the cleric spoke of his opposition to one of the proposed changes that Charles was considering. Charles was disturbed that the vicar knew of his ideas as he had only shared this in confidence with Archdeacon Colin, no-one else knowing anything about it other than Elizabeth, who was typing up the outline manuscript for the vision. On return to Bishop's House, Charles rang the Archdeacon who denied he had anything to do with the leak of information, blaming Elizabeth instead. Charles looked up the history of the cleric he had visited to discover that he was yet another of the clergy who had attended the same theological college as the Archdeacon. Charles realised that the Archdeacon was beginning to muster his cronies and briefing them to oppose Charles.

As Charles sat at his desk, he remembered Hugo's warning and questions concerning his ability to cope with conflict and how that might possibly undermine his confidence. The life-long difficulty of wanting to be loved by everyone entered Charles' thoughts once again. He had been so encouraged by his first year in office; the mainly successful visits to clergy and parishes and of meeting people who seemed genuine in wanting to restore the failing church. Now, after one phone call, Charles felt hot tears of despair running down his cheeks.

At that moment, there was a soft knock at the door and Elizabeth entered. Shocked at seeing his distress, she moved quickly towards him, placing her arm around his shoulders in an unselfconscious desire to offer comfort.

Elizabeth's presence so close to Charles electrified him. He could feel the warmth of her body and smell the fragrant perfume that she used. Charles was confused by the emotions flowing through him and mumbled to Elizabeth about his distressing conversation with the Archdeacon and the discovery that Colin was playing at 'church politics', by trying to build up a group of clerics to oppose Charles' future plans. Elizabeth listened quietly and then shared her experiences of how coldly the Archdeacon had treated her since taking up her post. Somehow, Elizabeth's soft voice and listening ear began to restore Charles to near normality as he wiped away the tears.

As Christmas approached, Charles realised that it would

be very different from the previous one. With the death of his grandparents during the past year, there would be a real sense of loss around the Christmas lunch-table. Also missing this year was Penelope, who had written in December explaining that she was beginning a world lecture tour, accompanied by Greta and would not arrive in Tuxbury until New Year's Eve, then was only able to stay for a few days before flying on to North America. Gladys, Alan and the children would arrive as usual on Christmas Eve armed with a cockerel and all the trimmings.

Charles had asked Elizabeth to organise a Christmas tree and she spent an afternoon decorating it for the children. While helping Elizabeth put the tree in place, Charles, fully aware that she had no family, enquired of Elizabeth how she was going to spend Christmas Day. Elizabeth was non-committal in her reply so Charles, on the spur of the moment, invited her to join him and the family for Christmas Day lunch. Hesitantly, Elizabeth accepted.

That night, Charles slid deeply under the covers of his bed. He wondered why he had invited Elizabeth? Was it simply an act of Christian compassion to offer a lonely person hospitality, or as he suspected, was there an underlying motive to his invitation? As Charles thought of Elizabeth, he noticed a stirring in his loins and his hand moved to satisfy his feelings. Charles imagined Elizabeth laying naked upon his bed with her full, rounded breasts and her dark pubic hair, before guiltily, moving back in his fantasy to Penelope's long, sensual legs. Afterwards, Charles counselled himself regarding the impropriety of such feelings, the necessity of remembering his vows of marriage and the teachings of his faith.

Christmas Day went well with Gladys preparing the lunch

while Charles completed the Christmas-tide services in the cathedral. The children were their usual boisterous and excited selves. Albert and Katherine loved Charles' home with its numerous rooms to explore and space to play on their newly acquired Amstrad computers. Elizabeth arrived at around one o'clock looking rather nervous and apprehensive, which was quickly recognised by Gladys, who immediately took her into the kitchen, placed a glass of sherry in her hand and invited her to help prepare and cook the vegetables. By the time lunch was served, Gladys and Elizabeth were firm friends, sharing stories that Charles had not even heard before. Before lunch began there was a toast to family members no longer present, with a moments silence and a few tears.

After lunch it was time for the family games, which firstly had to be taught to Elizabeth, when she confessed to not ever playing family games in her childhood. There was much laughter at Elizabeth's initial slowness at the game of 'Stations' where one had to race to get to an empty chair. However, as the game progressed, so did Elizabeth's speed and competitiveness, so much so that she outraced Albert on one occasion! Then, much to the merriment of everyone, when Charles was competing with Elizabeth in this rough and tumble game, she pushed Charles out of the way to get to the last spare seat first, only then turning to apologise for shoving the Bishop onto the floor! As Elizabeth came to help him up from the floor, he pulled Elizabeth down next to him and then tried to get to the spare seat but was prevented from doing so and disqualified by Gladys! Charles just laughed along with everyone else but secretly loved the close and informal contact with Elizabeth.

Later, after exhausting the list of games, a cold buffet

supper was instantly produced for all to share and at ten o'clock the party broke up as the exhausted children said their goodnights, with both Albert and Katherine giving everyone, including Elizabeth, a kiss goodnight.

After Elizabeth had left, Charles, Alan and Gladys sat drinking a nightcap, when Gladys turned directly to Charles and asked, "You seem to get on well with your new Personal Assistant then, Charles." Charles could see the little mischievous twinkle in Gladys eyes but he also recognised that behind the pointed question, was the wonderful perception that Gladys had always possessed regarding his unspoken feelings.

Gladys, Alan and the children left on Boxing Day to go and visit Alan's family while Penelope arrived four days later. It was indeed a 'flying' visit, spending only two nights before having to travel to Heathrow to catch her flight to New York. Penelope was excited about the lecture tour and about the recent discoveries of an almost complete Neolithic dwelling that had been uncovered, only slightly damaged and containing many artefacts. This was bringing forth new evaluations and theories, giving more clues about how that ten-thousand-year-old society operated.

After Charles waved goodbye to Penelope at the airport, he spent the return journey wondering about the future of their relationship. Could a marriage survive when two people lived apart at such a distance for long periods of time? Although they had made love on the first night, it had felt to Charles that it reflected the distance between their separate lives. Penelope seemed so far away during the lovemaking, apart from him, almost as if she was somewhere or with someone else. In one dark moment on that journey home in early January, Charles pondered on the possibility that there was a connection between his inability to form close and lasting relationships throughout his life, especially so with the opposite sex even in marriage, with the miles that separated his life from Penelope? Was it the loss of a mother-figure at such a young age that held him at a distance from the female gender? Being overly careful so as to not allow himself to be hurt again?

After the Christmas and the New Year break, Charles' life and ministry returned to its daily pattern with visits, meetings and civic duties all absorbing his waking hours, leaving him a few late hours in the day to work upon his vision for the way forward for the church. Then, in February and March, two letters arrived on his desk that would change his life.

The post to Bishop's House would arrive at 8 a.m. and Elizabeth would sort out any important letters and bring them to Charles' attention at their daily meeting at 9.30 a.m. In mid-February, Elizabeth placed a letter on his desk saying that she felt needed his urgent consideration. It was from a Mr Frank Hatfield.

Dear Bishop Charles,

We met briefly on your visit to our Parish last year but I am sure you will not remember me amongst all the many people you have met in the past eighteen months. However, I feel I have to write to you over an extremely serious matter concerning our Vicar, Reverend Stephen Toole. I wrote to Archdeacon Colin nearly six months ago and despite two reminders to him, I have not yet received a reply.

My twelve-year-old daughter, Felicity, has been a member of the church choir for several years but recently has refused to attend church. My wife, Paula, has eventually managed to get her to talk about refusing to go to church and in a very tearful conversation, Felicity explained that the Vicar had made 'approaches' to her over several months, commenting on her developing breasts and by 'accident' bumping into and touching her. It came to a head when he cornered her in a small vestry and forced his hand up her skirt, before Felicity was able to struggle free and run away.

I had included all this information in my original letter to the Archdeacon expecting a quick response but disappointingly, this has not materialised. We do not want, at this time, to go to the police as we have been loyal members of the church throughout our lives and most importantly, we do not want to cause more distress for our daughter, Felicity.

However, we are deeply concerned that if nothing is done by the church authorities concerning Reverend Toole, this clergyman may try to commit an even more serious offence against other young and vulnerable children.

Can we please ask that you urgently intervene in this matter?

Yours sincerely,
Frank Hatfield

Charles was shocked and utterly appalled at the contents of the letter. He requested Elizabeth to telephone the family immediately to ask if the Bishop could call on them that evening to discuss the situation. During the day, Charles discovered that Reverend Toole was at the same theological college as Archdeacon Colin and that he had come to his present rural parish four years ago, from a diocese in the south of the country. Charles continued to make enquiries through contacts he had in that diocese to discover that Reverend Toole had been asked to leave his previous parish for undisclosed reasons and that he was now single, having been separated, then divorced by his wife before he arrived in Tuxbury Diocese.

Charles was almost physically shaking with anger, especially so at the Archdeacon for his appalling attempts to sweep the matter under the carpet in order to protect one of his cronies. It was the calmness of Elizabeth that prevailed, with her sensible guidance and advice to carefully think through the appropriate reaction to the situation that prevailed. Charles sat quietly, contemplating more rationally the issues before him, whilst aware of the deep emotions the letter had ignited in him.

Charles had recently heard of stories of child abuse, both physical and sexual, in the Roman Catholic Church where priests had misused their position of authority by subjecting boys and girls to horrendous acts of rape and sodomy. Threatening the children with the 'fires of eternal hell' if they said anything to anyone. They convinced the children that it was their fault this act had happened, because they had been evil for tempting their parish priest. The policy of celibacy for clergy in the catholic church obviously proved too difficult for some, resulting in their sexuality being acted out in perverse and hurtful ways, damaging the lives of hundreds of young people over the ages.

As far as Charles had been aware, there were no similar cases in the Church of England. Now however, this incident posed the question to him as to whether such abuse in the Anglican Church had also been covered up in the past and hidden away from the public eye.

That evening, Charles travelled to the Hatfield's family home in the village of Puddlemore. He spoke with Felicity's parents and apologised profusely for the distress their daughter had suffered at the hands of Reverend Toole. Charles assured them that an immediate investigation and action would be taken and that Charles would personally keep in touch with the family. He had arranged for the vicar to meet him at Bishops House at 10 a.m. tomorrow, where the Bishop would request Reverend Toole's resignation and early retirement from all ministry. In the meantime, Charles would be grateful for the family's discretion about this matter as it would soon be resolved.

Charles asked if he might speak with Felicity so that he could listen to her experience of what had happened. After some consideration and because Charles had been so straight and apologetic to them, the parents agreed. Felicity was an attractive, young person, although nervous about speaking to the Bishop. However, Charles put Felicity more at ease immediately by remembering that when he had visited the parish last year, it was Felicity who had come out to the front and worn the Bishop's mitre during Charles' talk in the midst of the service. A small bond was forged between them, enabling Felicity to relax enough to speak hesitatingly but freely.

After hearing what Felicity had to say, Charles, then apologised for Reverend Toole's disgraceful behaviour, assuring her that she was not responsible for her vicar's inexcusable actions and adding that it was no way for any adult to behave, least of all a clergyman. Charles explained that Reverend Toole had betrayed the trust the church had placed in him and would therefore have to leave his position here in the village.

Charles continued talking and listening to Felicity for over an hour, asking her about her school, her interests and her friends in the village. Felicity spoke of her love of animals, both wild and tame and how she enjoyed hours out in the local woods and fields with her binoculars, cataloguing all that she observed. Briefly, childhood memories filtered back to Charles of his love of being out amongst the world of natural life and he shared with Felicity his watching at a badger's sett. It gradually emerged that Felicity hoped to go to university and train as a vet before returning to work in a country veterinary practice, as she loved being in the countryside and close to animals in their natural setting. Felicity also spoke about how she valued going to church with her family and after Reverend Toole left, she would return.

The following morning, Charles met Reverend Toole and informed him of his knowledge of the sexual assaults upon the twelve-year-old, Felicity Hatfield and that the matter may be referred to the police, depending upon the family's wishes. Charles made it perfectly clear to Reverend Toole that he would have to step down from his position immediately and that he should apply for early retirement, leaving the Puddlemore Vicarage by the end of the month. Reverend Toole burst into tears and between sobs, he offered apologies for his behaviour.

He confessed that he felt disgusted with himself for causing the distress he had inflicted upon Felicity and the Hatfield family. When Charles asked if this was the first occasion such an incident had happened, Reverend Toole replied that it had occurred once before in his previous parish, resulting in his wife leaving him, followed by a painful and acrimonious divorce. He continued by saying Archdeacon Colin had heard of his situation and kindly offered him his present job in return for loyalty to him. Reverend Toole, amid the flowing tears, explained that he missed his wife and children enormously and had mistakenly and inappropriately, reached out to Felicity for comfort.

Adopting a more compassionate tone, Charles affirmed that the sexual abuse by Reverend Toole towards Felicity Hatfield forced him, in his position as Diocesan Bishop, to bar him from ministry because of the risk he posed to young people. Charles ascertained that Reverend Toole had a home to retreat to which belonged to his late mother, clarifying that he would not therefore be homeless. Charles also asked Reverend Toole to promise that, as soon as he was settled, he would seek out appropriate psychotherapy or counselling to help him sort through his emotional problems in order to begin a new start in life.

Half an hour later, the Archdeacon stood in front of Charles, summoned by his Bishop. Charles explained what had happened with Reverend Toole and the action that he had taken. He informed the Archdeacon that he was extremely disappointed by his actions in this matter on two very important counts. Firstly, that Archdeacon Colin had been responsible for appointing someone whom he knew had a past history of inappropriate behaviour towards young people and secondly, that when the current abuse was brought to light by a loving, caring family, the Archdeacon had decided to bury his head and this offence in the sand. Charles stated firmly that the covering up of abuse of young people by clergy must not be tolerated and should always be dealt with speedily if any cases ever occur in the future.

Then Charles, acting on an idea from Elizabeth, requested the Archdeacon to go away and begin to draw up a discussion paper in order for the diocese to adopt a 'Protection Policy for Young People in Church'. Charles wished this to be discussed initially at the Bishops' Council meeting, followed by further debate and then enshrined as diocesan policy at the July Diocesan Synod.

Charles impressed upon the Archdeacon that he then wished this document to be a blueprint that they could take on to General Synod for adoption by the wider Church of England. This issue was so important that he wanted the Archdeacon to personally drive this policy forward. Charles continued that once the Archdeacon had consulted with other dioceses and with secular organisations such as Social Services prior to putting together his initial ideas, they would then spend an afternoon together beginning to collate an outline of the new policy.

Charles urged the Archdeacon to make this a priority in his workload insisting that it was time nationally, that the Church of England must openly face up to this issue. "I wish you, Archdeacon Colin, to spearhead this not only in our diocese but also across the whole of the Church of England."

The Archdeacon left, unsure as to whether he had been told off or been promoted. Charles smiled wistfully as the door closed, marvelling at Elizabeth's wisdom. The strategy, as explained by Elizabeth, was that by giving the Archdeacon such responsibility in this important area, it would leave him little time to plot against the Bishop's vision. Secondly, it would also propel the archdeacon into the national limelight and maybe lead to him being offered a bishopric elsewhere as a result.

It was now six months since Elizabeth had started work alongside Charles. In the beginning, Charles wondered if Elizabeth with so little experience of church life in the past, would be able to cope with the role. In those early days, there were moments when Elizabeth's lack of confidence showed. People of authority and supposed importance sometimes made her appear nervous and worried as to whether she had the ability to communicate with them. Charles speculated that maybe her humble upbringing and secondary modern education left her at a disadvantage in dealing with Public School, Oxbridge degree-level, educated people, who often came across as hugely confident and sometimes arrogant individuals.

Despite these early reservations, Charles observed with wonder and admiration how determined Elizabeth was to overcome any difficulties that she faced. It felt as if she was now beginning to blossom in her role as Personal Assistant, as well as a person in her own right. Charles quietly admitted to himself, that he loved being in her presence and he would often create and manufacture moments to invite her into his study to ask her opinion on a variety of issues. It was in one of those times together that Elizabeth had suggested that the Bishop might consider creating opportunities to gain the Archdeacon's trust, rather than participate in Colin's adversarial approach. For Bishop Charles to try to counter the Archdeacon's negative ways with positive solutions, encouraging Colin to come 'on board' by including him, rather than excluding.

As their working relationship developed, so also did their personal knowledge of each other. On one afternoon they had stopped work and were sharing tea and scones, when Charles asked Elizabeth a little more about her childhood in Pinton-on-Sea. Elizabeth's mood darkened and those beautiful eyes moistened and dulled.

Haltingly, Elizabeth spoke of difficult times in a home of parental arguments and shouting: of the continual memory of hearing her father's hand slapping her mother's face, of an abusive father endlessly keeping her awake at night with his talking at her through oppressive beer-laden breath and of him leaving without even a goodbye, never to return.

Then, of her mother, deserted and desolated, who over several years gradually became so depressed that she took her own life by drowning in the sea. For Elizabeth, it was a childhood where there was little or no joy and laughter.

By this time, tears were flowing down the cheeks of Elizabeth's face and Charles came forward and tenderly wiped away the rivers of sadness from her face with his white handkerchief. Then suddenly, Charles felt her moist lips upon his cheek. Elizabeth immediately apologised, shocked by her actions and coloured deeply. Charles sought to reassure Elizabeth about her impulsive moment and said how nice it was to be kissed, causing further blushes.

The following week, Charles asked Elizabeth if she might like to go to visit her mother's grave at Pinton-on-Sea. During their time together the previous week, Charles discerned that there was a lot of unresolved grief still bottled up inside Elizabeth and that to visit her mother's final resting place might be therapeutic for her. Having thought through Charles' suggestion, Elizabeth accepted his offer, saying that yes, it might be helpful. Later, at the graveside, Elizabeth had wept huge sobs of tears and Charles held her tightly to offer comfort. A little ray of sun shone in Elizabeth as they walked back to the car.

The second life-changing letter arrived a couple of weeks before Easter. It was from his wife, Penelope. By now, Elizabeth recognised Penelope's handwriting and obviously placed her letters on Charles' desk unopened. Charles, seeing the letter, presumed it was to let him know when Penelope would be coming over for the Easter break and left it until later before opening it. After his evening meal, Charles, in the privacy of his own rooms read the following:

Dear Charles,

You have been so very kind and loving to me over the time of our marriage together that I want to thank you for all that you have been to me. Thank you. You are the only living person I know that gave me a picture of your loving God, through the way you lived your life and almost made me want to find out more about this God-thing.

However, Charles, I need to be truthful to you and on reading this news I hope that you will try to understand me and why this has come about. As you are very much aware, I have found the sexual side of our marriage difficult and you probably realise that this was affected by a childhood experience of abuse. You helped me greatly through this with your tenderness and patience and again, I thank you.

Over the last few months, I have fallen in love with Greta and we now have a full relationship and live together. With Greta I do not find the sexual experiences threatening but fulfilling and liberating. Whether the freedom I feel being with a woman is a consequence of my adolescent experience, or whether it is my natural way of life which I did not earlier recognise, I do not know or understand at the moment.

Dear Charles, I do hope you can understand and realise that I do not wish to hurt you; that is the last thing I would want to do to such a kind and loving person. I am sorry that I have not had the courage to come and say all this to you in person but I am not really very strong and find it hard to express myself in relationships with spoken words, hence my letter.

I will not be with you over Easter as I feel you may need time and space to absorb the contents of my letter. I also do not wish to affect your work as a Bishop and am happy to remain as your wife and do not need a divorce. I will also visit occasionally whenever you need me by your side in an official capacity.

I do hope, Charles, that we can still remain good friends. I'm sorry to shock you with this news.

Love from

Penelope

Charles was shattered. Shocked to the core. Devastated. He had expected a typical Penelope letter with questions about: how Charles was keeping, what he had been up to, relating her progress concerning the excavation and any important discoveries they had uncovered and then finally, the date that she would arrive home for the Easter holiday. Not one of those usual comments was included. Instead, the letter had a totally surreal content informing him that his previously heterosexual wife was now a homosexual person; a lesbian, in love with another woman.

The news left Charles bewildered and perplexed. His mind whirled around in ever-increasing questioning circles. He was unable to think logically or with any sense of clarity. Sleep eluded him until the early hours of the morning when emotional exhaustion finally brought relief from his insomnia.

Awakening late the next day having missed Morning Prayer, Charles recalled that he had a full diary starting with a Bishops' Council meeting in the morning where the Archdeacon was going to present some initial thoughts about 'Child Protection in Church', a first draft which he had been enthusiastically working upon. Then he needed to rush onto a Civic Luncheon event with the Mayor and local council, where afterwards, Charles had to unveil a plaque and say a few words at the re-opening of the refurbished local museum. In the evening, he was out at a country parish fund-raising event to raise monies to re-hang their ancient bells in the church tower. A tiring, non-stop day where Charles had little time to think and which he got through on autopilot, burying his turbulent emotional state within him.

But Charles could not hide away from all the questions, the doubts and the pain. It was there every minute of his day - at the forefront of his mind as he drove to engagements, in quiet moments when he tried to pray, in seeing other happy couples as they walked hand-in-hand. Charles was approaching Holy Week and felt as if he was the one who was being crucified, rejected, cast-off and isolated with his best friend now walking away and betraying him. His own special Judas.

As he lay in bed that night the dilemma swamped him. Why hadn't he realised that Penelope was moving away into another relationship? Was it because of him? Was it because Charles so rarely spoke with Penelope of their feelings for each other? Was it simply the living so far apart, the lack of being together to deepen their marriage? Round and round through his mind the questions swirled. Then, in the latter part of the night, Charles spent hours thinking about how to reply to Penelope's letter.

Should he be annoyed and express his hurt to her, or be conciliatory and ask her to reconsider her decision, or finally be graceful and accept her moving on in life and wish her well for the future? Time and time again the words of his reply formed in his mind only to be constantly changed, reformed and re-jigged again and again in an endless state of movement, reflecting the confusion and distress within Charles' mind.

The following morning had been put aside to spend with Elizabeth getting up-to-date with the ever-growing pile of paperwork that needed his attention. Within five minutes of beginning, Elizabeth asked Charles if he was all right. Then ten minutes later she asked again. Both times Charles dismissed her inquiries with a gruff reply stating that he was fine. Within half an hour of starting, Charles told Elizabeth that he was too tired and could not concentrate, leaving the room in a state of near panic.

He rushed out of Bishop's House, driving fast and erratically down the drive, out into the countryside to a well-known beauty spot where he parked his car on the brow of a hill, overlooking the rolling green countryside below. Within moments he was asleep and it was early evening before he awoke in a distressed state. On returning to Bishop's House, he was surprised to see Elizabeth still there, waiting anxiously for him. This time there was no way of concealing his state of mind. Elizabeth made him a pot of tea and came to sit with him in the library.

Feeling the warmth of Elizabeth's presence as she held his hand, the tears started to roll down his face. Charles gave her Penelope's letter to read explaining that his marriage was at an end. Elizabeth listened as Charles went on to confide that throughout his life, he had always found it hard to make life-long relationships and here, he had failed again with Penelope. He felt useless, totally unable to give fully of himself, often holding back and afraid of being hurt and rejected if he did.

Charles explained that he was aware that he came over as

a kind, considerate and loving person to the many people he came into contact within the course of his role as a priest and Bishop but it was establishing and sustaining fuller, more long-lasting relationships, that he appeared incapable of doing.

After sitting and listening to Charles for well over an hour, Elizabeth suddenly asked Charles, "How old were you, Charles, when your parents died?"

Charles was dumbstruck, unable to reply. After a pause, Elizabeth continued, "When did you last have a kiss and cuddle with your mother and father?" Immediately the last night with his father and the games played, the story read and the kiss goodnight came flooding back. It was rapidly followed by the scene at his mothers' bedside in the Home for the Incurables, replayed in Charles' mind's eye. The long corridor, with their footsteps echoing off the walls, the small room with the iron bedstead, the jerking limbs of his mother and those guttural, almost inhuman cries of anguish. The soft kiss on her cheek that he gave to his mummy before leaving her for the last time. Then, the last picture in his memory of that day, was of his aunty Gladys crying and the smile on his mummy's peaceful face as he left his mother forever. Without parental love for so many years.

Gradually, Charles began to recover and he wiped his eyes. The sharing of his distress with someone, with Elizabeth and the remembering of his love for his mother and father and their love for him, had somehow brought relief to the intensity of the mental trauma he was struggling with. Without thinking he leant forward and kissed Elizabeth lightly upon the cheek and whispered, "Thank you." Again, Elizabeth blushed and they both laughed remembering that only a few weeks ago, they had shared a kiss when Elizabeth was upset.

During Holy Week and Easter, Charles had an extremely busy diary with little time to dwell too long on the ramifications of Penelope's letter for the future. He sent a short letter to Penelope thanking her for being so truthful and that he would write to her a fuller letter after the business of Easter had passed. Charles spent a long time struggling with his Easter Sunday sermon, with its themes of new life and joy eventually overcoming suffering and pain. The subject was more than a bit raw with Charles feeling the opposite as he felt well and truly stuck on Good Friday, still crucified. Charles tried his best to join in the happiness of Easter Day but inside him he was locked in despair and the darkness of emotional death. New life felt a million miles away from his real inner being.

On Easter Monday, Charles packed a case and set off for a pre-arranged ten-day break on the Isle of Iona. It was a long car journey to Oban to catch the ferry to Mull and as Charles drove, he thought back over the last couple of weeks. Surprisingly to Charles, Elizabeth immediately came to mind. He recalled their conversation ten days or so ago, remembering how still and calm she had been. Listening intently to Charles who was trying, at times quite incoherently, to offload his distress. Never interrupting, never giving easy answers but just sitting alongside and sharing his pain. Then those questions about cuddles and his parents.

Where, he wondered, did that come from? and yet, how restoring it had been in encouraging him to think back to the love he had shared with his mother and father.

As he approached the ferry terminal port of Oban, Charles thought how similar Elizabeth was to his aunty Gladys in her listening and in her understanding of his inner feelings.

Charles resolved that while on Iona, he must buy Elizabeth a little gift to express his appreciation of her waiting for him to return on that day and for her patient listening.

Iona is a mere slip of an island, three miles long by one mile wide, sited in the Inner Hebrides on the west coast of Scotland, lying off the larger island of Mull and accessed by a short ten-minute ferry crossing. When Charles arrived at the bottom of Mull at Fionnphort, a gale was howling and it was announced that due to the weather, this crossing was to be the last one that could be safely undertaken that day. As the boat rose and dipped as the seas and winds swept around the small vessel, Charles wryly, thought of the hymn 'For those in peril on the sea'! He was more than relieved when the boat reached the end of its short and scary journey.

Safely back on dry ground after dodging the waves on the landing stage, Charles turned right in the centre of the small village and a hundred yards on, located his hotel. Over the next couple of days, Charles took a morning walk around the island's pathways and tracks, crossing the countryside, then returning in time for lunch, before having an afternoon rest and taking dinner alone in the hotel. The rest and change brought him a measure of tranquillity but this was soon challenged by the reappearance of dark thoughts as Penelope and his failed marriage re-surfaced to the fore. Alone with his sense of failure, Charles began to stumble and slide unto depression.

Charles realised it was not the failing of his marriage that was the real issue but his inability to change, to move on through the difficulties of relationships. It seemed as if he was unable to recognise and face issues that may have their roots in his earlier life. Was he stuck in the grieving process, resistant to accepting his parents' horrendous endings? Charles asked himself if he had ever requested Gladys to tell him how the deaths occurred, the details involved. His mood darkened and he stayed more and more in his room, isolating himself from reality.

On the fourth day, Charles dragged himself out for a walk across the island's golf course. His desperate state was making his walking erratic and close to a wall, he crashed down onto the soft ground. He lay prone, seemingly unable to move, sobbing into the grass and soil. Charles felt he was being swallowed by the very earth on which he lay, face down into the awaiting abyss.

Almost tasting the grass and the soil beneath him, Charles struggled to breathe and turned his face to one side. As he did so, he noticed a small, blue flower, growing against all the odds, in the crack of a dry-stone wall. Charles marvelled at its simple beauty and wondered at the gift of life it represented. After lying looking at the little flower a while longer, Charles clambered to his feet and decided to try life again. To struggle forward and root himself again in earth's beauty and creation, to try to grow again, just like the small blue flower that had fought to survive.

On the way back to his hotel, Charles stopped at the Abbey Church, the home of the Iona Community. Iona with its long Christian history spanning fifteen hundred years when St Columba arrived from Ireland to set up a monastery on the isle. After the pillaging and destruction of the Vikings, then the sixteenth century Reformation, the Abbey had fallen into ruins until the twentieth century when it was restored and a new community established which encouraged modern day pilgrims to come and share in its unique and liberating worship.

Charles entered the quiet building and sat in silence. On the seat next to him was a leaflet of the service that had taken place the previous Sunday, on Easter Day. Charles picked it up and read from a hymn the words…

So, I set my life before you
All its passion, joy and pain,
Contradictions, strength and weaknesses
To receive your touch again.
Breathe your Spirit through its textures,
Shape its patterns, mend its wrong;
So, my dying and my living
May release your kingdom's song.

Again, and again, Charles read and re-read the words, allowing them time to sink into the very being of his person; trying to accept his strengths and faults. Attempting to allow God's love into him so he could learn to love himself more fully.

As Charles sat in the choir stalls, he looked across to the abbey wall facing him and marvelled at the stones, taken from the earth and piled upon one another to create this beautiful building of worship. Excavated, ripped out from the living earth after thousands upon thousands of years in creation and now a part of another beginning. Living stones, resounding to the words and songs of life and love, absorbing into its very texture the meaning of existence.

Then, slowly, a strange sensation crept over him as Charles seemed to merge into the very essence of the living stones and journey to the centre of earth's creation, to a place of great light and happiness. In this dreamlike state, he walked along a glowing tunnel bathed in a bright brilliance, holding the hands of two moments of love. But then, quietly and suddenly, one hand let go and was gone, the tunnel becoming less light and smaller. A little further on, the other hand released itself, disappearing into the darkening stones.

He was alone, deserted and sad, with the tunnel becoming increasingly narrow as the light faded, leaving him colder and more frightened. The darkness began to engulf and surround him. The stones about him seemed to cry out in mourning and shed tears upon a weakened Charles, as he felt he was beginning to drown in rivers of sorrow. In the darkness, he was now struggling on his knees, hemmed in on all sides, flattened into the hard stone. Occasionally, there was a brief holding of another hand that helped him stumble on and brought some light but the tunnel seemed endless, twisting and turning, going deeper into the night-time of his life, as he cried out in despair and fear, time and time again.

Finally, after what seemed like a life-time, Charles could see a small light in the distance. As he approached through a particularly difficult passageway, he could see someone standing in the light with love shining in their eyes. Charles reached out his hand and it was held. The darkness disappeared. He had journeyed through the depths to discover a new life of love.

Charles emerged from his sleep or was it a trance, a dream, or a moment of enlightenment: a vision? as the noisy, creaking door of the Abbey was opened and his quiet time in the building was ended. A coachload of American tourists, armed with their flashing cameras and gratingly loud southern drawl accents, invaded the peace. Unperturbed by the intrusion, Charles sneaked out of the back door with a lighter heart and a smile upon his lips. He had recognised the eyes of love that had greeted him at the end of his dark and winding tunnel of life.

Charles enjoyed the remaining days on the island, happily joining in the profound worship offered by the Community in the Abbey. He loved the grounding of their faith in the wonders of creation, rooted in the earth and wonder of God's world. He also appreciated their liturgy; it was so close to his heart, thoughtful and rich in depth of meaning.

He particularly liked the way the image of a traditional, white, Father God figure in the clouds had been replaced with language that reflected a creative force incorporating instead, a picture of a God that was inclusive for both genders.

Charles walked each day, criss-crossing the island, fighting through strong winds to get up to the top of the highest hill where he could see the island of Staffa in the far distance.

Towards the end of his holiday, Charles visited a silversmith's workshop he had discovered on the isle. He chose and purchased a silver chain with a Celtic cross as a gift for the one whose eyes had greeted him at the end of the tunnel. The next day, Charles stepped onto the ferry for the short crossing to Mull to begin his journey home. This time the sea was calm with just a gentle breeze, as the ferry tranquilly made its short journey across the Sound of Iona. Charles was looking forward to returning to Bishop's House.

On his first day back at work, Charles sat in the circle with his staff for Morning Prayer in the small chapel. During the time of quietness, Charles opened his eyes and looked across to where Elizabeth was sitting. She was sat very still with her eyes closed and appeared to be in a deep time of meditation. After a moment though, her eyes opened and she looked across to Charles and smiled. A great warmth seemed to flow through him, as he slowly re-closed his eyes, smiling in return.

Following Morning Prayer, Charles was sitting at his desk when there came that familiar soft knock on the door and Elizabeth entered, with her arms full of correspondence and matters to be dealt with urgently. They sat together for nearly two hours going through important items that Charles would need to respond to in the next few days. Elizabeth was so well organised and had dealt with many of the less vital issues but still needed to brief Charles upon her responses. Charles was finding it hard to concentrate on the business in hand, more aware than ever before of Elizabeth's beauty and persona, especially those eyes of love.

At 11.30 a.m. Elizabeth suggested a coffee break, going off to prepare and bring a tray of coffee for them both. Over their drinks, Charles told Elizabeth about his time on Iona, including a little about his initial struggles trying to come to terms with Penelope's letter but eventually managing to find some peace and resolution. Charles informed Elizabeth that he was going to write that evening to Penelope, accepting that her life had moved on and assuring her of his wish that they could indeed still remain friends. Charles was pleased that Elizabeth noticed that he was now less distressed and more like his former self, as he knew she had worried a lot about him before and over Easter.

At the end of the coffee break, Charles produced from one of the drawers in his desk, a little jewellery box which he gave to Elizabeth, thanking her for all the help she had given by listening to him and reminding Charles about his parents' love. Elizabeth opened the box and was genuinely delighted with the chain and cross. As Elizabeth placed it around her neck, Charles came to assist her with the fastening of the clasp. As he touched Elizabeth's skin, Charles was enthralled by its softness and texture and felt excited by the closeness of their bodies.

Clipping the clasp into place, Charles thought he felt a shiver go through Elizabeth as his fingers touched her neck. Charles retreated quickly to his side of the desk, confused at the mixture of emotions flowing through him. Anxious, yet uplifted by the pure sensation of touch.

That night, Charles wrote to Penelope.

Dearest Penelope,

Your letter with the news that Greta and you have fallen in love and are now living and sleeping together was undoubtedly a great shock to me. I know that you have spoken often of Greta and your friendship but I had always imagined that it was set within a working relationship. So initially, I felt deserted and struggled to come to terms with the situation.

After a busy Easter, I literally retreated to the Isle of Iona to sit and think through the implications of your letter. It is fair to say that in the first few days I became very depressed and in despair, feeling very sorrowful for the failure of our marriage. I thank you for explaining the difficulties you have experienced in our sexual union but I also have to put my hand up and accept equal responsibility for us moving apart. A marriage is about two people and usually its failure is due to both parties, so please do not blame yourself alone.

On my part, the loss of my parents at an early age in my life, has made it extremely difficult for me to make deep relationships. Buried within me I have always been afraid deep down that if I get too close to someone and then lose them, my childhood loss and pain will come flooding back. So, within our marriage I was also guilty of not loving you deeply enough and for that I am sorry. The past can be a very powerful influence in the present, as it seems to have been for us both.

I hope that you will be happy with Greta and that issues blocked away within you will be resolved through your love for each other.

I would be very happy for you to visit whenever you are able to in the future but in the meantime, I hope that we will continue writing to share news of our ongoing lives and of course, remain good friends.

With love and best wishes,

Charles.

A couple of weeks later, Penelope replied thanking Charles for his kind and considerate letter. She confirmed that she would visit during the summer holiday for a few days and looked forward to catching up with all his news.

The following Friday afternoon whilst enjoying tea and scones together, Charles asked Elizabeth if she would like to accompany him on a visit to his childhood roots. Although Charles formed the request as a question to Elizabeth, he dearly hoped that she would accept and be alongside him. Elizabeth understood Charles' underlying needs and readily accepted his invitation.

After visiting the local florist and purchasing three bunches of flowers including some red roses, Charles picked Elizabeth up from her flat at 10 a.m. and drove across country to his early childhood homes in the North Midlands.

In Sheddingworth, he showed Elizabeth his nan's small home and the school he attended until aged ten which was now disused and vandalised. He placed one of the bunches of flowers by the headstone on his nan's grave at the local Parish Church. Then, just three miles further on they came to his home town of Gattingford where he was born. It was over thirty years since Charles had been back to his original home and he had had to ring Gladys to remind him of the address. He was pleased that he had done so, as many of the roads containing the plain, terraced housing meant that many of the streets were so similar. Charles was shocked as to how much the town appeared to be in decline, with three of its four pits closed and several corner shops boarded up as a result of less spending power by the large group of unemployed miners.

Eventually, they located the house of his first four years of life. He stood with Elizabeth, looking and trying to remember. A tear ran down his cheek as he struggled to recall that early period of life. His wooden train set came to mind and he smiled as he revisited pushing it around its wooden track. Charles also remembered the shed in the back garden and wandered down the side passage to see if it was in place. To his delight, it was still there and Charles explained to Elizabeth how on some Saturday mornings his father would allow Charles to come into the workshop and watch. He remembered the smell of the wood and playing with offcuts to create some small toy.

But then, those last moments in the house tumbled back into his mind and that horrific sobbing of his mother on the sofa returned and finally, those last kisses of love came into his mind.

At the graveside where his father and mother lay, joined more recently by his grandparents' ashes, Charles placed the second bunch of flowers. He stood for several minutes in stillness, with Elizabeth by his side, holding her hand. Slowly, a peace filled his whole being, so instead of the many tears he thought he would shed, Charles began to smile broadly and his eyes were alight and shining. In those moments of quiet time, Charles could feel the resurrected love of his mother and father, both within him and by his side. He squeezed Elizabeth's hand as the healing love flowed through to him.

On the return journey, they detoured to Grange-next-to-Sea, stopping outside the home where he had lived for seven years with his grandparents until the age of seventeen. They walked through the woods at the back of the house, over the hill and onto the deserted beach. Again, memories returned as they sat together on the rocks, with a tranquil sea lapping its small waves onto the sandy beach as the sun began to descend.

In the early evening, they travelled back to Tuxbury, stopping at a village pub for a meal together. On returning to the car, Charles gave the third bunch of flowers, the red roses, to Elizabeth to say thank you for accompanying him on this important journey. Charles explained that he loved being with her and felt that she had helped him so much in his efforts to come to terms with his past. As he leant forward to kiss her on the cheek, Elizabeth had moved her head to look at the beautiful roses and instead, the kiss landed on her lips. They both realised the accident of the kiss but Charles was full of joy that their lips had touched. Driving back, he mused quietly to himself, on the saying that 'God works in many mysterious ways'!

Meanwhile, life continued in the diocese over the following weeks with Charles extremely busy trying to ensure that he had visited all the clergy in all the parishes before presenting his vision to the Diocesan Synod in early July.

Charles also met up with his group of friends from the 'think-tank' including his academic colleagues, Graham Sharpe and Brian Jones and together they discussed the outline of his vision. There was encouragement in their opinions but also warnings that in its present state, it may be too unacceptable for many to cope with. They felt that the section about the Disestablishment of the Church of England would be so controversial that it would deflect from the many other good ideas that the vision contained. They worried it would create so much negative publicity and opposition that all would be lost. Surely, they argued, it was better to begin with manageable goals, expanding the vision gradually. Hugo's words resonated through Charles' thoughts on his journey back to Tuxbury, 'slowly, slowly, step by step'.

He met regularly with Elizabeth, who was compiling the document, ensuring it was set out in a clear, easy to read format. He wanted to present it to members of Synod and then, begin a long but thorough consultation across the Diocese.

A part of the working relationship between Charles and Elizabeth was the need to be close, understanding one another and able to be singing from the same hymn sheet. But Charles was also aware that he just loved being in Elizabeth's company and found himself making any excuse to visit her office or to invite her to his study about some matter or other. Sometimes they would sit talking for hours in the late afternoon about issues in the vision, or about other matters of not much importance, just so that they could be together.

In early June, on the first sunny, warm day of summer, they met in the late afternoon to complete the first draft of the vision. Elizabeth was wearing a beautiful, floral summer dress and stood beside the seated Charles, explaining the paperwork in front of them on the desk. Charles was mesmerised as Elizabeth spoke and he struggled to concentrate.

The closeness of Elizabeth to him, the fabric of her dress brushing against his arm and the smell of her perfume were all overpowering for Charles. He recalled someone once speaking about Mary Magdalene's anointing of Jesus just before his death; how she gently massaged naard, a very expensive perfume, into his tired feet. They had referred to her action, as one of total love and commitment, a symbol of 'lingering love', because the aroma hung in the air for such a very long time.

Charles now felt this intense, 'lingering love' for Elizabeth. He could no longer contain it within himself and so, finally, after a long, exhaustive journey through a desert life of emptiness, Charles reached out with his hand to touch such wonderful love…

Epilogue: Elizabeth and Charles

Charles' hand continued slowly, higher, towards a different life. He was becoming flushed, a warm feeling flowing through him.

Elizabeth slightly adjusted her stance as his hand came close, giving her permission for him to continue, giving space to her and his desires.

Charles' hand touched her underwear, moving back and forth. He moved her knickers to one side and entered her.

Elizabeth could feel her excitement mounting as she felt his hand between her legs. Her breath coming in short gasps and then, as he entered her, she cried out softly in pleasure.

Charles continued his caressing of her, tenderly gliding in and out. Then standing up behind her, he quickly undid his trousers, pushed his underpants downwards, his erect member racing to be inside her.

Becoming aware that he was now behind her, Elizabeth quietly lifted higher her summer dress and eased her knickers down before bending further over the desk. She received him with a pleasurable gasp, feeling full, complete with him inside her.

Elizabeth's orgasm came suddenly and was ecstatic and life-changing. Charles came within seconds, gasping with incredible relief, joy and fulfilment.

After their passionate time together in the study, Charles

led Elizabeth up the stairs to his private rooms. They slowly undressed one another and lay naked on the bed together, tenderly touching and caressing. They stroked and kissed each other's intimate areas, bringing pleasure to one another. Finally, Charles entered Elizabeth again and together they made love, relishing the intense pleasure of their union.

Afterwards, they lay alongside each other in wonder at what had happened. The afternoon had long disappeared and the evening had darkened the room as the light faded. They each spoke of their lives and what had brought them to this first real moment of love. Gradually, they began to realise the extent to which these last few hours would change their lives forever. Nothing could ever be the same again. The vision was in another life, another time. A greater vision lay before them.

Charles laughed out loud at the irony of the situation, telling Elizabeth that after so many years of sadness and lack of love in his personal life, he had now, at long last, found true love but the attitude and response of the supposedly loving and caring church would be to forbid Charles' and Elizabeth's loving relationship. Their togetherness would be outlawed by the rules that had emerged over the centuries — canon laws that constrained and sometimes undermined the very tenets of their faith based on love. Indeed, the church establishment would condemn and ostracise them both. Charles chuckled, thinking how his Archdeacon would have a 'field-day' leaking the news to an intrusively hungry media.

After many hours of talking and discussion, Charles and Elizabeth both knew that their future life and love would be together with one another but outside the institution and ethos of a rule-bound and conservative Anglican Church. Together they sat and wrote their letters of resignation. Later, after making love again, they bathed and decided that initially, they would live together in Elizabeth's flat until the future became clearer. Charles packed two suitcases of clothes, leaving behind all clerical wear. He also packed the box that contained his childhood red and blue toy train and some other personal items.

Placing their letters of resignation upon his desk in the study, they left the Bishop's House just after midnight for the last time, together, hand-in-hand. Charles drove down the drive to the junction with the ring road. As he pulled out of the drive, he looked across at Elizabeth and saw such incredible love for him in her beautiful, brown eyes. Charles noticed the chain and Celtic cross around Elizabeth's neck that she had worn each day since he had given it to her two months ago. Reaching out, Charles held Elizabeth's hand and said, "Thank you," for sharing such wonderful love with him.

He did not see or hear the oncoming joyrider, drug- and alcohol-fuelled, driving at ninety m.p.h., with the police in hot pursuit. Metal smashed against metal, ripping into their car. The impact was horrific. Charles' vehicle was turned over twice, ending upon its flattened roof with windows smashed and doors opened and buckled.

Both Charles and Elizabeth died instantly, hand-in-hand, locked together. Their love sealed in a metal tomb, now untouchable by the world. Love that would now always remain pure and precious, hidden away from the sensationalism of the front pages of the gutter press. Love unblemished. Love everlasting.

Scattered across the road were the remains of Charles' red and blue train set with his precious engine, devoid of its wheels, lying on its side in the gutter.

The wind rose and a gust blew through the still-open

French window doors in the Bishop's study. The letters of resignation fluttered off the desk and into the waste bin, ready to be emptied in the early morning by the cleaner and placed into her large collecting, black, plastic bag. The vision remained sealed to the desk, until the following day, when Archdeacon Colin gathered up all the papers into his briefcase, locking them in a cupboard in his office at the Archdeaconry. Charles' Reformation was to be hidden away behind the discreet church's decaying doors and closed minds, unlike Luther's First Reformation which was nailed to a cathedral door for all to see.

Outside, the rain began to fall endlessly and the darkness enveloped and choked the church, as it progressed slowly and steadily on its downward path of decline towards oblivion.

The pureness of true love, alive in the healed lives and spirits of Elizabeth and Charles, remained locked away from the established church. An institution unfulfilled and smothered by bureaucratic pettiness and worldly, non-spiritual attitudes — despite the goodness and love of so many individual people. The main artery to its heart blocked by misinterpreted, ancient doctrine and out-of-date, dogmatic, canon law, rules and regulations; hindering the flow of freeing love within its body.

Love and sadness, hope and despair, still inseparable.

Alpha and Omega.

Appendix One

Charles' Vision for the Future — First Draft

(This document was recovered in 2015 when the Archdeaconry building in the Cathedral Close was being sold to provide much-needed funds to keep the Diocese of Tuxbury financially afloat. The Vision paper was found in the same briefcase and cupboard where it had been hidden away nearly thirty years before).

Introduction

The premise behind this 'Vision for the Church's Future' is that the only way to arrest the decline of the church in western society is to be 'radical' and to return to the very basics of the Christian life, as expressed in the words and actions of Jesus Christ. Jesus was unique in being very concerned and alongside the 'have-nots' of society, speaking out against worldly power and its misuse. Too often, the church has mimicked those worldly influences and ignored the true calling of Christ.

A new way forward means cutting through all the trappings and distortions that have accumulated over many centuries in the Church of England. To put aside the numerous additions and exaggerations that have occurred throughout the ages. To discard the legalistic, endless rules and canons that have helped to stifle the 'spirit' of Christ, embroiling the faith in a straightjacket of restrictive laws. Rather than following in the footsteps of the Pharisees, the church needs to allow freedom for the spirit of Christ's love to flourish.

It is urgent for the church to follow a root and branch restructuring, in order to return to the true message of Jesus. To focus upon the values of love, peace, truth, justice, forgiveness, compassion, simplicity and equality for all. The church needs to rediscover Jesus the Jew, taking into account the cultural setting and customs that made more sense to his listeners than to us, in our uninformed and misunderstood present-day interpretation of his words.

After the first century AD, the largely gentile-led early Christian church often came to the teachings of Jesus from a Greco-Roman perspective, rather than a Jewish one, frequently not understanding the subtleties of the context in which Jesus taught. Then, later, having become tied to state establishments, the church has either been content to lazily take things literally that were meant to be understood symbolically and has actively encouraged a simplistic 'black and white' understanding for its own political ends.

Our faith has become wrapped up in multiple layers of sentimental 'stories' that were developed by early generations; or even reduced to a focus of endless modern distractions such as maintaining of old buildings. Too often today, the public think of the 'church' as a building, not people actively living out a particular way of life based on Jesus' teaching and actions. We need to return to the beginning again and re-discover the spirit and love of the radical Jesus.

So how can we do this?

What follows are a series of 'reforming' ideas in order that the church might move forward by returning to the basics of

Jesus' teachings. Some of these thoughts are for the church at a national level, others for the training of clergy and then, most importantly, for all in our local parish churches, the very grassroots of our faith communities.

This is a paper to ignite thought and discussion across our diocese, not a complete answer for all our ills. It may appear quite controversial and revolutionary to some but then so was Jesus' presence and teaching, back in the first century. Surely, we need now to adjust and become more relevant to the modern, rational and scientific society that we inhabit in the late twentieth century. It is together that we need to prayerfully decide on the future path for our church. We cannot continue to sit and do nothing, watching the pews emptying, yet maintaining the status quo. Society is already and will increasingly turn away from the church, seeing it as irrelevant to modern times.

I commend this 'Vision' paper to you. Please approach its content in a positive frame of mind so that you might make your contribution to a new beginning.

The Church — Nationally

To return to the pureness of Jesus' teaching, the Church of England needs to remove itself from the power structures of the state. It cannot be a radical voice if it is always looking over its shoulder to see whether it is upsetting the governing powers. By being an arm of the state, sitting in the House of Lords, we are inescapably tied to the 'establishment'. Sending delegates to Parliament demonstrates that the church is hand-in-hand with worldly authority, thereby on occasions, compromising the spiritual message of Jesus.

One very vivid example of this is regarding peace. Jesus

was quite clear in his teaching that as his disciples, we are asked 'to turn the other cheek' and not respond to violence with violence, as this only creates a scenario for further war and death as history has proven. The early Christians were all pacifists, refusing to serve in military forces. It was only when the early church became the Roman state religion that Jesus' teaching of peace was jettisoned in return for power. The church compromised itself and the Gospel with a 'just war' policy in return for the support of the state.

Today, the Church of England continues to support wars because of its alignment to those in government. A clear example of this was in 1914, when all clergy were instructed to preach from the nation's pulpits urging young men to volunteer for war, by telling them that if they did not do so they would be betraying their country and their loved ones. It took a lot of courage and faith in those days to be a conscientious objector and follow Jesus' words of peace.

So, we need to move away from the restricting influence of the state, to be released to speak out more boldly on issues such as poverty, injustice, equality and peace, as Jesus did in his time. This will inevitably mean the dis-establishment of the Church of England sometime in the future, enabling a new beginning of freedom to express the 'good news' of Christ without inhibitions.

(This section NOT to be included in the first Vision draft to Synod.)

Secondly, as we are freed from the models of worldly power, it gives the church the opportunity to restructure its own levels of authority. To look again as to how the church can actively reflect Jesus' teaching on equality where all are important in the sight of God.

In recent years, Willy Brandt has produced an incredibly impressive 'Brandt Commission Report' regarding the inequality found across our world. He speaks of the divide between the rich nations of the northern hemisphere and the poor countries of the southern hemisphere. How all too often, the rich continually exploit the poor countries, taking their resources whilst paying well below an acceptable rate. The divide, Brandt explains, is becoming dangerously wide and inequality could lead to a threat to world peace if the poorer nations turn to violence to gain their fair share.

He writes: 'A new century nears and with it the new prospect of a new civilisation. Could we not begin to lay the basis for that new Community with reasonable relations among all people and nations and to build a world in which sharing, justice, freedom and peace might prevail?'

The Brandt Commission Report suggests that the massive gap in the standards of living experienced between the northern and southern countries, should be corrected by the transfer of resources from north to south so that more equality of opportunity exists. The poor in the south desperately need help now from the rich nations of the north. Brandt warns that our failure to act to bring equality, will have an enormous effect in the future if we do not change our ways. He counsels that in an age of developing communications, the poor will not tolerate their poverty while observing the rich having an excess of the fruits of the world.

The church as an expression of the world has, over time, copied this 'wealth' philosophy into its own structures with leaders such as past Popes holding vast riches, lands and armies to influence the course of the world. In our own Church of England, we still have vast inequality with Bishops living in palaces and lowly curates in small, often crowded, old, terraced homes. The church has a hierarchy that rewards status with a wage structure favouring those with most power. Jesus and his disciples held a 'common purse' where all were treated equally. Maybe it is time to return to the example of Jesus and insist that all who serve Christ be paid the same, that all are treated equally; to get our own 'house' in order before we preach to the wider world.

In our vision we must try to discover ways forward to support efforts to bring more equality to the world, if we wish to live life fully in the image of Jesus. Finance is a key element in worldly affairs and is often a transparent expression of inequality, poverty and injustice. In the world, a great deal of power is held by the richest people. As the national church is correctly judged to be wealthy, we need to urgently review the ethics of our own financial arrangements in order to avoid hypocrisy, when we speak out for a more equal sharing of wealth in the community. There is enough for all and no one should be starving in this world in today's modern society.

Equality is not just about the differences between nations, it also includes the need to treat people of different skin colours equally. Mr Enoch Powell's disturbing 'rivers of blood' speech clearly demonstrates an underlying prejudice and discrimination against black people in our country. There is a great deal of work for a reformed church to do in the area of race relations starting within ourselves and our churches, so that people may live together in harmony and with equal opportunities.

Another issue in the realm of equality is the position of women in the Church of England. It is a travesty of justice that women are not allowed to fully explore God's call to vocation within the church. If we are to serve the people of this country in a changing world where women are moving towards an equal position in society, the church, likewise, must move to include women in all areas of church life, including becoming priests and bishops. God calls all to serve, not just the male gender. There are many women who believe that they have a genuine calling to ministry, which needs to be acknowledged and prayerfully explored by the church, which presently is inhibited from doing so by the exercising of male dominance.

Another national issue facing the Church of England is the ever-increasing time and resources spent on the maintenance and repair of church buildings. The 'church' is for many now the building, rather than being the followers of Jesus. The building is distracting congregations away from the real purpose of being Jesus' love, care and compassion in the world, to solely concentrating all their efforts to raising monies to keep an ancient monument in a good condition. A new way forward needs to be agreed upon where a place to worship, no matter how ancient or beautiful, does not become the main focus of a congregation's mission. There are much more important issues facing our declining church than the decaying stones of our buildings.

Clergy Training

The old model of clergy training which centres mainly upon a traditional view of biblical studies, is out-of-step with today's society. Biblical studies need to take a wider view of the history and culture of the Jewish people who were its authors. There is also now a need to include in the training a 'people-based' model which includes in-depth study of the social sciences, psychology, sociology and philosophy in the curriculum of theological colleges. The main focus of ministry is surely to act out the Gospel of Christ's love, by serving and being alongside people. To do this well, I believe requires a wider understanding of humanity and the deeper issues within society.

A crucial step in enabling clergy to develop these skills is to help them become more aware of themselves, of their strengths and weaknesses. College courses need to provide programmes in self-awareness and encourage ordinands to be open to an honest self-assessment and evaluation. This will enable the prospective leaders in church communities to be confident of themselves, yet humble enough to discover how the beam in their own eye can prevent them from helping remove the speck from the other's eye.

After college, the training process needs to continue. During the curacy and beyond, diocesan-based development programmes need to include a variety of extensive courses, including attending a counselling skills programme to enhance the ability to listen at a deeper level, both to themselves and to others. Clergy need to learn to sit quietly and hear the real, sometimes hidden, concerns being expressed, rather than just rush to give, superficial answers or the 'quick-fix'.

For their important work with the dying, all clergy should attend a ten-week CRUSE bereavement course in order to understand the process of death and the stages of grief. Another helpful opportunity would be for clergy to complete a three-month placement in a Hospice, where they can face and explore the huge life issues of loss and grief. The above would be one of the cornerstones together with other experiential training in areas such as prisons, disability centres, hospital and sick visiting, to name but a few.

Teaching is also a central skill for clergy. Leading children's services, taking school assemblies, setting up Youth Clubs and Holiday Clubs are all important opportunities when working with and passing on the messages of our faith to younger generations. Many clergy, through lack of training, simply talk at young people and do not possess the necessary communication skills - this needs to change. All clergy during their curacies, would benefit from a term's course in which to discover positive ways to connect with our children in schools and in church.

The use of new technology in presenting bible stories, interactive teaching, learning through questions and visual aids are all to be encouraged, in the promotion of the skills clergy can usefully acquire for teaching young people as well as adults.

Training for clergy should continue beyond the three or four-year curacy. Whatever office or appointment a priest or deacon may exercise their ministry in, be they chaplains, rural deans, diocesan officers, archdeacons, bishops and even archbishops, training should be a means of continual development and a source of personal fulfilment for all. It may well be that we need a national educational structure working alongside the diocesan training department which together, will be responsible to develop these new ways forward. It is earnestly proposed that all clergy are provided with both spiritual and personal development according to their individual situation and requirements.

The overall aim is to continually equip clergy with updated resources and skills to enable them to provide a relevant approach for a modern and fast-changing society. It is imperative that the church be in touch with and channel the love of God, not least into its care of the clergy as well as into a society faced with today's issues and concerns.

The Parishes

This section of the paper is addressed particularly to our diocese. It is here that everyone in the parishes need to be involved and committed if we are to save our Church of England. As mentioned earlier, the church is not a building, it is the people of God, it is YOU. What I am going to say in the next few lines, is I believe, vitally important to moving forward and halting the decline in our way of life. So please, can I ask you to listen, read and give serious prayerful consideration to the ideas presented to you? I am not asking you to agree to everything. These are thoughts which I wish to open to you for discussion and debate over the next two years. A base or platform from which to move forward.

1. For each parish to undertake an 'audit'. This will involve a study group to be set up by each Parochial Church Council who will eventually report its findings back to the full Council, including an open meeting for all members.

2. The purpose of the audit will be two-fold. Firstly, to look deeply at the area which the parish serves and compile a detailed dossier of the community and its needs, looking at: housing, employment, schools and youth work, health, social issues such as unemployment, homelessness, loneliness, addictions and many other areas that are relevant to your particular parish. Nothing about life in your parish should be excluded.

3. Secondly, to give a full account of all church-based activities at the present time. Listing: services, meetings, any schoolwork undertaken, visiting by clergy or laity, the social

life of the church, hospital connections, occasional services such as baptisms, marriages, funerals and their follow-up. Include in your report all that your church achieves and also does not accomplish.

4. Another important part of looking at your church are your building(s). How often is it used? What facilities does it have? How can it be utilised more effectively? Can you add to it, or maybe even change it in some way so that it can become a multi-functional place, serving other needs as well as worship? If you have a church hall, how is it that used?

5. Once the information is gathered and presented in a report, hopefully in the first year, the Parochial Church Council will then need to find substantial time to discuss and debate its contents during the second year.

6. The next stage is for the church to come up with a re-evaluation of its role based on the information gathered. To prayerfully formulate a 'Plan for the Future' as to how the church can respond to the community's needs and be relevant to its local area as we move forward towards the twenty-first century.

7. The 'Plan for the Future' is vital and is to become the template, the focus of the church's life. A plan to place the church back in the centre of the community as it was many years ago, by serving the needs of your community.

8. For each parish, the plan will be unique with its own characteristics and ways forward. The answers produced will be different for all, dependent upon the area and the needs of the people the church is called to serve.

9. For example, in some of the more northern parts of our diocese, where parishes are witnessing the closing of the mines, there is a great need for the church to be there to support

the unemployed miners and their families. This might translate into the church building being re-ordered to provide the local community with a meeting place for those unemployed. Something like a Job Breakfast Club could bring together two avenues of support with advice on job applications and food to sustain.

10. Another example, which may be identified in the plan, possibly in more rural areas, might be the problem of loneliness. In response, a group of parishioners could offer visiting, or set up a social group, transporting folk into a central meeting place for tea, cakes and a chat one afternoon a week.

11. The avenues and opportunities for the 'living' church to move on are endless if we are courageous enough to grasp these moments. I know it will mean change from some traditional ways that may be precious to you but if we do not look to the future, there will be no future. Churches and chapels are already closing and being declared redundant. We need to move forward.

12. Each parish's 'Plan for the Future' will need to be revisited and reassessed every five years, to ensure it keeps in step with the fast-changing world.

Conclusion

I am very much aware of the enormity of the enterprise I am placing before you in the Tuxbury Diocese over the coming years but the reality of decline is facing the church and we cannot ignore it, if we believe in the words and actions of Jesus.

The usual Sunday Attendance in the Church of England across our country in 1980 was one million, three hundred and seventy thousand and four hundred (1 370 400). Five years later in 1985, it had fallen to one million, two hundred and sixty-four thousand, six hundred (1 264 600). A decline of over 100 000 in the space of half a decade, nearly eight per cent. This is the most serious situation facing our Christian faith in centuries. We do need to respond by action. We cannot afford to sit quietly by and witness the collapse of 'church', as at the moment that ending appears to be racing towards us.

Our society has and is, changing rapidly. We belong to a scientific and rational world where knowledge has increased our understanding of the planet. Scientists and intellectuals have widened our horizons over recent centuries. People like Galileo and Darwin have overturned past religious beliefs with concrete, material and factual evidence. In doing so, these recent discoveries have undermined long-held Christian doctrine. The footnote in the King James Bible informing us in the Book of Genesis that the world was created in the year 4004BC is an obvious example of a dogma which is out-of-date. Modern technological advances have had a similar effect, with space travel exploding the belief that heaven was just beyond the clouds.

Our faith needs to be based on an experiential, spiritual journey, prayerfully continuing both together and as individuals, an ongoing exploration of the teaching of Jesus. We need to be open-minded as well as open-hearted, thinking through rather than turning our backs on modern developments in research and biblical study which can assist us in our understanding and spiritual growth.

As a church, we need to review many areas of our faith in the light of the modern setting in which we live. Stagnant old declarations, arguments or so-called 'answers' will no longer do in today's world. No longer can we hold on to a literal interpretation of the Jewish writers use of 'stories' in the first century Gospels. We need to revisit, understand and preach the underlying truth and meaning which the authors were expounding. Thinking people of the late twentieth century can no longer accept just a literal interpretation of the bible — which is to many people today, simply 'unbelievable'! We need to revise the way we explore our Gospels, searching together for a deeper understanding and living out its true and timeless message of love.

Therefore, I call you all to a new beginning. A new era of exploring again our faith. A time to bring our Christian values alive in a way that are relevant to this ever-changing world in which we live. I call you to be heralds of a Second Reformation.

Let us all come together in prayer, patience, understanding and love for one another. Let us realistically 'Plan for the Future' and begin to reverse the church's decline.

Charles +

July 1987

Appendix Two

Average Adult Sunday Attendance in the Church of England

1980 to 2015

1980 – 1 370 400

1985 – 1 264 600

1990 – 1 259 800

1995 – 1 126 700

2000 – 963 300

2005 – 870 600

2010 – 780 000

2015 – 660 000

In this period of thirty-five years, Sunday attendance at the Church of England has fallen by over fifty percent.

In 1980, 11.1% of the population attended a church on Sundays.

In 2015 that had fallen to 4.7%

In 2015 the average age of those attending the Church of England was sixty-eight years.

It is predicted that in another generation, i.e., thirty years, those attending will be less than 200 000.

Churches and chapels across Britain have been closing, and/or declared redundant at an alarming rate, since the beginning of the new millennium.